NEBOSH NATIONAL CONSTRUCTION CERTIFICATE

UNIT NCC1: MANAGING AND CONTROLLING HAZARDS IN CONSTRUCTION ACTIVITIES - PART 2

Element 7: Fire Safety

Element 8: Chemical and Biological Health - Hazards and Risk Control

Element 9: Physical and Psychological Health - Hazards and Risk Control

Element 10: Working at Height - Hazards and Risk Control

Element 11: Excavation Work and Confined Spaces - Hazards and Risk Control

Element 12: Demolition and Deconstruction - Hazards and Risk Control

Contributors

Mr Roger Passey, CMIOSH, MIIRSM

Dr T Robson, Bsc (Hons), PhD, CFIOSH, MRSC, CChem

For information on all RRC publications and training courses, visit: www.rrc.co.uk

RRC Module No: NCC1 - PART 2

ISBN: 978-1-909055-89-6
Third edition Summer 2018

ACKNOWLEDGMENTS

RRC International would like to thank the National Examination Board in Occupational Safety and Health (NEBOSH) for their co-operation in allowing us to reproduce extracts from their syllabus guides.

This publication contains public sector information published by the Health and Safety Executive and licensed under the Open Government Licence v.2 (www.nationalarchives.gov.uk/doc/open-government-licence/version/2).

Every effort has been made to trace copyright material and obtain permission to reproduce it. If there are any errors or omissions, RRC International would welcome notification so that corrections may be incorporated in future reprints or editions of this material.

Whilst the information in this book is believed to be true and accurate at the date of going to press, neither the author nor the publisher can accept any legal responsibility or liability for any errors or omissions that may be made.

Element 7: Fire Safety

Contents

Element 8: Chemical and Biological Health - Hazards and Risk Control

Element 9: Physical and Psychological Health - Hazards and Risk Control

Contents

Element 10: Working at Height - Hazards and Risk Control

Element 11: Excavation Work and Confined Spaces - Hazards and Risk Control

Contents

Element 12: Demolition and Deconstruction - Hazards and Risk Control

Revision and Examination

NCC2 Practical Application

Suggested Answers

Introduction

Course Structure

This textbook has been designed to provide the reader with the core knowledge needed to successfully complete the NEBOSH National Certificate in Construction Health and Safety, as well as providing a useful overview of health and safety management. It follows the structure and content of the NEBOSH syllabus.

The NEBOSH National Construction Certificate consists of three units of study. When you successfully complete any of the units you will receive a Unit Certificate, but to achieve a complete NEBOSH National Construction qualification you need to pass the three units within a five-year period. For more detailed information about how the syllabus is structured, visit the NEBOSH website (www.nebosh.org.uk).

NEBOSH National Certificate in Construction Health and Safety

Unit NGC1: Management of Health and Safety	
Unit NCC1: Managing and Controlling Hazards in Construction Activities	
Element 1	Construction Law and Management
Element 2	Construction Site - Hazards and Risk Control
Element 3	Vehicle and Plant Movement - Hazards and Risk Control
Element 4	Musculoskeletal Hazards and Risk Control
Element 5	Work Equipment - Hazards and Risk Control
Element 6	Electrical Safety
Element 7	Fire Safety
Element 8	Chemical and Biological Health - Hazards and Risk Control
Element 9	Physical and Psychological Health - Hazards and Risk Control
Element 10	Working at Height - Hazards and Risk Control
Element 11	Excavation Work and Confined Spaces - Hazards and Risk Control
Element 12	Demolition and Deconstruction - Hazards and Risk Control
Revision and Examination Guide	

Unit NCC2: Health and Safety Practical Application
The Practical Assessment

Assessment

To complete the qualification, you need to pass two formal written exams (one for Unit NGC1 and one for Unit NCC1), as well as a safety inspection of your workplace, including a short report to management (Unit NCC2).

Each written exam is two hours long and consists of one long question (20% of the marks) and ten short questions (each being 8% of the total marks). You must answer all questions.

The practical assessment requires you to undertake a safety inspection in your workplace and write a short report on your findings.

Further information and help on the Unit NCC1 exam is given in this textbook in the Exam Skills sections at the end of each element and in the Revision and Examination chapter at the end. Information and guidance on the Unit NCC2 practical application is also given at the end of this textbook.

HINTS AND TIPS

As you work your way through this book, always remember to relate your own experiences in the workplace to the topics you study. An appreciation of the practical application and significance of health and safety will help you understand the topics.

Keeping Yourself Up to Date

The field of health and safety is constantly evolving and, as such, it will be necessary for you to keep up to date with changing legislation and best practice.

RRC International publishes updates to all its course materials via a quarterly e-newsletter (issued in February, May, August and November), which alerts students to key changes in legislation, best practice and other information pertinent to current courses.

Please visit www.rrc.co.uk/news-resources/newsletters.aspx to access these updates.

Other Textbooks in the Series

- NEBOSH National General Certificate - Management of Health and Safety
- NEBOSH International General Certificate - Management of International Health and Safety
- NEBOSH National Fire Certificate - Fire Safety and Risk Management
- NEBOSH International Fire Certificate - International Fire Safety and Risk Management
- NEBOSH International Certificate in Construction Health and Safety - Managing and Controlling Hazards in International Construction Activities
- NEBOSH National Diploma Unit A - Managing Health and Safety
- NEBOSH National Diploma Unit B - Hazardous Substances/Agents
- NEBOSH National Diploma Unit C - Workplace and Work Equipment Safety
- NEBOSH International Diploma Unit IA - Managing Health and Safety
- NEBOSH International Diploma Unit IB - Hazardous Substances/Agents
- NEBOSH International Diploma Unit IC - Workplace and Work Equipment Safety

RRC International is continually adding to its range of textbooks.

Visit www.rrc.co.uk/publications.aspx for a full range of current titles.

Fire Safety

Learning Outcomes

Once you've read this element, you'll understand how to:

1 Describe the principles of fire initiation, classification and spread and the additional fire risks caused by construction activities in an existing workplace.

2 Outline the principles of fire risk assessment.

3 Outline the principles of fire prevention and the prevention of fire spread in construction workplaces.

4 Identify the appropriate fire detection, fire alarm systems and fire-fighting equipment for construction activities.

5 Outline the requirements for an adequate and properly maintained means of escape in the construction workplace.

6 Outline the factors which should be considered when implementing a successful evacuation of a construction workplace in the event of a fire.

Contents

Principles of Fire Initiation, Classification and Spread and Fire Risks Caused by Construction Activities

IN THIS SECTION...

- Three things must be present for a fire to start: fuel, oxygen and heat.

- The five classes of fire (determined by the types of fuel) are:

  - Class A (organic solids).

  - Class B (flammable liquids or liquefiable solids).

  - Class C (flammable gases).

  - Class D (metals).

  - Class F (high temperature fats).

- Fire can spread through a workplace by various means of transmission, including direct burning, convection, conduction and radiation.

- Additional risks of fire within construction are faulty or misused electrical equipment, deliberate ignition (arson), hot work, heating and cooking appliances and smoking.

Basic Principles of Fire

The basic principles of fire and combustion can be represented by the fire triangle.

The three things required for a fire to start are:

The fire triangle

- **Fuel** - a flammable or combustible material or substance (e.g. paper, wood, petrol, diesel, propane, oil or paint).

- **Oxygen** - in the air all around us (21%) and consumed during combustion when it chemically combines with the fuel. Oxygen can also come from oxygen-rich chemicals (oxidising agents) such as ammonium nitrate.

- **Heat** - ignition source, to start the combustion process. (Once a fire starts, it continues to produce its own heat.) Sources are sparks, heaters, smoking and sunlight.

The first thing to come from a fire is invisible vapours. Once the vapours ignite, the fire produces heat, a flame and smoke. Smoke is made up of hot combustion gases such as carbon monoxide, carbon dioxide and solid particles of soot. It will also contain (sometimes toxic) residues from substances that burn (e.g. burning plastics will produce acidic fumes).

The fire triangle is useful for two reasons. It represents:

- **Fire prevention** - keep the three elements apart and fire cannot start.

- **Fire-fighting** - remove one of the elements and a fire will go out.

> **DEFINITION**
>
> **FIRE**
>
> A chemical reaction that uses fuel and oxygen and creates heat and light.

TOPIC FOCUS

The **fire-fighting** triangle:

- **Remove oxygen** - smother the fire (using a fire blanket, foam, dry powder).
- **Remove heat** - cool with water or carbon dioxide.
- **Remove fuel** - starvation - turn off the gas/electricity/oil supply.

Classification of Fires

Fires are commonly classified into five categories according to the fuel type. The classification is useful as the basis for identifying which extinguisher to use:

- **Class A** - solid materials, usually organic, e.g. paper, wood, coal, packaging material and textiles.
- **Class B** - flammable liquids or liquefiable solids, e.g. petrol, diesel, paraffin, oil, grease.
- **Class C** - gases, e.g. methane, propane, butane, acetylene and mains gas.
- **Class D** - metals, e.g. aluminium, magnesium.
- **Class F** - high temperature fat, e.g. cooking fat.

Note that there is no Class E fire. This was avoided to prevent confusion between Class E and Electricity. Electricity is not a fuel (although it can be a heat/ignition source).

Basic Principles of Heat Transmission and Fire Spread

Once a fire has started, there are four methods by which it can spread:

- **Convection**

    The principle that hot air rises and cold air sinks. Hot gases created from the fire rise straight up:

    – **In a building**, the gases will hit the ceiling and spread out in a layer beneath it. On contact with other combustible materials, these hot gases may cause them to ignite.

    – **Outdoors**, these convection currents carry hot embers, which may fall to the ground and carry the fire to another location.

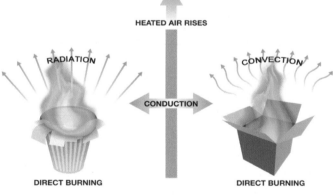

Fire spread

- **Conduction**

    Heat can be transmitted through solid materials. Some materials (metals, and copper in particular) heat very efficiently. Steelwork, pipes and cables running from room to room can carry the heat through and spread a fire.

- **Radiation**

    Heat energy can radiate through air as infrared heat waves travelling in straight lines, and can pass through transparent surfaces (e.g. glass). Radiant heat generated from a fire shines onto nearby surfaces and is absorbed, and if the material heats up enough it can burst into flames.

- **Direct Burning**

  Where a flame simply spreads through a material that is on fire, until it is all consumed.

Additional Risks and Consequences of Fire During Construction Activities

There are many reasons why fires start during construction activities. Some of the more common ones are:

- **Hot work** - many construction tasks involve heat and naked flames, e.g. use of propane torches, tar-boilers, asphalting burners, welding and burning. Even some remote site lights may be propane-powered.

- **Electricity** - faulty wiring, especially in temporary site circuits; overloaded conductors; misused equipment; and incorrect use of electrical equipment, especially power tools, in inappropriate environments.

- **Smoking** - especially carelessly discarded smoking materials, such as cigarette ends and matches.

- **Cooking appliances** - fat pans, toasters, etc. in welfare areas left unattended.

- **Heating appliances** - electric fan heaters and portable space heaters, often left unattended and used on site for drying clothes.

- **Deliberate ignition** (arson) - fires started because the construction site is close to public access areas and is an easy target, perhaps by persons not wanting building carried out there, or by young people playing.

TOPIC FOCUS

Arson

In criminal law, arson is defined as: *'the act of intentionally or recklessly setting fire to another's property or to one's own property for some improper reason'*.

Arson is a common problem on construction sites for a range of possible reasons, for example:

- The location of the site in relation to other premises, schools, etc. or in an inner city location which makes it vulnerable.

- The site is unsecured, without adequate perimeter fencing.

- The site does not have security officers in attendance or doing patrols.

- There is little or no security lighting.

- Flammable or combustible materials are stored in unsecured areas close to the perimeter of the site.

- Former employees may have a grudge against the contractor or site management.

- Attacks may be made by opportunist vandals, especially children during school holidays.

It is important to consider and control all of these factors to reduce the risk of arson and ensure workers report anyone seen acting suspiciously on or around the site.

- **Unsafe use and storage of flammable substances** - petrol, diesel, propane gas cylinders are used and stored on site.

- **Mechanical heat** - generated by friction between moving parts of site machinery, e.g. motors, bearings, tight drive belts, etc.

Unsafe use and storage of flammable substances can cause fire on site

TOPIC FOCUS

Friction

Friction is two or more materials or surfaces moving against one another, giving off heat.

Without lubrication or cooling substance, such surfaces become very hot or produce sparks, either of which may be sufficient to cause ignition.

Friction can:

- Be caused by impact - one material striking another.

- Result from surfaces rubbing together or 'smearing' (steel, coated with a softer material, is subject to high bearing pressure with sliding or grazing).

Fire can be disruptive on a construction site, particularly because of the many different contractors and their equipment in use and stored on site. Losses are normally covered by insurance.

The biggest danger is to people, which is a greater risk where construction activities are carried out in a public place that remains in use, e.g. the high street. More people die in fires from smoke inhalation than from burns.

Additional Risks of Fire

Some construction methods use different technologies and materials to produce less expensive buildings that are also often quicker to erect than those of conventional materials and building methods. Some of these materials and components, often produced and assembled off-site, are more prone to fire while they are unprotected during construction. This will particularly affect timber-frame buildings.

The consequences of the use of such materials and methods of construction is often faster propagation of flames and much quicker fire spread among partly-assembled or constructed buildings and the parts awaiting assembly into those buildings. This in turn leads to quicker collapse of burning buildings and spread to properties nearby.

STUDY QUESTIONS

1. Identify the process of heat transmission/fire spread shown in the following images.

    (a)

    Source: Safe Practice "Fire Safety"

    (b)

    Source: Safe Practice "Fire Safety"

    (c)

    Source: Safe Practice "Fire Safety"

2. What additional method of heat transfer/fire spread is not illustrated by Question 1?

3. Explain briefly how each of the following might start a fire:

    (a) Friction.

    (b) Space heater.

4. Identify the three ways of extinguishing a fire.

5. Identify the fire classification of each of the following types of fire:

    (a) Butane gas cylinders burning in a storage compound on a construction site.

    (b) Fire in a paint store on a construction site.

    (c) Fire in a construction site office.

(Suggested Answers are at the end.)

Fire Risk Assessment

IN THIS SECTION...

- The onus is on an employer to ensure fire safety on construction sites by carrying out a fire risk assessment.

- Fire risk assessment is a five-step process of identifying hazards; identifying people at risk; identifying and implementing the precautions needed; recording the findings of the assessment; and reviewing it.

- Construction sites are to have site specific emergency plans in place in case of fire, and control and evacuation measures should be well documented and known.

The Requirement for a Fire Risk Assessment

The **Regulatory Reform (Fire Safety) Order 2005 (RRFSO)** (there is separate legislation in Scotland - the **Fire Safety (Scotland) Regulations 2006**) has made significant changes to the way in which employers and people in control of premises are required to manage fire safety:

- Fire certificates for premises are no longer required.

- Emphasis is now on the owner or occupier having in place a fire risk assessment (originally introduced in an amendment to the **Management of Health and Safety at Work Regulations 1999**).

Under the **RRFSO**, the basic requirements that must be addressed by all 'responsible persons' can be summarised as:

- Conduct a **fire risk assessment** for the premises over which you have control.

Fire risk assessment

- Identify the fire hazards and risks associated with the premises.

- Identify the people (or groups of people) at risk, and anyone especially at risk.

- Remove or reduce the risks as far as is reasonably practicable.

- Put in place general fire precautions to deal with any remaining risks.

- Implement additional preventive and protective measures if flammable or explosive substances are used or stored on the premises.

- Develop and implement appropriate emergency procedures.

- Record the significant findings of the risk assessment and actions you have taken to remove/reduce risk.

- Review the risk assessment:

  - Periodically.

  - After significant changes in the workplace.

  - When there is reason to believe it may no longer be valid.

TOPIC FOCUS

Under the **RRFSO** a '**responsible person**' is anyone who has control of premises or has a degree of control over certain areas or systems, for instance:

- The employer for those parts of premises which staff may go to.

- The managing agent or owner for shared parts of premises or shared fire safety equipment (e.g. fire warning systems or sprinklers).

- The occupier, e.g. self-employed persons or voluntary organisations (if they have control).

- Any other person who has some control over part of the premises.

It is usually obvious who the responsible person will be, but there may be times when the responsibility is shared among a number of people.

Enforcement of the requirements of the **RRFSO** is principally the responsibility of:

- **The Fire and Rescue Authority:**

    - For the majority of workplaces.

- **The Health and Safety Executive:**

    - For **construction sites**.

    - For nuclear installations.

    - For ships (under construction/repair).

- **Local Authorities:**

    - For sports grounds.

The most common means of enforcement is the issue of Notices by Inspectors.

MORE...

www.gov.uk/government/collections/fire-safety-law-and-guidance-documents-for-business

Conducting a Fire Risk Assessment

The fire risk assessment:

- Is the basis for planning and maintaining all aspects of fire prevention and fire precautions on a construction site.

- Should follow the same 'five steps' principles as other risk assessments.

- Should address three significant topics: a site plan; the fire hazards and their level of risk; and the fire control and evacuation measures.

TOPIC FOCUS

The '**five steps**' for fire risk assessment are:

- **Step 1: Identify the Fire Hazards**

  This means looking around the construction site, including existing buildings that are being worked on and temporary accommodation, for sources of heat, fuel and oxygen which, together, might lead to fire.

- **Step 2: Identify the People at Risk**

  - Consider **anyone** who could be on site, not just workers in the immediate area, e.g. contractors, delivery drivers, passers-by, and people present outside normal working hours such as site security guards.

  - Include visitors and members of the public.

  - Include individuals or groups who may be particularly at risk, e.g. young or inexperienced workers; people with mobility or sensory impairment; pregnant workers; etc.

- **Step 3: Evaluate the Fire Risks, Remove or Reduce the Risks and Protect People from Any Remaining Risk**

  This involves consideration of the:

  - Likelihood of fire breaking out, which can be minimised by the use of appropriate **preventive measures**.

  - Consequences (severity) of any harm, which can be minimised by the use of appropriate **protective measures**.

- **Step 4: Record the Significant Findings and Actions Taken to Remove/Reduce Risk**

  - Develop and implement an appropriate **emergency plan**.

  - **Inform and instruct** relevant persons on the actions to be taken in the event of a fire.

  - **Train** employees, particularly those with specific duties, e.g. fire marshals.

- **Step 5: Review**

  The fire risk assessment must be reviewed:

  - If you suspect that it may no longer be valid.

  - After any incident (fire) or 'near miss'.

  - After significant changes to the site.

  - Periodically.

Temporary Workplaces

In construction activities temporary accommodation is often provided for workers, e.g. site huts, canteens and mobile offices. Such accommodation must be considered in the fire risk assessment and site emergency plan (see later), and constantly reviewed to cover any changes that are made during the construction project.

Shared Workplaces

Where construction work takes place in existing premises that are shared, either by the construction contractors and occupants (e.g. a school or shopping centre) or by different construction contractors, then its fire risk assessment must consider the activities of all parties involved, and any existing local fire safety plans should be incorporated to form part of the overall site plan. All parties must be made familiar with the risk assessment and the fire precautions required.

Site Specific Emergency Plan

The fire risk assessment should include a site specific emergency plan, locating all main fire hazards and protective measures on site. It should be kept in the Construction Phase Plan. The precautions identified will become part of the site induction training and evacuation procedure for all parties.

Identification of the Fire Control and Evacuation Measures

On construction sites, in both temporary site accommodation and existing premises, consideration must be given to how a fire should be dealt with if the precautions are ineffective. This should cover the following points:

- Warning systems - alarms and detectors.
- Fire-fighting equipment.
- Evacuation procedures and escape routes, including signs and emergency lighting.
- Testing, maintenance and inspection procedures, including fire drills.

STUDY QUESTIONS

6. What three topics must be addressed in a fire risk assessment?

7. What considerations should be made when identifying fire hazards in the fire risk assessment?

8. What should a site-specific emergency plan cover and where should it be kept?

(Suggested Answers are at the end.)

Fire Prevention and Prevention of Fire Spread

IN THIS SECTION...

- Fire can be prevented by:
    - Eliminating or reducing the use and storage of flammable and combustible materials on site.
    - Controlling ignition sources, including hot work such as welding.
    - Operating safe systems of work, including hot work permits.
    - Ensuring the safe storage, transport and use of LPG and other gas cylinders.
    - Maintaining good housekeeping standards.
- Restrictions should be in place to limit the amounts of highly flammable liquids (up to 50 litres) and flammable liquids (up to 250 litres).
- Structural measures can help to prevent fire and smoke spread, such as considering the properties of common building materials and the protection of openings and voids.
- Only suitable approved electrical equipment should be used in flammable atmospheres.

Control Measures to Minimise the Risk of Fire in a Construction Workplace

Use and Storage of Flammable and Combustible Materials

Potential fuels that will be identified in a site fire risk assessment include:

- **Combustible materials** - cardboard packaging, paper, wooden pallets, scaffold boards, etc.

- **Flammable materials**:
    - Liquids such as petrol, diesel, paint and thinners.
    - Gases such as propane, butane and methane.

Control measures (in order of preference):

- **Eliminate** these materials from the site (although total elimination is rarely achievable). Unwanted and old stocks should be removed as a start.

Packaging materials need to be stored safely

- **Substitute** a high-risk fuel source for a lower risk material, e.g. replacing petrol-driven generators with diesel-powered units, lowering the flammability risk.

- **Minimise** (reduce) the amounts of materials kept and used. This needs:
    - Good stock control and waste management systems.
    - Close control of items such as empty wooden pallets (used for delivering blocks, bags, etc.).
    - A system that ensures regular returns.

- **Safe storage** and **safe use** of materials, for example:
    - Drums of flammable liquid (within the maximum limit) should be on bunded pallets, in a secure fenced compound in a safe location, with fire precautions in place.

– Separation of combustible and flammable materials into different storage areas.

– Instead of tipping the drums to get liquid out, use a hand-pump to avoid tipping and spills (and reduce manual handling).

TOPIC FOCUS

Storage areas for flammable and combustible materials on site should be:

- Securely fenced, ventilated buildings or open-air compounds.

- Separate from other parts of the site and away from emergency exits.

- Accessible to fire-fighters.

- Properly marked/signed.

- Provided with two escape routes.

- Large enough to allow clear spaces to be maintained around stacks of materials, taking care that the stacked materials themselves do not cause a hazard.

Control of Ignition Sources

Most fires in the workplace are caused by a lack of control over sources of ignition. These are preventable by carefully designed working systems and practices:

- **Electrical equipment** should be routinely inspected and tested to prevent faults that could cause sparks and overheating going unnoticed.

- **Hot work**, such as welding, should be controlled with a permit to work when carried out in sensitive areas.

- **Smoking** should be controlled and limited to restricted areas on site (welfare areas).

- **Cooking and heating appliances** should be safely located and used carefully. They should not be left unattended.

- **Mechanical heat** (overheating) can be controlled by good maintenance programmes.

- **Bonfires** (often used for burning waste) should not be permitted on site.

- **Deliberate ignition** (arson) should be prevented by good site security, perimeter fences, CCTV, security lighting and good control of combustible waste, i.e. stored away from buildings in a secure area.

Welding on a Construction Site

Welding (including flame cutting and burning) involves many fire risks, both from gases used in the process and from electricity, both creating a high energy spark of flame. The precautions required include:

- Select a suitable welding method, e.g. electric, gas (oxy-acetylene or oxy-propane), or gas and metal such as TIG or MIG.

- Correct siting and positioning (upright) of gas cylinders.

- Use of flashback arrestors to gas cylinders.

- Carry out a **COSHH** risk assessment for materials and fume from the welding.

- Ensure appropriate PPE is worn, e.g. aprons, gloves and goggles.

- Use of welding screens in sensitive areas.

- Adequate training and competence of all welding operatives.
- Provision of suitable fire extinguishers.
- Use of a permit-to-work system for hot work.
- Regular fire safety checks during and after welding.
- Removal of all flammable and combustible materials from the welding area.

TOPIC FOCUS

Fire Hazards and Precautions in Building Refurbishment Work

Fire hazards:

- Hot work (welding, burning, cutting, soldering).
- Use of flammable materials (solvents, gas cylinders, etc.).
- Use of combustible materials (packaging, wrapping, filling materials).
- Electrical work - especially on poorly maintained systems.
- Use of defective portable electrical equipment, including extension leads.
- Overloading an electrical system used in the work and use of socket adaptors.
- Workers smoking or burning rubbish on site.

Precautions:

- Use of hot work permits.
- Regular fire safety checks in the hot work area (during and after work).
- Use of burning/welding/soldering equipment by qualified persons only.
- Consider fabrication of components off site.
- Portable appliance testing and maintenance of electrical systems.
- Proper control of flammable and combustible materials used or stored.
- Regular removal of rubbish.
- Prohibiting of smoking and burning rubbish.

Systems of Work

These should be in place to minimise the risk of fire. Risk assessment will determine what systems are appropriate, including:

- **Permits to work** - controlling hot work, work on electrical systems.
- **Careful control of storage areas** - especially where flammable materials are kept.
- **Refuelling** - careful refuelling of vehicles and plant on site in safe areas.
- **Prevention and control of spillages** - use bunded storage systems and pump-transfer (instead of pouring from drums).
- **Control of waste** - segregation in areas away from fire risks and regular removal of waste materials from the site.

Permit-to-Work Procedures

Welding, flame cutting, use of blow lamps or bitumen boilers, soldering equipment and portable grinding equipment can all pose a serious fire hazard through the production of sparks, heat or a naked flame.

These hazards must be controlled to prevent fires occurring, especially in areas where flammable materials such as paint, timber, plastic, thinners, adhesives, etc. are stored or used. One method is to use a written permit-to-work system applicable to all workers involved, i.e. employees and contractors.

A **hot work permit** ensures that:

- Formal arrangements are in place as a safe system of work.

- There is appropriate co-ordination with other people or activities to avoid any conflicts.

- Time limits are provided within which it is safe to carry out the work.

- Ignition sources (hot work) will not be introduced until combustible/flammable materials have been moved away from where the work is to be carried out.

- Fire-fighting measures are in place to tackle any fire that may occur, including having in place a fire-watcher (a person to monitor the area during and after operations to identify and extinguish sparks).

- Specialised PPE, e.g. breathing apparatus, is provided.

- Appropriate methods of communication are used.

TOPIC FOCUS

Hot Work Permit Requirements

A hot work permit should contain the following details/precautions:

- Area safety inspection to ensure flammable materials are removed from the work area or adequately protected from heat and sparks.

- The fire-fighting equipment to be available in the work area.

- Location and nature of work.

- Name of person in charge.

- The permitted time span of the activity and the level of supervision required.

- The actions to be taken when the work is finished, including initial and subsequent checks that there are no smouldering or hot materials which could allow a fire to break out later.

Further precautions for hot work in confined spaces:

- Air monitoring may be required to determine air quality and any hazardous conditions (a confined space permit may also be needed).

- Cylinders of flammable gases and oxygen should not be taken into confined spaces because of the risk of serious fire or explosion from a build-up of fuel gases, e.g. from a leak.

- All hot work equipment should be removed from the confined space whenever work stops - even for a break.

Safe Storage, Transport and Use of Cylinder Gases

Liquefied Petroleum Gas (LPG) (propane or butane) and cylinders of other gases such as oxygen and acetylene are used in hot work processes on construction sites. LPG is also used to power some vehicles and floodlighting units.

Characteristics of cylinder gases include:

- **LPG** - a colourless liquid which readily evaporates into a gas to form a flammable or explosive mixture. It is heavier than air and can collect in drains, gullies, cellars and excavations, where it can accumulate and lead to possible asphyxiation. It is not easily detected by smell. It can cause frost burns to the skin, and presents a fire/explosion risk - especially in a confined space or where ventilation is poor. LPG hoses should be colour-coded orange.

- **Oxygen** - an odourless gas which supports combustion and in high concentrations will cause material to burst into flames. It should never be used to enrich or sweeten the atmosphere, should be stored at least three metres away from acetylene, LPG or any other cylinders, and the hoses should be colour-coded blue.

- **Acetylene** - a gas which will form an explosive mixture with air and must be transported upright. Hoses for acetylene are colour-coded red.

Hazards

- If struck by moving vehicles or materials, dropped or tipped over, cylinders may incur unseen damage, which may cause leaks, fire and explosion.

- They may leak from poor connections and fittings, with the same results.

- Cylinders can also give rise to possible manual handling problems - a proper risk assessment is required.

Safe Storage

Requirements for gas cylinder storage:

- Store outside in a secure, lockable location away from buildings and protected from sunlight.

- Warning signs should be displayed, including ones indicating where an explosive atmosphere may occur.

- Cylinders should not be stored beneath overhead power cables or in the path of falling materials.

- Ensure that the number of cylinders is kept as small as is reasonable.

- Only take on site what is needed, and return to the store on completion.

- Ignition sources should be eliminated from the area.

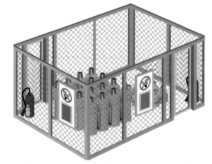

Gas cylinders safely stored outside

- Cylinders should be stored upright (unless designed otherwise, e.g. LPG-fuelled forklift trucks) with valves uppermost and chained securely.

- Cylinders should be secured in a safe storage area constructed of non-combustible material which is adequately ventilated and in a safe position (at least three metres away from buildings/structures/drains/excavations), e.g. a meshed cage in the open air.

- Ideally, different gases, and empty/full cylinders should be segregated (e.g. do not store oxygen and LPG together) and away from bulk containers.

- Suitable fire extinguishers should be available (e.g. foam, dry powder).

- The two principal sets of regulations covering gas cylinders are the **Carriage of Dangerous Goods and Use of Transportable Pressure Equipment Regulations 2009**. (the "**Carriage Regulations**") and the **Pressure Equipment (Safety) Regulations 2016**.

Specific requirements for LPG cylinder storage:

- An LPG storage area is classified as a hazardous place and will be "zoned" under the **Dangerous Substances and Explosive Atmospheres Regulations 2002** (**DSEAR**). If LPG bottles are stored correctly in a secure cage, well away from sources of ignition, then the area should fall into Zone 2.

Zone 0	Zone 1	Zone 2
Explosive gas atmosphere present continuously or for long periods.	Explosive gas atmosphere likely to occur in normal operation.	Explosive gas atmosphere not likely to occur in normal operation; if it does it is only for short time.

- LPG should not be stored near any cellars, drains or excavations.

- Each cylinders should be clearly marked "Highly Flammable LPG" showing the design pressure and temperature.

- Correct LPG regulators should be used and orange colour-coded hoses.

Transport

- Cylinders on site should be transported upright using suitable trolleys to avoid manual handling problems, or lifted by cranes using a special carrier.

- Vehicles transporting cylinders should be suitable and fit for the purpose, e.g. do not use an enclosed van. Cylinders should be secured from undue movement in an upright position.

- Drivers should:

  - Be specifically trained, e.g. in relation to hazards and precautions.

  - Be provided with PPE (e.g. gloves).

  - Have **ADR Instructions in Writing** (which have replaced the previous "Tremcard" system and are now only required in the language of the driver for the journey) in their possession showing the appropriate precautions in the event of an incident.

Use

All cylinders are to be properly installed and connections leak-tested before use. Only trained persons are to install and use cylinder gases.

Particular uses and precautions include the following:

- **Hand-Held Tools**

  Blow lamps, torches and roofing irons need to be used at the correct pressures and have non-return valves fitted and suitable flash-back arrestors. When they are in use, keep the area free of combustible materials. Fire checks should be carried out following completion of any work.

- **Tar Boilers**

  Cylinders should be kept at least three metres away or protected by a heat shield, be clear of traffic and supplied with a robust, steel-reinforced, braided hose. The tar boiler equipment should be properly supervised with experienced operators, properly sited to avoid spillages, never be left unattended or towed while alight, and never be positioned on roofs - unless proper precautions are taken, e.g. a non-combustible base used.

- **Site Huts**

  Flammable vapours may accumulate inside and give rise to a fire and/or explosion risk. Such areas need to be adequately ventilated both at top and bottom, and the equipment fitted with flame failure devices. The cylinders should be kept in the open air, protected from inclement weather, outside the hut. Maintenance and repair of heaters and appliances should be carried out by registered Gas Safe Register personnel.

Good Housekeeping

Good housekeeping is fundamental to fire safety and should ensure that:

- Combustible and flammable materials are regularly removed from work areas.

- Items that can't be removed are covered with fire-retardant blankets.

- Waste bins are emptied regularly, so that there is no accumulation of combustible materials.

- Site areas are regularly cleaned and kept free of litter and rubbish.

- Safe disposal of all waste materials is arranged. 'Unofficial' rubbish burning must be banned.

- Skips are placed at least three metres from buildings and other structures.

- Pedestrian routes are always kept clear.

Storage of Small Quantities of Flammable Liquids

Category 3 "**flammable liquids**" have a relatively low flash point (between 23°C and 60°C) and are therefore relatively easily ignited with an ignition source (such as a match) at normal room temperature.

Category 2 "**highly flammable liquids**" have a lower flash point (<23°C) and a boiling point of 35°C or more and are therefore easier to ignite at normal indoor and outdoor temperatures.

Category 1 "**extremely flammable liquids**" have a similar low flash point (<23°C) and a boiling point of less than 35°C and are therefore very easy to ignite at normal indoor and outdoor temperatures.

When in use in the workplace, the quantity of flammable liquids should be minimised:

- Up to 50 litres of highly flammable liquids.

- Up to 250 litres of flammable liquids.

Storage requirements:

- Store only in appropriate (usually metal) containers with secure lids.

- Containers should be correctly labelled.

- The need to decant highly flammable liquids from one container to another should be minimised, reducing the risk of spillages.

- Area should be well ventilated.

- Drip trays and proper handling aids should be provided.

- Method/procedure for dealing with spillages and disposal of empty containers and contaminated materials should be in place and understood.

Structural Measures to Prevent the Spread of Fire and Smoke

Building design can be a significant factor in preventing both the outbreak and spread of fire. The main features which influence this are the:

- Layout and construction of the building or the site premises.

- Materials with which buildings are constructed and those used in decoration and furnishings.

If a fire starts within a building, it should be contained and prevented from spreading. This can be done by designing the building in such a way that it is divided up into **compartments**, each surrounded by fire-resistant materials.

There are two types of fire compartment or cell:

- Those designed to keep a fire in - areas of high risk such as plant rooms or flammable stores.

- Those designed to keep a fire out - high loss effect areas such as document archives or computer rooms, and escape routes.

The walls, floors and doors which form the boundary to a fire compartment must generally provide a 60-minute resistance to fire.

The walls, floors and doors which subdivide fire compartments must generally provide a 30-minute resistance.

To allow movement between these compartments, fire doors are fitted. These should:

- Be rated to withstand fire for a minimum of 30 minutes.

- Have a self-closing device.

- Be fitted with an intumescent strip.

> **DEFINITION**
>
> **INTUMESCENT STRIP**
>
> 'Intumesce' means 'to swell'.
>
> Intumescent strips, seals or foam are placed in door frames and other openings (e.g. service ducts between floors) and will swell with the heat from a fire and seal the gap, preventing the passage of air (which might feed the fire), smoke and flames.

- Have a vision panel of fire-resistant glass.

- Be clearly labelled (e.g. "Fire Door - Keep Shut").

Properties of Common Building Materials

Fire affects different building materials in different ways. Controls must therefore ensure that appropriate materials are used in a structure.

Material	Fire Characteristics
Concrete	Usually very resistant to fire and does not collapse catastrophically. May 'spall' - throw off small chunks.
Steel	Severely affected by high temperature - will expand, twist and warp (buckle). Structural elements can be pushed apart, leading to catastrophic collapse. It will also conduct heat and increase the possibility of fire spread.
Brick	Fired clay bricks are very resistant to fire.
Timber	Thin timber will burn easily and quickly fail. Thicker timber may char on the outside, protecting its inner core - it will fail slowly.

To strengthen construction materials in a fire situation:

- Concrete is mixed with lighter aerated aggregates and reinforced with steel. Fire resistance depends on the type of aggregate used and the thickness of the concrete over the reinforcing rods.

- Steel is usually strengthened by encasing it in concrete or fire-resistant board.

- The integrity of bricks is enhanced by thickness, rendering or plaster, being a non-load-bearing wall, and the lack of perforations or cavities in the bricks.

- Timber and other surfaces can be treated with fire retardant or resistant finishes and intumescent coatings.

TOPIC FOCUS

The **fire resistance of timber** depends on the 'Four Ts':

- The **thickness** or cross-sectional area of the piece.

- The **tightness** of any joints involved - in general, the fewer joints, the better.

- The **type** of wood - generally, denser timber has better resistance (the surface chars, but because conduction is poor, the internal timber still performs structurally).

- Any **treatment** received, e.g. flame-retardant treatment is often applied to such materials as plywood or chipboard sheets.

Other Building Materials

- **Stone** - granite, limestone and sandstone are commonly used for cladding. Provide good fire resistance but may be subject to "spalling" when used as cladding.

- **Building blocks** - clay or concrete, used as bricks in structures - provide excellent fire resistance, provided that the foundations and supporting structure can keep the wall in place during the fire.

- **Building boards** - used for cladding and insulation; combustible but not easily ignited.

- **Building slabs** - thick versions of board, used as substrates for roofing. Fire resistance is dependent on the materials used such as plywood, OSB (a structural panel made of wood strands sliced in the long direction and bonded together with a binder under heat and pressure) or timber boards; although concrete, wood wool or profiled metal can also be used.

  Current building regulations require all building slabs to be fire resistant, with more stringent standards for those used in buildings over 18m high.

- **Glass** - will break and cannot be used as a fire barrier, unless wired or treated (copperlight).

- **Insulating materials** - modern materials are non-combustible.

- **Lime** (plaster) - generally has good fire resistance.

- **Paint** - most paints are flammable; combustible when a dried finish. Flame-retardant and intumescent paints are available. When exposed to heat, these bubble rather than burn, giving additional protection to the painted timber.

- **Plastics** - thermoplastics will easily melt; thermosetting plastics will not, but will deteriorate in a fire.

Protection of Openings and Voids

Voids beneath floors and above ceilings, as well as openings around pipework and other services, lift shafts, air handling ducts, etc. can allow air to feed a fire, as well as assisting in the spread of fire and smoke. To help control this:

- Debris should not be allowed to accumulate in voids.

- When necessary, openings should be bonded or fire-stopped with non-combustible material.

- Ventilation ducts and gaps around doors must have the facility to be stopped in the event of a fire. This can be achieved by the use of baffles, self-closing doors and intumescent material which expands when subject to heat, thereby sealing the opening.

- It is important that any new openings made in a fire-resistant compartment are reinstated or protected in some way, e.g. when cables are run through a hole in a wall, the opening could be filled with a spray-in intumescent foam.

> **DEFINITION**
>
> **FIRE STOPPING**
>
> A **firestop** is a fire protection system made of various components used to seal openings and joints in fire-resistance rated wall or floor assemblies. For penetrating cables, these are also known as Multi Cable Transits (MCTs).

Use of Suitable Electrical Equipment in Flammable Atmospheres

The **Dangerous Substances and Explosive Atmospheres Regulations 2002 (DSEAR)** intend to eliminate or reduce the risks of fire (and explosion) arising from the hazardous properties of substances, particularly where they create a flammable or explosive mixture in air.

Part of the elimination or reduction of risks requires the use of intrinsically safe electrical fixtures, fittings and equipment in such atmospheres. Where such atmospheres may occur, the area must be split into hazardous and non-hazardous zones and marked with signs at points of entry.

The zones and categories of electrical equipment are shown below:

Zone 0	Zone 1	Zone 2
Explosive gas atmosphere present continuously or for long periods.	Explosive gas atmosphere likely to occur in normal operation.	Explosive gas atmosphere not likely to occur in normal operation; if it does, it is only for short time.
Cat 1 Electrical Equipment	**Cat 2 Electrical Equipment**	**Cat 3 Electrical Equipment**
"i" intrinsically safe. **BS EN 60079-11:2012**	"d" flameproof enclosure. **BS EN 60079-1:2014**	Electrical type "e". **BS EN 60079-7:2015 Explosive atmospheres. Equipment protection by increased safety "e".**

In addition, suitable earthing of all equipment and plant is required, and all maintenance controlled to prevent sparks being created (use of a permit to work).

STUDY QUESTIONS

9. How might you minimise the risk of fire in a woodworking area?

10. What precautions should be taken when using flammable liquids?

11. What hazards are associated with LPG?

12. What are the requirements for safe storage of LPG?

13. Upon what does the fire resistance of each of the following building materials depend?

    (a) Timber.

    (b) Reinforced concrete.

    (c) Brick walls.

14. Describe the effects of fire on an unprotected steel beam.

15. Describe how flame-retardant paint protects covered timber.

16. Describe the conditions that determine the three zones used to identify hazard areas (UK **DSEAR**).

(Suggested Answers are at the end.)

Fire Detection, Fire Alarm and Fire-Fighting Equipment

IN THIS SECTION...

- Fire safety relies upon systems to detect and warn of fire, and a means of fighting a fire.

- Consideration of fire safety systems must include:

  - Common fire detection and fire alarm systems.

  - The siting, maintenance, inspection and training requirements with regard to portable fire-fighting equipment.

  - The advantages and limitations of extinguishing media: water, foam, dry powder and carbon dioxide.

Common Fire Detection and Alarm Systems

Fire Detection

In the simplest of workplaces, where all parts can be seen by occupants and the risk of fire is low, fire detection can rely on nothing more than a person seeing or smelling the fire. In larger workplaces, or where early detection is critical, e.g. remote or unoccupied places, detection systems should be used:

System	Features
Smoke/fume detectors	Very common. Will detect small particles in smoke, are very sensitive and give early warning. They have ionising or optical sensors, but can give false alarms in humid, dusty or smoky atmospheres.
Heat detectors	More suitable for some situations. Detect heat from a fire, but are less sensitive and give later warnings. They can detect heat by fixed temperature or the rate of rise in temperature (fusion or expansion heat detectors). They may not detect a slow, smouldering fire giving off smoke but little heat.
Flame detectors	These are optical sensors and will detect flames by ultraviolet and infrared systems.

Fire Alarms

On small, compact sites, word of mouth might be adequate, but in all other cases, alarm systems should be fitted as early as possible in the construction phase, maintained in good working order and repaired.

Problems can arise if wiring operations lead to the alarm system being disabled (deliberately or otherwise) even for a short length of time, particularly where construction occurs in an existing workplace. Alternative means of raising the alarm need to be planned in the event of this happening, and the occupants informed.

All alarm systems must be maintained and tested regularly and the results recorded. Any faults discovered must be rectified and the system re-checked.

Fire alarm

- **Manual Systems**

  These are suitable for small workplaces of low risk and include rotary gongs, iron triangles, hand bells, whistles and horns. They can only raise the alarm over a limited area and for a limited time. There should be a means for the person raising the alarm to make it more widespread - by using a phone or public address system, or a manual/electric system.

- **Interlinked Smoke Alarms**

  Used in remote locations, these units detect the smoke (or flames) and sound an alarm, not just stand-alone, but often in a linked circuit.

- **Manual/Electric Systems**

  These are systems which are initiated from an alarm call point (a 'break glass' unit). When pressed, the alarm is sounded throughout the premises (or a particular part of them). It may also relay an alert to the fire service.

- **Automatic Fire Alarms**

  These are not normally present on small construction sites. They are made up of automatic detectors and manual call points linked through a central control box to alarms (and sometimes flashing beacons). A person can activate them on seeing a fire, or they will initiate automatically if no-one is around.

Note: in noisy environments, visible warnings (flashing lights) may be needed in addition to audible alarms. Similar provision may be appropriate for hearing-impaired workers.

Portable Fire-Fighting Equipment

Small fires can be dealt with quickly using portable fire extinguishers, but this should only be attempted where the person is trained to do so and it is safe, without putting them at risk.

Extinguishing Media

- **Fire extinguishers** - coloured red, with an identifying colour code to denote the extinguishing agent contained (e.g. water, carbon dioxide, foam, powder or vaporising liquid).

- **Fire blankets** - a fibre blanket used to smother small fires. Very useful in a kitchen where there may be burning fat, and also for smothering burning clothing.

- **Hose reels** - sited in fixed locations in buildings to allow fire teams to fight larger fires.

- **Sprinkler systems** - built-in systems sited in buildings, warehouses and at large flammable tank locations - they work automatically off (usually) thermal detectors.

Portable fire extinguisher

Note: where sprinkler systems are installed, they should be deactivated before hot work is carried out that could set them off.

TOPIC FOCUS

Fire Extinguishers

Under BS EN 3-10:2009, all fire extinguishers are now **red**, with colour identification to denote the extinguishing agent contained.

Common types of fire extinguishers and their uses include:

- **Water** (red with white lettering) - suitable for Class A fires. It works by cooling the fire. A standard water extinguisher is not suitable for use on Class B, D or F fires or live electrical equipment (this might lead to risk of shock). Certain specialised water extinguishers are available for use on Class B and F fires.

- **Carbon dioxide** (black colour coding) - suitable for Class B fires and fires involving live electrical equipment. It works by smothering the fire. It is not suitable for use on Class D or F fires. It must be used with care because the body of the extinguisher gets very cold during use and can cause a freeze-burn injury. Carbon dioxide is an asphyxiant gas and so care must be exercised when using in an enclosed space.

- **Foam** (cream colour code) - suitable for Class A and B fires. It works by smothering the fire or by preventing combustible vapours from mixing with air. Some specialist foam can be used on electrical fires but, again, you must be certain that you are using the right type. As the foam is wet, it is not suitable for Class F hot fat fires.

- **Dry powder** (blue colour coding) - suitable for all classes, with the exception of Class F, and use on live electrical equipment. It works by cooling the flames and may chemically interfere with the combustion process. It can be very messy and the powder must not be inhaled.

- **Halon** (green colour code) - suitable for Class A and B fires, especially live electrical equipment. However, under the Montreal Protocol halon is now very limited and is replaced with other gas or vaporising liquids.

- **Fire blankets** (in red box or wrapper) - suitable for Class B and F fires.

Siting

Portable fire-fighting equipment should be:

- Located at fire exit doors and along escape routes.

- Positioned close to specific hazards (e.g. a flammable store) on site, in clearly marked locations.

- Easily accessible (kept clear) at all times.

Maintenance and Inspection

To ensure they are always available and work when we need them, extinguishers are to be routinely inspected and maintained by means of:

- **Frequent routine inspections** - to make sure they are in their correct locations and that they appear to be full and in working order (with the firing pin still tagged, or a gauge reading full). This can be done as a housekeeping check or routine site inspection.

- **Planned preventive maintenance** - a regular service usually done by qualified persons or fire safety engineering companies. This ensures the condition of the extinguisher body, its operating system and its contents.

Training

Employees need enough fire safety training to:

- Understand the theories and principles of fire.

- Be able to raise the alarm when necessary.

- Know what actions to take if they hear the alarm.

- Know when and when NOT to tackle a fire.

- Know when to leave a fire that has not been extinguished.

> **MORE...**
>
> **Fire Safety (Employees' Capabilities) (England) Regulations 2010**
>
> www.legislation.gov.uk/uksi/2010/471/contents/made
>
> **Fire Safety (Employees' Capabilities) (Wales) Regulations 2012**
>
> www.legislation.gov.uk/wsi/2012/1085/contents/made

Training on the use of fire extinguishers should be enough so that they can:

- Identify the correct type to use on a particular class of fire (and which not to use).

- Use a fire extinguisher to effect their escape or save their life in a fire situation.

The intention is not to make them fire-fighters, and employers must take into account the health and safety capabilities of employees when entrusting them with fire safety tasks. This will apply at all levels of employee training, including competent persons, fire marshals, etc.

Advantages and Limitations of Extinguishing Media

All extinguishers have the limitation of short duration and relatively small amount of extinguishing agent; therefore they are only suitable for small fires. Some other advantages and limitations include:

Extinguishing Agent	Advantages	Limitations
Water	Good cooling medium for Class A fires. No chemicals involved. Inexpensive material.	Not suitable on most Class B, D or F fires or on live electrical equipment.
Carbon dioxide	Smothers quickly. Non-toxic. Suitable for Class A and B fires and live electrical equipment.	A gas cylinder under pressure. Not suitable on Class D fires. Use with care - rapidly exhausting gas can cause freeze-injury if touched. Noisy and can startle a user.

Extinguishing Agent	Advantages	Limitations
Foam	Suitable for B fires and fires involving live electrical equipment. Smothers a fire. Valuable where burning liquids are 'running' (moving along the ground, as in a spillage).	Not suitable for Class B, C, D or F fires. Messy. Not easy to correctly use unless trained.
Dry powder	Suitable for Class A, B, C and D fires, and on live electrical equipment. Smothers a fire.	Not suitable for Class F fires. Can be messy. Some noise when exhausting the powder.
Vaporising liquid (**Halon in very limited situations**)	Suitable for Class A and B fires, especially live electrical equipment. Smothers a fire and interferes chemically with the combustion process.	Expensive medium. Uses a gas cylinder under pressure. Noisy when released. Some can be harmful if inhaled.

TOPIC FOCUS

AQUEOUS FILM FORMING FOAM (AFFF)

Aqueous Film Forming Foam (AFFF) extinguishers have a dual Class A and Class B rating which allows them to be used against both solid and liquid burning fires. These extinguishers also have a conductivity rating of 35kV which means that, although they are not specifically designed for use on electrical fires, they can be safely used on electrical equipment up to 1,000V.

The reason why an "aqueous" medium can be used on electrical equipment is that the method of delivery is by spray nozzle, which breaks up the flow of extinguishant. This prevents a continuous electrical path between the user and the electrical apparatus.

STUDY QUESTIONS

17. What are the limitations of manual alarm systems and how may they be overcome?

18. Identify the three ways in which fire may be detected and state the types of automatic detector associated with each.

19. Identify the classes of fire for which each of the following extinguishing agents/devices are suitable:

    (a) Water.

    (b) Carbon dioxide gas.

    (c) Dry powder.

    (d) Foam.

    (e) Fire blankets.

20. State the colour coding requirements for portable fire extinguishers.

21. Outline the main points to be covered in training in the use of fire extinguishers.

(Suggested Answers are at the end.)

Means of Escape

IN THIS SECTION...

- The means of escape is the safe route that a person takes from wherever they happen to be in a building or on site, to a place of safety outdoors.

- The distance a person has to travel, the number of escape routes available and their width, the design of the route (i.e. stairs and passageways) and of fire doors along the route and the provision of suitable assembly points all have to be considered.

- It is important that the escape route is properly signed and provided with escape lighting where necessary.

Requirements for Means of Escape

In order to evacuate a fire situation safely there must be one or more escape routes available for people to use and the following principles can be applied:

- A means of escape is to be available for every person in the workplace, whether they are in an office, workshop, out on a construction site or on scaffolding.

- The means of escape should allow an able-bodied person to travel the entire distance of the route alone and unaided.

- They should not have to use machinery (e.g. a passenger lift) except in special circumstances (when it must be rated for escape purposes).

- The means of escape must take the person from wherever they are in the workplace to a place of safety outdoors.

- Two or more escape routes may have to be available in case one becomes blocked or otherwise unusable.

- The distance that a person has to travel along the route from its start to the final exit out of the building (or the assembly point on site) should be as short and straight as possible and may be limited to a maximum distance.

- The width of corridors and passageways in buildings and walkways on site should allow the free and fast movement of the numbers of people who might be anticipated (there are minimum widths applied).

- Escape routes should be clearly signed and appropriately lit.

- Escape (emergency) lighting should be provided where necessary in case the mains power fails.

- All escape routes should be clear of obstructions (stored materials, vehicles or inappropriate doors).

The means of escape and emergency plans must be regularly reviewed as construction work progresses to ensure they are always suitable and sufficient. As structures change, routes may become blocked or may no longer be the best route for occupants to take.

> **DEFINITION**
>
> **MEANS OF ESCAPE**
>
> The safe route that a person takes from wherever they happen to be in a building or on site, to a place of safety outdoors.

Escape routes are to be kept clear of obstructions

Stairs and Passageways

Stairs and passageways (corridors) used as means of escape should be:

- Protected against fire ingress to a higher degree than other parts of a building. (This is to keep them free from flames and smoke so they can be used for escape. The walls, floor and ceiling will need to be fire-resistant and doors along the route should be fire doors.)

- Kept free from obstructions and the storage of materials and products that would be fuel in a fire.

Doors

Doors along the escape route must:

- Be suitably fire-resistant for the location (see earlier).

- Be easily opened by a person escaping.

- Be wide enough to allow unimpeded passage.

- Open in the direction of travel (not always a strict requirement where occupancy numbers are low).

- Be able to be opened at all times while people are in the building (i.e. not locked or chained while the building is occupied).

Lighting

> **DEFINITIONS**
>
> **EMERGENCY SAFETY LIGHTING**
>
> Provides illumination to protect occupants who remain in the premises during a supply failure - applies to buildings for which a staged evacuation plan is implemented. It is adequate to allow occupants to stay in an area of the building during a power failure, but is not enough for functional tasks to be continued.
>
> **ESCAPE LIGHTING**
>
> Lighting that comes on automatically to illuminate an escape route.

Escape routes must be adequately lit, and where normal lighting is not adequate or will be lost in a power failure, additional lighting may be necessary. In the simplest of situations this could be a rechargeable torch, but larger workplaces will require escape lighting. This should:

- Illuminate:
  - The escape route.
  - Fire safety signs and equipment.
- Be maintained in working order.
- Undergo routine testing.

Signs

Escape routes must be easy to follow. Fire safety signs should be provided to direct occupants to and along routes. These signs (called 'safe condition' signs) must:

- Comply with legislative standards.

- Have appropriate pictograms in addition to any wording.

- Be fixed in places where they are easily seen and not easily obstructed.

A fire escape sign on an escape light unit

Signs can be standard coloured signs, light-retentive (glow in the dark) or attached to escape light units.

Assembly Points

Escape routes lead to an **assembly point**, where people gather once outside a building or away from danger areas on site. It will be in the open air and away from any further danger from the fire. At this location a roll call is taken to ensure everyone has escaped safely.

Assembly points should be:

- Clearly signed.

- A safe distance from a building or site hazards.

- In a safe location (away from traffic routes and storage areas).

- At a location where further escape is possible if needed.

- Out of the way of emergency service vehicles attending the fire and their personnel.

The location should be continually reviewed as construction work progresses.

In some cases a '**refuge**' is provided inside a building, which is a temporary location in a place of comparative or relative safety, in a fire-protected area, where people may wait for a short time, e.g. people with impaired mobility waiting for assistance to evacuate further.

TOPIC FOCUS

Travel Distances

- The distance people need to go to escape (the travel distance) should be as short as possible. The travel distance should be measured from the farthest point in a room to the door to a protected stairway or, if there is no protected stairway, to the final exit from the building.

- If there is only one escape route, the travel distance should not normally be more than 18 metres. This distance should be shorter (12 metres or less) in any parts of the premises where there is a high chance of a fire starting or spreading quickly.

- The distance can be longer (up to about 25 metres) where the chance of a fire starting or spreading quickly is very low.

- If there is more than one escape route, the travel distance should not normally be more than 45 metres (around 25 metres in areas where the risk of fire is high and about 60 metres in areas where the risk of fire is very low).

STUDY QUESTIONS

22. What is the purpose of signs used along an escape route?

23. Outline the main requirements for an escape route.

24. What is an assembly point, and how might it differ from a refuge?

(Suggested Answers are at the end.)

Evacuation of a Construction Workplace

IN THIS SECTION...

- Every construction workplace must have procedures to ensure the safe evacuation of people from danger areas in the event of fire.

- Some procedures will require nominated persons to carry out certain duties, e.g. fire marshals or someone to take the roll call.

- Employees should be trained in fire procedures and nominated persons trained in their specific roles.

- Fire drills allow employees to practise their emergency response and help management to monitor the effectiveness of the emergency arrangements.

- Special procedures may be required to ensure safe evacuation of the infirm or disabled.

Emergency Evacuation Procedures

Fire procedures ('action in the event of fire') must be in place to instruct employees in what actions to take in the event of fire. They need to know what to do if they find a fire, or hear the alarm (indicating someone else has found a fire). The safety message is simple - get out and stay out!

Fire procedures

Appointment of Fire Marshals

However many employees there are, responsibility for action in the event of fire should be assigned to specific persons. Some premises may have fire marshals (or fire wardens) who are responsible for the following actions:

- Ensuring all occupants leave by the designated safe escape routes.

- Searching all areas to ensure that the area is clear (people have left).

- Ensuring that fire escape routes are kept open and clear at all times.

- Ensuring all doors and windows are closed on leaving the area.

- Conducting the roll call at the assembly area (in the absence of senior management).

- Meeting the fire service on arrival and informing them of any relevant details.

- Ensuring special assistance is available to the disabled or infirm (perhaps using 'evac-chairs' in multi-storey areas).

- Investigating the location of the fire (as indicated by the fire alarm system controls).

Some sites may operate a 'fire team' who have the dual role of investigating the fire alarms and fire-fighting (they will be specially trained for this).

Fire Instructions and Training

All workers and others on site must receive sufficient information to know what to do in the event of fire. Site induction should give information on the:

- Location of relevant escape routes.

- Location and operation of the fire warning system in their working area.

Appropriate training should be given to those employees who:

- May have to use fire extinguishers or other fire-fighting equipment.

- Have a fire marshalling role.

- Will assist the infirm or disabled.

- Are members of a fire team.

Records of all training should be kept.

Fire Drills

These are generally planned events that:

- Allow all employees to properly practise the evacuation procedure.

- Give management an opportunity to test the procedure's overall effectiveness.

Time taken to evacuate and attendances should be recorded, and notes made of any shortcomings in the system. All shortcomings should be resolved.

Roll Call

On reaching the assembly point, a roll call must be held in order to account for everyone and make sure that no-one is missing:

- Arrangements should be in place for taking the roll call - a list of names of all on site.

- The roll call is conducted by pre-designated persons (commonly senior members of staff or fire marshals).

- Using a register may not be practical on all sites, so fire marshals may have to carry out area checks.

- If anyone is not accounted for in the roll call, the fire officer in charge must be notified as soon as the fire service arrives.

Provision for the Infirm and Disabled

- People with hearing or other physical disabilities must be accommodated in the evacuation plan.

- People in wheelchairs and the infirm must be provided with assistance.

- Provision must be made for other groups such as children or elderly persons.

Provision for the disabled

STUDY QUESTIONS

25. What should take place at an assembly point following an evacuation?

26. List the actions for which fire marshals/wardens are responsible when an evacuation takes place.

(Suggested Answers are at the end.)

Summary

This element has dealt with hazards and controls relevant to fire in the workplace.

In particular, the element has:

- Outlined basic principles of fire safety - including the fire triangle, the five classes of fire, how fire can spread, and some common causes of fire on construction sites.

- Looked at the five steps to fire risk assessment:
  - identify the hazards;
  - identify who may be harmed and how;
  - identify what precautions are in place and what more may be needed;
  - record the risk assessment; and
  - review the assessment periodically.

- Explained how fire can be prevented by controlling potential fuel sources (e.g. safe storage and use of flammable liquids) and potential sources of ignition (e.g. hot work), including the use of suitable electrical equipment in flammable atmospheres.

- Outlined the structural measures that assist in containing fire and smoke if a fire starts, and how to protect openings and voids.

- Described the general principles of fire detection and alarm systems.

- Discussed the main types of fire extinguishers, such as water, carbon dioxide, foam and dry powder, and the advantages and limitations of each type.

- Outlined the main characteristics of means of escape, including travel distances; number of routes available; width of routes; design of doors in the escape route; assembly points; safety signs; and escape lighting.

- Described basic requirements for evacuation: fire marshals; training and information; fire drills; roll call; and special procedures for the disabled and infirm.

Exam Skills

Approaching the Question

Think now about the steps you would take to answer the question:

Step 1. Read the question carefully. Note that this question is about fire risk in a refurbishment project.

Step 2. Now highlight the key words. In this case, they might look like this:

A major hazard on a **refurbishment project** is fire.

(a) **Identify THREE** activities that represent an **increased fire risk** in such a situation. **(3)**

(b) **Outline the precautions** that may be taken to **reduce the risk** of a fire occurring. **(5)**

Step 3. Next, consider the marks and time available. In this question, there are eight marks so it is expected that around eight or nine different pieces of information should be provided. The question is helpfully signposted into two parts. The part (a) action word is 'identify', so select and name activities - for three marks, three activities need to be identified. Part (b) has the action word 'outline' and is worth five marks, so this part must have at least five precautions to be taken to reduce risk. The question should take around eight minutes in total.

> **Note:** If you are specifically asked for three points, and you are confident in your first three answers, you don't need to waste time providing more - you won't get additional marks. If, however, you are not limited to a specific number (as in part (b)), we can assume from the mark scheme that there are five marks available, but providing an additional couple of precautions may increase your chance of gaining maximum marks for that section.

Step 4. Read the question again to make sure you understand it and have a clear understanding of fire risks and precautions. (Re-read your notes if you need to.)

Step 5. The next stage is to develop a plan - there are various ways to do this. Remind yourself, first of all, that you need to be thinking about 'fire risk'. When you see the action word 'outline', you need to give the most important features.

> Your answer must be based on the key words you have highlighted. So, in this case, we need to identify three activities that increase fire risk and outline precautions to take to reduce the risk of fire.

Now have a go at the question. Draw up an answer plan, and then use it as the basis to write out an answer as you would in the exam.

Remember, you can always contact your tutor if you have any queries or need any further guidance on how to answer this question.

When you have finished, compare your plan and full answer with those that follow.

Suggested Answer Outline

Activities	Precautions
• Hot work. • Use of flammable substances. • Electrical work. • Individuals smoking. • Burning rubbish on site.	• Permits to work to control hot work. • Fabricate components off site (minimise/avoid hot work). • Inspection of work areas prior to, during and after hot work. • Regular clearing away of rubbish. • Proper storage of flammable substances. • Testing of electrical systems and equipment. • Prohibit bonfires on site. • 'No smoking' policies enforced.

Example of How the Question Could be Answered

(a)   Three activities increasing fire risk include:

- Hot working, e.g. use of blowlamps when plumbing.

- Work requiring electrical tools using the existing wiring system of the site, which may be overloaded by the use of industrial electrical tools.

- Smoking on the site with the possible disregard for rules that prohibit smoking.

(b)   Precautions to reduce the risk of a fire include inspection and testing of the electrical system to ensure it has the load-carrying capacity for the tasks being undertaken, and that equipment used is inspected and tested prior to use. Hot work precautions include the use of permits to work, which may have agreed safe working practices such as the use of a fire-watcher (a person to monitor the area during and after operations to identify and extinguish sparks) and the provision of standby fire extinguishers to control sparks. The work area should be inspected prior to work being started to identify (and remove) rubbish which may ignite, and the area should be inspected when work has been completed to ensure no smouldering materials are left behind. Flammable substances such as paints should be stored in a suitable, labelled container away from sources of ignition. 'No smoking' on site policies must be enforced by supervision and communicated to all the site users prior to them entering the site. Safety inspections can check for evidence of the rule being broken by looking for discarded cigarette ends. The practice of burning rubbish on site should also be prohibited to prevent bonfires from spreading.

Reasons for Poor Marks Achieved by Candidates in Exam

- Citing general fire precautions rather than those related to refurbishment projects.

- Referring to the provision of fire extinguishers. The question was concerned with stopping fires starting rather than putting them out, so this gained no marks.

- Failing to separate answers into the two parts - structuring your answer to address the different parts of the question is necessary in these two-part questions.

- Illegible handwriting - you need to be aware that examiners cannot award marks if they cannot read what you have written.

Chemical and Biological Health - Hazards and Risk Control

Learning Outcomes

Once you've read this element, you'll understand how to:

1 Outline the forms of, classification of, and the health risks from exposure to, hazardous substances.

2 Explain the factors to be considered when undertaking an assessment of the health risks from substances encountered in construction workplaces.

3 Explain the use and limitations of workplace exposure limits, including the purpose of long-term and short-term exposure limits.

4 Outline control measures that should be used to reduce the risk of ill health from exposure to hazardous substances.

5 Outline the hazards, risks and controls associated with specific agents.

6 Outline the basic requirements related to the safe handling and storage of waste on construction sites.

Contents

Forms, Classification and the Health Risks from Hazardous Substances

IN THIS SECTION...

- In construction activities, many different forms of chemical hazards occur - dusts, fibres, fumes, gases, mists, vapours and liquids.

- Biological agents, such as fungi, bacteria and viruses, can be hazardous to health.

- Chemicals are classified according to their hazardous properties: toxic, harmful, corrosive, irritant or carcinogenic.

- There are differences between acute and chronic health effects of hazardous substances.

Introduction to Forms, Classification and the Health Risks from Hazardous Substances

Exposure to chemical hazards can occur:

- Intentionally - by using chemicals in our work.

- Unintentionally - from spillages and accidents.

In either case, exposure has to be prevented, and where we can't prevent it, it must be controlled so that no harm is caused to those who may be exposed.

Exposure can lead to immediate health effects (e.g. carbon monoxide can cause asphyxiation) or even physical effects (battery acid can burn the skin).

Some hazardous substances can have both short-term and long-term effects, e.g. concrete or stone grinding dust can cause immediate coughing and respiratory distress, and can lead on to permanent lung damage from prolonged or repeated exposure.

Spillages can lead to unintentional exposure to hazardous substances

Forms of Chemical Agents

Chemicals may be in the form of a substance (a chemical element or compound) or a preparation (a mixture of substances). These exist in a variety of physical states and this will affect the way chemical hazards occur in construction activities. The physical forms of chemicals are:

- **Dusts** - small solid particles created by grinding, polishing, blasting, road sweeping and mixing materials (e.g. cement), which become airborne.

- **Fibres** - asbestos and other Man-Made Mineral Fibres (MMMF) have different characteristics from dust particles. Important dimensions are the length and diameter of the fibre and the length to diameter ratio.

- **Fumes** - fine solid particles which are created by condensation from a vapour (e.g. welding fume) given off in a cloud. Metallic fume is usually the oxide of the metal and is toxic.

- **Gases** - a formless chemical which occupies the space in which it is enclosed (e.g. carbon dioxide, acetylene).

- **Mists** - small liquid droplets (aerosol) suspended in the air, created by activities such as paint spraying.

- **Vapours** - the gaseous form of a liquid or solid substance at normal temperature and pressure (e.g. solvent vapours given off by acetone).

- **Liquids** - a basic state of matter; free flowing fluid (e.g. water at room temperature).

The form they are in can significantly affect how they might enter the body (discussed later).

Forms of Biological Agents

Biological agents are micro-organisms. We will look at three types:

- **Fungi** - plant matter lacking chlorophyll and reproducing by spores. Examples include mushrooms, mould and yeasts. Fungal diseases can appear as asthmatic and/or influenza-type symptoms from inhaling dust or air contaminated by fungi, such as dry rot in roofs, or fungal infections such as athlete's foot.

- **Bacteria** - single-cell organisms found in vast numbers in and on the human body. Some are harmless, some are beneficial (certain gut bacteria) and some cause diseases, e.g. Legionnaires' disease or Weil's disease (leptospirosis). Construction activities near waterways could pose a risk from Weil's disease.

- **Viruses** - very small infectious organisms that increase by hijacking living cells to reproduce and generate more viruses. Many cause disease, e.g. hepatitis and AIDS.

Health Hazards Classification

The **Globally Harmonised System of Classification and Labelling of Chemicals (GHS)** is a single internationally agreed system of chemical classification and hazard communication using labelling and Safety Data Sheets (SDS).

It includes harmonised criteria for the classification of:

- **Physical hazards**, e.g. explosive, oxidising, highly flammable.

- **Health hazards**, e.g. toxic, harmful, irritant, carcinogenic.

- **Environmental hazards**, e.g. harmful to aquatic organisms, dangerous for the ozone layer.

TOPIC FOCUS

The main **classifications of chemicals hazardous to health** can be summarised as follows:

- **Toxic** (or very toxic) - small quantities cause death or serious ill health if inhaled, swallowed or absorbed via the skin.

- **Harmful** - may cause death or serious ill health when inhaled, swallowed or absorbed through the skin in large doses.

- **Corrosive** - destroys living tissue on contact, such as sulphuric acid and hydrochloric acid in chemical cleaners, e.g. for masonry or brickwork.

- **Irritant** - causes inflammation of the mucous membranes (eyes and lungs) or skin from immediate, prolonged or repeated contact.

- **Carcinogenic** - may cause cancer (abnormal growth of cells in the body) when inhaled, swallowed or absorbed via the skin.

Criteria for classifying chemicals have been developed for the following GHS health hazard classes:

- **Acute Toxicity**

  These chemicals cause acute toxic effects after ingestion, skin absorption or inhalation. They are allocated to one of five toxicity categories and category 1 toxic chemicals are those requiring the lowest dose to cause a toxic response.

- **Skin Corrosion/Irritation**

  These chemicals cause:

  - irreversible corrosive damage to the skin,

    or

  - irritation of the skin which is reversible.

- **Serious Eye Damage/Eye Irritation**

  These chemicals cause:

  - serious tissue damage in the eye or serious physical decay of vision,

    or

  - irritation of the eye which is reversible.

- **Respiratory or Skin Sensitisation**

  These chemicals cause sensitisation, which means they can produce an allergic reaction that will gradually worsen as exposure is repeated. There are two types:

  - **Respiratory sensitisers** - these can cause asthma and similar effects if inhaled (e.g. wood dusts and isocyanates).

  - **Skin sensitisers** - these can cause allergic dermatitis on contact with the skin (e.g. epoxy resin used in adhesives and paints). Bad cases can cause absence from work. It can be reportable under RIDDOR in certain cases.

- **Germ Cell Mutagenicity**

  Mutagenic chemicals may cause genetic mutations that can be inherited.

- **Carcinogenicity**

  Carcinogenic chemicals may induce cancer or increase its incidence.

- **Reproductive Toxicity**

  Chemicals that are toxic to reproduction may cause sterility or affect an unborn child. Known as teratogens, they are substances that cause harm to the foetus or embryo during pregnancy, causing birth defects while the mother shows no signs of toxicity. Common teratogens include ethanol, mercury compounds, lead compounds, phenol, carbon disulfide, toluene and xylene.

- **Specific Target Organ Toxicity (Single and Repeated Exposure)**

  All significant health effects, not otherwise specifically included in the GHS, that can impair function (both reversible and irreversible, immediate and/or delayed) are included in this class. Narcotic effects and respiratory tract irritation are examples of this.

DEFINITION

DERMATITIS

A skin disease (sometimes called eczema) in which the skin's surface protective layer is damaged, leading to redness/swelling of hands and fingers, cracking of skin and blisters on hands/fingers, flaking/scaling of skin, and itching of hands/fingers with cracks.

MORE...

Information on dermatitis is available in the HSE publication INDG233 *Preventing contact dermatitis and urticaria at work* available at:

www.hse.gov.uk/pubns/indg233.pdf

- **Aspiration Hazard**

  Aspiration is the entry of a liquid or solid directly through the mouth or nose, or indirectly from vomiting, into the trachea and lower respiratory system. Some hydrocarbons (petroleum distillates) and certain chlorinated hydrocarbons are aspiration hazards. Acute effects include pneumonia, varying degrees of pulmonary injury or death.

Acute and Chronic Health Effects

It is important to understand the difference between acute (short term) and chronic (long term) health effects from exposure to hazardous substances:

- **Acute effects** occur quickly after exposure (i.e. in seconds, minutes or hours), often from large amounts of a substance, e.g. inhaling high concentrations of chlorine gas causes immediate respiratory irritation. These effects are often reversible.

- **Chronic effects** take time to appear (i.e. months or even years), after exposure to smaller amounts of a substance over a longer period of time, e.g. working with lead can take months to accumulate high levels of lead in the blood. These effects are mostly irreversible.

In terms of prevention, chronic effects present the most difficult control problems. This is because:

- The effects occur over a long period, so the hazard is not recognised.

- The level of contamination required to produce chronic effects is often tolerated by people because they do not experience acute symptoms.

- Symptoms occur slowly, so they are not recognised until an advanced condition of harm has developed.

- When symptoms are recognised, the harm may be too advanced for full recovery - sometimes no recovery is possible.

- Symptoms are often confused with 'normal' ill health or with 'getting older'.

- Symptoms are not always easily identifiable in groups of people with the same exposure, owing to the effect of differing 'personal' metabolisms.

Many hazardous substances can have an acute **and** chronic effect. For example, inhaling solvent vapours can have an almost immediate narcotic effect (acute) and long-term repeated exposure to lower levels can cause liver damage over a number of years (chronic).

> ## STUDY QUESTIONS
>
> 1. State the physical forms of chemical agents which may exist in the workplace.
>
> 2. Identify the five main health hazard classifications of chemicals.
>
> 3. Define the characteristics of mist and fumes, and identify a potential source of each in construction activities.
>
> 4. Distinguish briefly between acute and chronic ill-health effects.
>
> (Suggested Answers are at the end.)

Assessment of Health Risks

IN THIS SECTION...

- There are four main 'routes' by which hazardous substances enter the body: inhalation, ingestion, absorption through the skin and injection through the skin.

- The body has defence mechanisms to keep hazardous substances out and to protect from their harmful effects. The respiratory system is protected by the sneeze reflex, nasal cavity, ciliary escalator and macrophages.

- Knowledge about routes of entry is used during the assessment of health risks and to determine appropriate control measures.

- Information about the substances can be gathered from product labels, material safety data sheets and exposure limit lists, although there are limitations with this information.

- Assessments sometimes require that basic surveys are carried out using equipment such as stain tube detectors, passive samplers, smoke tubes, dust monitoring equipment and dust lamps. There are some limitations in their use.

Routes of Entry

Hazardous substances enter the body through **absorption**. They can be absorbed through the skin, the lining of the lungs or the gastrointestinal tract.

The way a substance gets to these absorption locations is along a **route of entry**. Absorption may take place anywhere along the route.

Some substances can cause physical harm from contact, e.g. battery acid burning the skin from spillages. Others, such as epoxy resin, can sensitise from touching the skin.

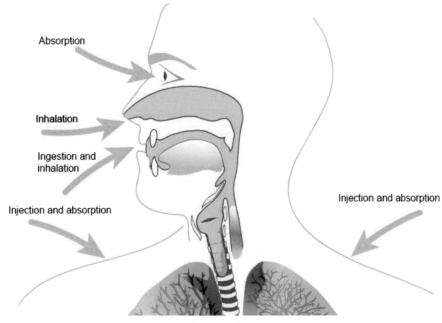

Routes of entry

TOPIC FOCUS

There are four main **routes of entry** for hazardous substances into the body:

- **Inhalation** - the substance is breathed in through the nose or mouth and travels along the respiratory passages to the lungs. The lung is the most vulnerable part of the body, as it can readily absorb gases, fumes, soluble dusts, mists and vapours. This is the main means of entry of biological agents.

  There are two types of dust:

  - Inhalable - particles of all sizes that can be inhaled into the nose and mouth and upper reaches of the respiratory tract.

  - Respirable - particles smaller than 7 microns (7/1,000 mm) that can travel deep into the lungs.

- **Ingestion** - the substance is taken in through the mouth and swallowed, travelling the whole length of the gastrointestinal tract through the stomach and the intestines. This may occur:

  - As a result of swallowing the agent directly.

  - From eating or drinking contaminated foods.

  - From eating with contaminated fingers.

  All forms of chemicals may be ingested, and some biological agents may also enter the body by this route.

- **Absorption** through the skin - the substance passes through the skin from direct contact with the agent or from contact with contaminated surfaces or clothing. It is mainly liquid chemicals which enter the body in this way, although other forms of chemical may either sufficiently damage the skin to gain entry or find their way through the eyes.

- **Injection** through the skin - the substance enters directly into the body by high pressure equipment or contaminated sharp objects piercing the skin. Chemical liquids, and sometimes gases and vapours, may enter the body in this way. Biological agents are often injected - either on needles, etc. or by biting from an insect or infected animal.

Although not a main route of entry, aspiration can also occur - where a substance already swallowed is regurgitated and can be inhaled into the lungs - usually if a person is unconscious.

Defence Mechanisms

The body's response against the invasion of substances likely to cause damage can be divided into **superficial** and **cellular** defence mechanisms.

Superficial

The skin provides a barrier against organisms and chemicals, but can only withstand limited physical damage. Some forms of dermatitis arise as a result of this damage, leading to thickening and inflammation of the skin which is both painful and unsightly.

The **respiratory tract** has a series of defences against inhaling contaminants:

- **The 'sneeze' reflex** - immediate irritation causing sneezing to expel contaminants.

- **Nasal cavity filters** - substances and micro-organisms down to 10 microns are trapped by nasal hairs and mucus.

- **Ciliary escalator** - the bronchioles, bronchi and trachea are lined with small hairs (cilia); mucus lining these passages is gradually brought up by these cilia out of the lungs. Particles above 7 microns trapped in the mucus are cleaned from the lungs by this mechanism.

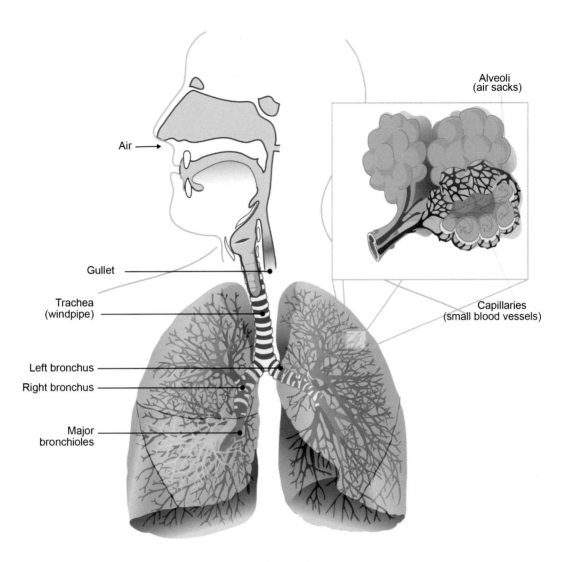

The respiratory system

Cellular

- **Macrophages** - scavenging white blood cells attack and destroy particles (fewer than seven microns) that lodge in the alveoli (the gas-exchange region in the lungs) where there are no cilia to protect them.

- **Inflammatory response** - any particles that cannot be removed by the macrophages are likely to trigger an inflammatory response, causing the walls of the alveoli to thicken and become fibrous. This can be temporary or result in permanent scarring (as with silicosis).

- **Prevention of excessive blood loss** - blood clotting and coagulation prevents excessive bleeding and slows or prevents the entry of contaminants into the blood.

Factors to be Considered when Assessing Health Risks

Where there is a potential for construction workers to be exposed to hazardous substances, it will be necessary to assess that potential to ensure that harm does not occur. This is a requirement of the **Control Of Substances Hazardous to Health Regulations 2002 (COSHH)**.

The risk assessment carried out to satisfy these regulations is often called a '**COSHH** Assessment'. There are five steps to **COSHH** assessment:

1. Gather information about the substance used, the people who might be exposed and the work activities carried out.

2. Evaluate the health risks - are current controls adequate?

3. Identify any further controls and implement them.

4. Record the risk assessment and actions taken.

5. Review and revise.

When identifying the hazardous substances on the construction site remember that many are created by the work carried out, e.g. welding metal creates a metal fume; spraying paint creates an aerosol mist; these hazardous substances do not come pre-packaged and labelled, but are created by the construction work activities.

We will see later that you can collect information about hazardous substances by referring to various information sources. This information can be used to evaluate the health risks associated with the actual work practices.

TOPIC FOCUS

Factors to consider when carrying out an **assessment of health risks**:

- **Hazardous nature** of the substance - is it toxic, harmful, carcinogenic?

- **Physical form** of the substance - is it a solid, liquid, vapour or dust?

- The **quantity** of the hazardous substance present on site - including total amounts stored and the amounts actually in use or being created at any one time.

- Potential **ill-health effects** - will it cause minor ill health or very serious disease? And will this result from short-term or long-term exposure?

- **Duration** - how much exposure and for how long? Will it be for just a few minutes, or last all day?

- **Routes of entry** - will it be inhaled, swallowed, absorbed?

- **Concentration** - will a substance be used neat or diluted? What is the concentration in the air?

- **The number of people** potentially exposed and any vulnerable groups or individuals - such as expectant mothers or the infirm.

- **The control measures** that are already in place - such as ventilation systems and PPE.

All these factors have to be taken into account when doing the **COSHH** assessment, and then the adequacy of any existing control measures can be decided and additional controls and precautions selected.

MORE...

For more information on **COSHH**, visit:

www.hse.gov.uk/COSHH/index.htm

Carcinogenic sign

Sources of Information

To assist the assessment of health risks, further information will be required. This can be obtained from product labels, safety data sheets and exposure limit documents.

The **Classification, Labelling and Packaging Regulation (CLP)** and the **European Registration, Evaluation, Authorisation and Restriction of Chemicals (REACH) Regulation** are the foundation of general chemicals legislation.

Product Labels

When supplying dangerous substances/mixtures, a product label must give the following information:

- Name, address and telephone number of the supplier.

- The nominal quantity of the substance/mixture (though this may be elsewhere on the package) - but only where it is made available to the general public.

- Product identifiers:

  - for substances: name and identification number (EC number, CAS number or inventory number);

  - for mixtures: trade name, and the identity of all the substances (maximum of 4) in the mixture which contribute to its classification.

- Hazard pictograms.

- Signal word (as applicable).

- Hazard statements (as applicable).

- Precautionary statements (as applicable).

- Supplementary information.

> **DEFINITION**
>
> **SAFETY DATA SHEET**
>
> Provides all necessary information about the substance - for transport safety and to assist in carrying out the **COSHH** assessment.
>
> Note: Often wrongly called '**COSHH** Sheets' they are, in fact, nothing to do with the **COSHH Regulations** but rather relate to **REACH**.

Sulphuric Acid 50%

Danger

Causes severe skin burns and eye damage.

Do not breathe mist. Wash hands thoroughly after handling. Wear protective gloves/clothing and eye/face protection.

IF SWALLOWED: Rinse mouth. Do NOT induce vomiting.
IF ON SKIN (or hair): Remove/Take off immediately all contaminated clothing. Rinse skin with water/shower. Wash contaminated clothing before reuse.
IF INHALED: Remove victim to fresh air and keep at rest in a position comfortable for breathing. Immediately call a POISON CENTER or doctor/physician.
IF IN EYES: Rinse cautiously with water for several minutes. Remove contact lenses, if present and easy to do. Continue rinsing.

Store locked up.

Dispose of contents/container in accordance with local regulation.

EC 231-639-5
CAS 7664-93-9

Net volume:
25 Litres

Supplied by: Amoeba Chemicals
Addison Lane, Bolsover, Derbyshire
Tel: +44 (0)3445 6298

A label showing the key information about the hazardous nature of the product

HSE Guidance Note EH40

This contains the lists of workplace exposure limits for use with the **COSHH Regulations**. The lists are reviewed annually and include information on materials under review for inclusion or for a change of category, plus lists of materials classified as: 'may cause cancer' and 'may cause cancer by inhalation'.

Manufacturers' Safety Data Sheets

Article 31 of **REACH** requires suppliers of dangerous substances and preparations to provide safety data sheets (this requirement was formerly within **CHIP**).

Safety data sheets are intended to provide users with sufficient information about the hazards of a substance or preparation for them to take appropriate steps to ensure health and safety in the workplace in relation to all aspects of its use, including its handling, transport and disposal.

They are not COSHH Assessments and should not be taken as such.

TOPIC FOCUS

Safety data sheets contain the following information:

- Identification of the substance or preparation, and supplier - name, address and emergency contact phone numbers.

- Hazard identification - a summary of the most important features, including likely adverse human health effects and symptoms.

- Composition and information on ingredients - chemical names, classification code letters and risk phrases.

- First-aid measures - separated for the various risks, and specific, practical and easily understood.

- Fire-fighting measures - emphasising any special requirements.

- Accidental release measures - covering safety, environmental protection and clean-up.

- Handling and storage - recommendations for best practice, including any special storage conditions or incompatible materials.

- Exposure controls and personal protection - any specific recommendations, such as particular ventilation systems and PPE.

- Physical and chemical properties - physical, stability and solubility properties.

- Stability and reactivity - conditions and materials to avoid.

- Toxicological information - acute and chronic effects, routes of entry and symptoms.

- Ecological information - environmental effects of the chemical, which could include patterns of degradation and effects on aquatic, soil and terrestrial organisms, etc.

- Disposal considerations - advice on specific dangers and legislation.

- Transport information - special precautions.

- Regulatory information - e.g. labelling and any relevant national laws.

- Other information - e.g. list of relevant risk phrases, any restrictions on use (non-statutory supplier recommendations).

Safety data sheets must be supplied (paper or electronic) free of charge when the substance is first provided. They must be kept up to date and revised and reissued accordingly.

Limitations of Information in Assessing Risks to Health

The sources of information we have seen are important, but have limitations in assessing health risks:

- They contain general statements of the hazards, but do not take into account local conditions in which you will use the substances, which will affect the risk.

- The information can be very technical and difficult to understand by the non-specialist.

- Substances affect different people in different ways - this is not taken into account in the generalities used.

- Information is about a substance or preparation in isolation - no account is taken of the effects of mixed exposures.

- The information was good at the time it was written; it represents current scientific thinking, so there may be hazards present that are not currently understood.

Role and Limitations of Hazardous Substance Monitoring

Hazardous substance monitoring sets out to measure how much of a contaminant is in the air (inhalation is the only route of entry that we can positively measure), and we use this, together with time exposure, to assess the risks to health of substance exposure.

To carry out hazardous substance monitoring we use various types of sampling equipment to collect and measure how much contaminant is in the air.

TOPIC FOCUS

Sampling Techniques

The first task in our basic survey is to collect the sample of air so that it may be analysed. We need to consider (depending on the risk level of the contaminant being assessed):

- **Location of the sample** - it may be taken in the general working atmosphere, in the operator's breathing zone, or at a position close to the contaminant generation or use.

- **Method of analysis** - this may involve sampling and analysis in the same instrument, or taking the sample collected and analysing it using different equipment, perhaps in a laboratory away from the point of collection.

- **Duration of the sampling** - is the survey looking at short- or long-term exposures?

Hazardous substance monitoring surveys generally fall into three main categories:

- A **spot** or **grab** sample - a snapshot of airborne concentration at one moment in time - usually analysed on the spot.

- A better method of obtaining a time-weighted average is by **collecting a sample over a period** and then analysing it. This is the usual technique for personal monitoring.

- A **continuous monitored** sample (usually high-risk areas) - where a sample is collected and continuously analysed over a period of time. Such systems may be linked to an alarm system if safe levels are exceeded.

There are two basic **methods of sampling**, based on the way in which the sample is collected:

- **Diffusion** or **passive sampling** - where the air sample (along with any contaminants in it) passes over the sampling system naturally, through an absorbent material which can be removed for later analysis.

- **Mechanical** or **active sampling** - where a pump forces air flow through the sampling device - used for both spot and continuous sampling.

Stain Tube Detectors

These are easy to use and useful for analysing gas and vapour contamination in air at one moment in time (spot sampling).

The principle of operation is simple - a known volume of air is drawn over a chemical reagent contained in a glass tube. The contaminant reacts with the reagent and a coloured stain is produced. The degree of staining can give a direct reading of concentration.

The instrument comprises a glass tube containing the chemical reagent fitted to a hand-operated bellows pump or piston-type pump. Many types of tube are available, with different chemicals that react to different gases and vapours.

To operate:

- Select the appropriate tube.

- Snap off the end of the tube to open it.

- Place the open end on the pump and break off the other end.

- Squeeze the bellows or operate the pump for a specified amount (e.g. number of squeezes of the bellows).

This draws air through the detector tube, the chemical in the tube changes colour and the concentration of the contaminant can be read from a scale marked along the tube.

The following diagram illustrates the principle:

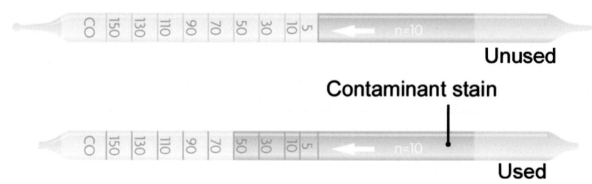

Stain tube before and after use. Note the closed and open ends of the tube. Arrow shows direction of air flow. n = 10 indicates that 10 strokes on the hand bellows are required. These tubes are sensitive to carbon monoxide (CO). Final concentration is given as 50 parts-per-million (ppm)

Limitations of stain tube detectors:

- Provide a spot-sample for one moment in time rather than an average reading.

- Can have an accuracy of +/-25%, which is not particularly accurate.

- Correct number of strokes must be used; losing count and giving too few/too many will give inaccurate results.

- Volume of air sampled may not be accurate due to incorrect assembly interfering with the air flow (through leaks, etc.) or incorrect operation.

- Can be cross-sensitive to substances other than the one being tested for.

- Designed to operate at about 20°C and one atmosphere pressure. Problems may be caused by variations in temperature and pressure away from these standard conditions.

- Tubes have a shelf storage life; out-of-date tubes may be inaccurate due to deterioration of the reagent.

- There may be variations in the precise reagent make-up between tubes.

Passive Samplers

These use absorbent material to sample contaminants without using a pump to draw air through the collector. They give a measure of concentration over a period of time (long-term sampling) and can be used for gas or vapour. There are two main types of design:

- The **badge (or dish) sampler** has a flat, permeable membrane supported over a shallow layer of sorbent.

- The **tube-type sampler** has a smaller permeable membrane supported over a deep metal tube filled with sorbent.

They allow gas or vapour to diffuse to an absorbent surface. At the end of sampling, the sampler is sent for laboratory analysis, although some work on a colour-change principle similar to litmus paper. Working on a colour-change principle allows visual assessment against a standard chart.

Limitations of passive samplers:

- Do not provide any immediate indication of the contamination concentration - results have to be analysed (unless colour changing).

- Only measure accumulated concentrations over the period for which they are in use - cannot be easily used to calculate time-weighted averages.

- Only sample contamination where they are located or, in the case of badges, where the wearer is - cannot be easily used to take spot-samples in various parts of the workplace.

- Badges are easy to take off, rendering them ineffective.

- Size of the sample is imperative. If the samplers are only used intermittently or only a small sample is used, results may be misleading.

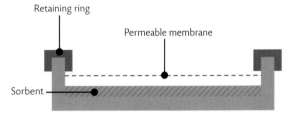

Badge sampler

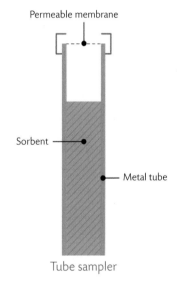

Tube sampler

Oxygen Meters

Direct reading instruments are available to monitor and warn of concentrations of the toxic gases carbon dioxide, carbon monoxide or hydrogen sulphide in the atmosphere, as well as the essential gas, oxygen, in naturally occurring respirable air. They are usually reliable and accurate.

They indicate concentrations of oxygen in the atmosphere on a simple dial or digital readout. To do this, an air sample diffuses into the sensor through a special membrane, where the resultant electrochemical process produces electric current directly proportional to the oxygen concentration.

These instruments can be pre-set to a given oxygen concentration which activates an audible or visual alarm system. They are used both as personal monitors and to measure room concentrations of oxygen (e.g. in a confined space).

The normal percentage of oxygen in air is 21%, most of the remainder (78%) being nitrogen.

Limitations of oxygen meters:

- Sensitive (but accurate) sensors, so are sometimes delicate and need careful handling.
- Need some skill to accurately set and monitor.
- Battery needs to be proven for capacity before use.

Smoke Tubes

These are simple devices that generate non-toxic smoke in a controlled chemical reaction. They are similar in appearance and operation to stain tubes, and to operate you break open the tube and attach a rubber bulb to emit the smoke.

Smoke tubes are used to assess the strength and direction of airflow. The smoke they release is carried away by the air currents in the local environment and the movements observed. Such smoke tests are ideal for checking the effectiveness of ventilation and extraction systems, air-conditioning systems and chimneys. They can be used to detect leaks in industrial equipment, to assess relative air pressures used in certain types of local ventilation systems and to provide general information about air movements in the general work area.

Limitations of smoke tubes:

- Do not give a quantitative measure of concentration, only a qualitative indication of air movement.
- Smoke particle size will probably be different from the size of contaminant particles, so the smoke may move in air currents in a different way.

Dust Monitoring Equipment

Dust Lamp (Tyndall Lamp)

Airborne dust in the workplace which is not visible to the naked eye can be visualised using a dust lamp.

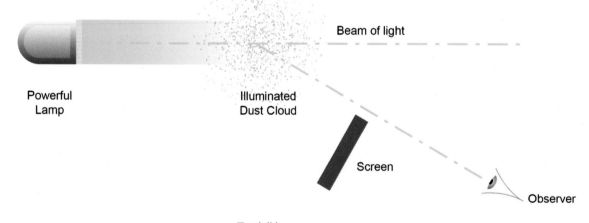

Tyndall beam apparatus

A strong beam of light is shone through the area where a cloud of finely divided dust is suspected. The eye of the observer is shielded from the light beam and the dust cloud is made visible. The method is used to determine how exhaust ventilation systems are working.

Limitations of dust lamps:

- Do not provide numerical data, only a qualitative indication.

- Provide no differentiation between contaminants and any other dusts.

Indirect-Reading Filtration Equipment (Dust Sampler)

Dust exposure can be measured using a sampling train made up of an air pump, tube and sampling head. This can be worn by a worker to give a personal sample covering their work period, or placed in a static location to get a background sample.

Air is drawn through and dust is collected onto a pre-weighed filter; it is sent to a laboratory where it is weighed again and the amount of dust in the air calculated. This will be an average value over the chosen period of time.

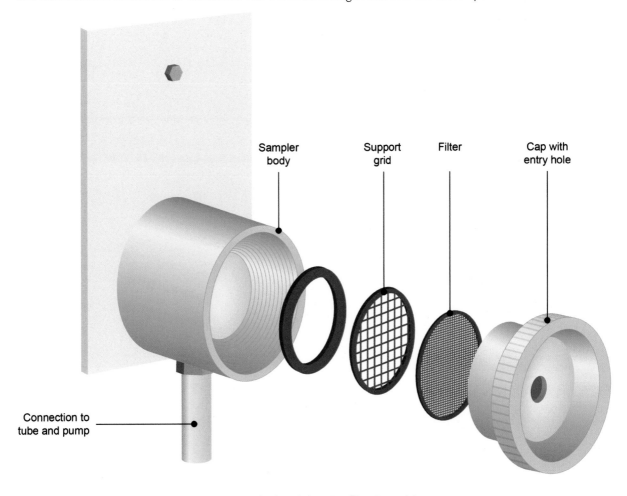

Dust sampler head showing filter in position
Based on original source MDHS 14/4 General methods for sampling
and gravimetric analysis of respirable, thoracic and inhalable aerosols, HSE, 2014 (www.hse.gov.uk/pubns/mdhs/
pdfs/mdhs14-4.pdf)

Limitations of dust samplers:

- Only suitable for calculating average exposures over long periods (minimum four hours).

- All the dust is assumed to be the contaminant dust for calculation purposes (unless more extensive analysis is carried out).

- Easy to misuse.

STUDY QUESTIONS

5. Identify the routes of entry of chemicals into the body.

6. What is the difference between an inhalable substance and a respirable substance?

7. What information is generally provided on the product label of a substance that is classified as dangerous for supply?

8. What is the purpose of safety data sheets?

9. What is the difference between passive and active sampling devices?

10. Give three limitations in the use of stain tube detectors.

11. What are smoke tubes used for?

(Suggested Answers are at the end.)

Workplace Exposure Limits

IN THIS SECTION...

- Workplace Exposure Limits (WELs) are maximum concentrations of airborne contaminants, normally measured across a particular reference period of time, to which employees may be exposed.

- Short-term exposure limits combat the sudden, acute effects of exposure; long-term exposure limits combat the long-term chronic effects.

- There are limitations to the effectiveness of workplace exposure limits in ensuring that employees are not exposed to harmful levels of hazardous substances.

The Purpose of Workplace Exposure Limits

The purpose of Workplace Exposure Limits (WELs) is to put a ceiling in place so that employees will not be exposed to concentrations of airborne substances (either for short durations of time or for long periods of the working day) where scientific evidence suggests that there is a risk to their health.

WELs have legal status under **COSHH Regulations** and can be found listed in the HSE Guidance Note EH40. If a WEL is exceeded, then a breach of the **COSHH Regulations** has taken place; this might lead to enforcement action or prosecution.

> **DEFINITION**
>
> **WORKPLACE EXPOSURE LIMITS (WELs)**
>
> Maximum concentrations of airborne contaminants, averaged across a particular reference period of time, to which employees may be exposed.

> **TOPIC FOCUS**
>
> **Units of Measurement of Exposure**
>
> The two main units used for measuring airborne concentrations are:
>
> - Parts per million (ppm).
>
> - Milligrams per cubic metre of air (mg/m^3, or $mg\ m^{-3}$).
>
> Vapours and gases are measured in ppm (parts per million), which refers to the number of parts of vapour or gas of a substance in a million parts of air by volume. Particulate matter - dusts, fumes, etc. - is measured in mg/m^3, which refers to the milligrams of the substance per cubic metre of air.
>
> One further unit of measurement is used in relation to fibres (e.g. asbestos):
>
> - Concentrations of fibres are expressed in fibres per millilitre of air ($fibres\ ml^{-1}$).

Long-Term and Short-Term Limits

The two reference periods commonly used for workplace exposure limits are:

- **15 minutes** - short-term exposure limit.

- **8 hours** - long-term exposure limit.

The reasons for having two limits are:

- **Short-Term Exposure Limits (SLTELs)** combat the ill-health effects (acute effects) of being exposed to very high levels of the substance for quite short periods of time.

- **Long-Term Exposure Limits (LTELs)** combat the ill-health effects of being exposed to relatively low concentrations of a substance for many or all hours of every working day throughout a working lifetime (chronic effects).

Significance of Time-Weighted Averages

Workplace exposure limits are Time-Weighted Average (TWA) exposures. They are calculated by measuring a person's average exposure over a specific reference period of time, either **15 minutes** (short-term exposure limit) or **8 hours** (long-term exposure limit). Consequently, they do not provide a limit for airborne concentrations measured over a very short period of time (say 1 or 2 seconds). Although such instantaneous measurements are useful as part of a monitoring programme to identify peak concentrations, only time-weighted averages can be used to legally assess exposure against WELs.

Limitations of Exposure Limits

WELs are designed to control the absorption into the body of harmful substances after they have been inhaled. They are not concerned with absorption from swallowing or through contact with the skin or eyes. So they will not take into account high levels of solvent that are present in a person who has had skin contact with it for a period of time - only that which they have inhaled.

They take no account of human sensitivity or susceptibility. This is particularly important in the case of substances which produce an allergic response - once a person has become sensitised, the exposure limit designed to suit the average person has no further validity.

Other limitations include:

- They do not take account of the synergistic (combined) effects of mixtures of substances, e.g. the use of multiple substances.

- They do not provide a clear distinction between 'safe' and 'dangerous' conditions.

- They cannot be applied directly to working periods which exceed 8 hours.

- They may become invalid if the normal environmental conditions are changed, e.g. changes in temperature, humidity or pressure may increase the harmful potential of a substance.

Application of Workplace Exposure Limits

WELs are designed to control absorption into the body of airborne harmful substances following inhalation. EH40 contains the list of substances for which WELs have been set, together with the LTEL and STEL values of these WELs, and can be used to determine whether exposure to an airborne contaminant has been adequately controlled as required by the **COSHH Regulations**. Adequate control of exposure to an airborne contaminant which is hazardous to health means not exceeding the WEL, or for a substance that is carcinogenic, mutagenic or causes asthma, reducing exposure to as low as is reasonably practicable.

Principle of Reducing Exposure Levels

The operation of WELs is based on controlling risk by reducing the workplace exposure to the contaminant. Therefore, the **COSHH Regulations** require that exposure to harmful substances should be reduced to the lowest level reasonably practicable:

- Eliminating exposure is the best way to control risk. Although this has been adopted for certain chemicals (e.g. carcinogens), it is impractical in most situations when we take into account the requirements of working processes. Therefore, limitation of the risk becomes the next best strategy.

- In practice, reducing exposure may mean more than simple compliance with the stated WEL. Under the **COSHH Regulations** requirement, if it is reasonably practicable to get contamination levels even lower, then that standard should be achieved.

STUDY QUESTIONS

12. What is Guidance Note EH40?

13. What is a Workplace Exposure Limit (WEL)?

14. What do you understand by the term 'time-weighted average' in relation to a WEL?

15. Give three examples of the limitations of WELs.

16. What two reference periods are commonly used with TWAs?

(Suggested Answers are at the end.)

Control Measures

IN THIS SECTION...

- Exposure to hazardous substances should be prevented or, if that's not possible, controlled to below the workplace exposure limits.

- There are principles of good practice for the control of exposure: minimisation of emissions; consider routes of exposure; appropriate and effective controls; use of PPE; checks on effectiveness of controls; provision of information and training; and ensuring controls do not increase risk to health and safety.

- Measures to achieve the principles of good practice include: eliminate or substitute the substance; change the process; reduce exposure time; enclose or segregate; local exhaust ventilation; dilution ventilation; respiratory protective equipment; other PPE; personal hygiene; and health surveillance.

- Further controls may be required for substances that can cause cancer, asthma or damage to genes that can be passed from one generation to another.

Duty to Prevent Exposure

The **COSHH Regulations** require the employer to prevent exposure to substances hazardous to health if it is reasonably practicable to do so. The employer might:

- Change the process or activity so that the hazardous substance is not needed or generated.

- Replace the substance with a safer alternative.

- Use the substance in a safer form, e.g. pellets instead of powder.

Adequately Control Exposure

If prevention is not reasonably practicable, exposure is to be adequately controlled. This will require putting in place measures appropriate to the activity and consistent with the risk assessment, following the hierarchy of controls.

Under the **MHSWR** and **COSHH** the general hierarchy of control is to:

- Eliminate or substitute the hazard by using a less hazardous agent.

- Change the process, i.e. vacuum instead of brush.

- Reduce the time of exposure by providing regular breaks.

- Use physical or engineering controls to reduce the risk at source and provide general protection (segregation, enclosure, ventilation).

- Manage the task or person by job design and provide (as a last resort) personal protective equipment.

> ## DEFINITION
>
> **ADEQUATE CONTROL**
>
> Under **COSHH**, adequate control of exposure to a substance hazardous to health means:
>
> - applying the eight principles of good practice set out in Schedule 2A of **COSHH**;
>
> - not exceeding the WEL for the substance (if there is one); and
>
> - if the substance causes cancer, heritable genetic damage or asthma, reducing exposure to as low as is reasonably practicable.

Ensuring WELs are Not Exceeded

The HSE has established WELs for a number of substances hazardous to health. These are intended to prevent excessive exposure to the substance by containing exposure to below a set limit. Correctly applying the **principles of good practice** will mean exposures are controlled below the WEL.

TOPIC FOCUS

The Principles of Good Practice

The are eight principles of good practice, these are outlined below:

- **Principle 1**

  Design and operate processes and activities to minimise emission, release and spread of substances hazardous to health.

- **Principle 2**

  Take into account all relevant routes of exposure - inhalation, skin and ingestion - when developing control measures.

- **Principle 3**

  Control exposure by measures that are proportional to the health risk.

- **Principle 4**

  Choose the most effective and reliable control options that minimise the escape and spread of substances hazardous to health.

- **Principle 5**

  Where adequate control of exposure cannot be achieved by other means, provide, in combination with other control measures, suitable PPE.

- **Principle 6**

  Check and review regularly all elements of control measures for their continuing effectiveness.

- **Principle 7**

  Inform and train all employees on the hazards and risks from substances with which they work, and the use of control measures developed to minimise the risks.

- **Principle 8**

  Ensure that the introduction of measures to control exposure does not increase the overall risk to health and safety.

Control Measures Used to Implement the Principles of Good Practice

Elimination or Substitution of Hazardous Substances

It may be possible to eliminate or substitute the substance by:

- Eliminating the process or type of work that requires the use of (or creates) the substance (e.g. outsourcing a paint-spraying operation).

- Changing the way that the work is done to avoid the need for the substance (e.g. screwing items together rather than gluing).

- Disposing of unused stock of substances that are no longer needed.

- Substituting the hazardous substance for one non-hazardous (e.g. switch from an irritant to a non-hazardous floor cleaner).

- Substituting a hazardous substance for one that has a lower-hazard classification (e.g. exchange a solvent paint for a water-based paint).

- Changing the physical form of a substance (e.g. use pellets instead of powder).

Process Changes

It may be possible to change a process so that risks can be reduced, for example:

- Brush painting rather than spraying reduces airborne mist and vapour.

- Vacuuming, rather than sweeping up, reduces dust levels.

- Damping of a substance during mixing or when clearing up also reduces dust levels.

Reduced Time Exposure

Ill-health effects caused by hazardous substances are often related to the length of time of exposure and the dose (amount) of the contaminant. Reducing the time will reduce the dose (extending the time increases the dose). We should therefore look to minimise the time people work with hazardous substances, especially with those having acute effects. If a short-term exposure limit (15-minute TWA) exists for the substance, this must not be exceeded. We can achieve this by:

- Providing regular breaks away from contact with the hazardous substance.

- Job rotation - where exposure of an individual is reduced by sharing the dose with other workers.

Enclosure and Segregation

Where it is not possible to reduce exposure, then we have to consider physical controls which enclose the hazard and segregate people from the process involving it.

Total enclosure of a process which generates dust or fumes will prevent the escape of airborne contaminants which could be inhaled by operators nearby. However, it may still be necessary to access equipment or material within that area, so the use of robotically-controlled, remote handling systems may be incorporated, allowing access without disturbing the integrity of the enclosure.

Where isolation of the source is difficult, it may be more practical to enclose the workers to ensure that they remain segregated from the hazard (e.g. in a control booth).

Local Exhaust Ventilation (LEV)

A Local Exhaust Ventilation (LEV) system will contain and collect dusts, vapours and fumes where they are generated, and prevent them spreading further into the workplace. The contaminants will be filtered out and the clean air exhausted outside the workplace.

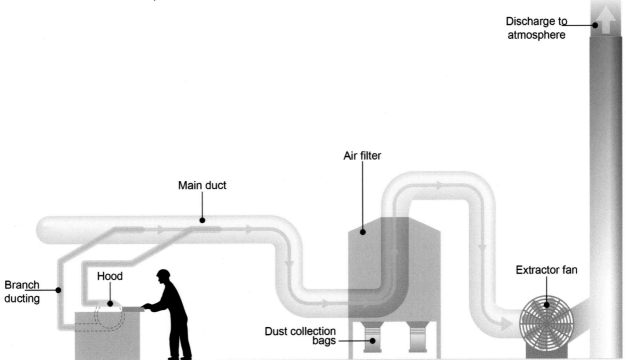

A typical LEV system extracting sawdust from a bench-mounted circular saw

TOPIC FOCUS

A **typical LEV system** consists of:

- An **intake hood** that draws air containing the contaminant in at the point it is created.

- **Ductwork** that carries the air from the intake hood.

- A **filter system** that cleans the contaminant from the air to an acceptable level.

- A **fan** that provides the air movement through the system.

- An **exhaust duct** that discharges the clean air to atmosphere.

Examples of LEV include:

- **Glove boxes** - total enclosures, often used in laboratories, which are accessed through flexible gloves and kept under negative pressure to prevent any release of contaminant.

- **Fume cupboards** - partial enclosures, again used in laboratories, accessed through a vertical sliding sash, with the enclosure kept under negative pressure so that the airflow is through the sash into the hood to prevent any release of contaminant.

A variety of different intake hoods are used on LEV systems, but they can be categorised into two main types:

- **Captor hoods** - hoods which can be positioned as near as possible to the hazard and capture contaminants by a negative airflow into the hood before they reach the operator, e.g. those used to extract woodworking dust or welding fume.

- **Receptor hoods** - large structures designed to capture contaminants which are being directed naturally into the hood, so that less air movement is needed to achieve uptake (e.g. a large intake hood above a bath of molten metal - the metal fume will be hot and rising up into the hood on convection currents).

> MORE...
>
> For more information on LEVs, visit:
>
> www.hse.gov.uk/lev/index.htm

Factors that Reduce Effectiveness

The effectiveness of LEV systems can be affected by:

- Poorly positioned intake hoods.
- Damaged or leaking ducts.
- Excessive amounts of contamination.
- Ineffective fan due to slow speed or lack of maintenance.
- Blocked filters.
- Build-up of contaminants in the duct.
- Sharp bends in the duct.
- Unauthorised additions into the system.

Inspection and Monitoring

LEV systems must be routinely inspected and maintained to ensure their continuing effectiveness:

- **Regular Visual Inspections**
  - To check the integrity of the system, signs of obvious damage and build-up of contaminant inside and outside the ductwork.
  - Filters should be regularly checked to ensure they are not blocked (some have a collector can which can be emptied).
  - The exhaust outlet should be clear.
- **Planned Preventive Maintenance**

  May include:
  - Replacing filters.
  - Lubricating fan bearings.
  - Inspecting the fan motor.
- **Periodic Testing**

  To ensure that air velocities through the system remain adequate.
  - Can be done by visual inspection of the captive system using a smoke-stick, measuring air velocity at the intake and along the ductwork using an anemometer, and measuring static pressures with manometers and pressure gauges.

LEV provided as a control measure for **COSHH** substances should be thoroughly examined by a competent person every 14 months or otherwise in accordance with Schedule 4 of **COSHH**: "Frequency of thorough examination and test of local exhaust ventilation plant used in certain processes".

> MORE...
>
> Further information on LEV can be found in HSG258 Controlling airborne contaminants at work: *A guide to local exhaust ventilation (LEV)*, available at:
>
> www.hse.gov.uk/pubns/books/hsg258.htm

Dilution Ventilation

This operates by diluting the contaminant concentration in the general atmosphere to an acceptable level, by efficiently changing the air in the workplace over a given period of time, e.g. a number of complete changes every hour.

The air changes might be achieved:

- **Passively** - by providing low-level and/or high-level opening louvres.
- **Actively** - using powered fans.

This type of ventilation is intended to be effective in removing gas contaminants (sometimes fumes) and to keep overall concentration of any contaminants below the WEL.

Dilution ventilation is appropriate where:

- The WEL of the hazardous substance is high.
- The rate of formation of the gas or vapour is slow.
- Operators are not in close contact with the contamination generation point.

If a powered system is used, fans must be sited appropriately. If the contaminant is:

- **Lighter** than air, it will naturally rise up inside workrooms and be extracted at high level.
- **Heavier** than air, it will sink to the floor and low-level extraction will be more suitable.

Limitations of dilution ventilation systems:

- Not suitable for the control of substances with high toxicity.
- Do not cope well with sudden releases of large quantities of contaminant.
- Do not work well:
  - On dust.
  - Where the contaminant is released from one point source.
- Dead areas may exist where high concentrations of the contaminant are allowed to accumulate.

  Dead areas are those areas in a workplace which remain dormant, so the air in them is not changed. This is usually due to the air-flow patterns produced by poor positioning of extraction fans and inlets for make-up air. Dead areas can move from one place to another as a result of changing the positions of fans and make-up air inlets, or by the intrusion of other air through windows and doors. Moving the position of machinery or workbenches can have similar effects.

Respiratory Protective Equipment (RPE)

Purpose and Application

The general principles of PPE can be applied to RPE, in that it is worn by workers to reduce the possibility of harm from exposure to a hazardous substance. This is called a **safe person strategy**. Ideally, the safe person strategy is a second line of defence against a potential hazard - control at source, or a **safe place strategy**, should be the first aim.

There will be situations where personal protection is the most appropriate method to deal with a particular hazard, e.g. when the cost of controlling the hazard at source is high and the time required for protection is short. Classic situations which typify these conditions are:

- Work involving planned maintenance, e.g. during plant shut-downs.

- One-off tasks generating airborne contaminants, e.g. demolition of a building by pulling it down.

- Failure of primary safety systems or emergency situations, e.g. a chemical leak from an on-site storage tank.

> **DEFINITION**
>
> **RESPIRATORY PROTECTIVE EQUIPMENT (RPE)**
>
> Any type of PPE specifically designed to protect the respiratory system, e.g. self-contained breathing apparatus.

Types of RPE and their Effectiveness

There are two main categories of RPE:

- **Respirators** - designed to filter the air from the immediate environment around the wearer.

- **Breathing apparatus** - provides breathable air from a separate source.

We will now go on to describe the different types of equipment and their effectiveness.

Respirators

These come in a variety of types:

- **Filtering Facepiece Respirator**

  This is the simplest type, consisting of a piece of filtering material worn over the nose and mouth and secured by elastic headbands. Fit around the chin and face depends on the tension in the headbands; a flexible metal strip enables the user to bend it over the bridge of the nose to ensure a personal fit.

  This type of respirator is useful to prevent inhalation of dust or fibres (and sometimes gas and vapours), but is not suitable for high concentrations of contaminant, for use against substances with high toxicity, or for long duration use.

A worker using a filtering facepiece respirator to prevent inhalation of wood dust

Use and Benefits	Limitations
Cheap.	Low level of protection.
Easy to use.	Does not seal against the face effectively.
Disposable.	Uncomfortable to wear.

- **Half-Mask or Ori-Nasal Respirator**

A flexible rubber or plastic face-piece which covers the nose and mouth, with one or two filtering canisters (cartridges) that contain the filtering material. It gives a much higher level of protection than the filtering facepiece respirator.

When the wearer inhales, a negative pressure is created inside the facepiece; this means that any leak in the respirator or around the seal will allow contaminants in.

A worker wears a half-mask respirator to seal asbestos lagging around a pipe

Use and Benefits	Limitations
Good level of filtration.	No built-in eye protection.
Good fit achievable.	Negative pressure inside facepiece.
Easy to use.	Uncomfortable to wear.

- **Full-Face Respirator**

This is similar to the half-mask (also with canister filters) but has a built-in visor that seals in the eyes and face. This type gives a high level of protection against airborne contaminants and protects the eyes. This can be important where contaminants may splash, cause irritation or be absorbed through the eyes.

A full-face respirator with filtering canister (or cartridge)

Use and Benefits	Limitations
Good level of filtration.	Restricts vision.
Good fit achievable.	Negative pressure inside facepiece.
Protects the eyes.	Uncomfortable to wear.

- **Powered Visor Respirator**

  - A powered fan blows filtered air to the wearer.

  - Usually made up of a helmet and face visor, with the air drawn in through a filter in the helmet, and fed down over the face inside the facepiece.

  - Powered by rechargeable battery.

This type of respirator does not have a tight seal around the face, and is especially suited to dusty, hot environments where the stream of air moving over the face is a benefit. Similar is the **powered clean air respirator** which has the filter remote from the visor, usually worn on the belt, and fed to the visor through a tube.

Powered visor respirator

Use and Benefits	Limitations
Intermediate level of filtration.	Heavy to wear.
Air movement cools wearer.	No tight face seal.
Air stream prevents inward leaks.	Limited battery life.

Breathing Apparatus (BA)

This can be classified under three general headings:

- **Fresh-Air Hose BA**

  This is the simplest type, where a large diameter hose is connected to the user's face mask. Air is either drawn down the hose by breathing or blown down by a low speed/low pressure fan.

Use and Benefits	Limitations
Air is from outside the workroom.	Hose must be tethered.
Supply of air is not time-restricted.	Bends or kinks make breathing difficult.
	User is restricted by length of hose.

- **Compressed Air BA**

  Similar to the fresh-air hose BA, but air is supplied through a small-bore hose at high pressure. Pressure is stepped-down by a regulator and supplied at low pressure to the user's face mask.

Use and Benefits	Limitations
Supply of air is not time-restricted if a compressor is used.	Hose can be long, but not endless.
Positive pressure inside facepiece.	
Wearer is not burdened with cylinder.	

- **Self-Contained Apparatus**

  Breathable air is supplied from a pressurised cylinder worn by the user. This type of BA gives the wearer complete freedom of movement, but it is the most heavy and bulky type. The air cylinder does have a limited capacity.

Use and Benefits	Limitations
Complete freedom of movement.	Supply of air is time-restricted.
Positive pressure inside facepiece.	Equipment is bulky and heavy.
	More technical training is required.

Selection, Use and Maintenance

RPE must be selected carefully to ensure that it is suitable.

TOPIC FOCUS

Key factors in the selection of RPE:

- Contaminant concentration and its hazardous nature (e.g. harmful, toxic).

- Physical form of the substance (e.g. dust, gas, vapour).

- Level of protection offered by the RPE.

- Presence or absence of normal oxygen concentrations.

- Duration of time that it must be worn.

- Compatibility with other PPE that must be worn.

- Shape of the user's face and influences on fit.

- Facial hair might interfere with an effective seal.

- Physical requirements of the job, e.g. the need to move freely.

- Physical fitness of the wearer.

The level of protection offered by an item of RPE is usually expressed as the Assigned Protection Factor (APF). This is a measure of how well the RPE keeps out the contaminant and is given by the formula:

$$APF = \frac{\text{Concentration of contaminant in workplace}}{\text{Concentration of contaminant in facepiece}}$$

Any RPE selected must meet the relevant standards (e.g. 'CE' marked).

Users of RPE should receive appropriate information, instruction and training. In particular, they should:

- Understand how to fit the RPE.

- Have a face-fit test to ensure suitability and fit (Reg. 7 of **COSHH**).

- Know:

  – How to test the item during use to ensure it is working effectively.

  – The limitations of the item.

  – Any cleaning requirements.

  – Any maintenance requirements (e.g. how to change the filter).

Maintenance and cleaning of RPE must be carried out in accordance with the manufacturers' instructions and any legal requirements (e.g. **COSHH** requirements for keeping a record of inspections, replacement parts, etc.). This should include the need to repair or replace worn or damaged items. Maintenance should be carried out by trained, competent personnel.

Other Protective Equipment and Clothing

There are other types of PPE used to protect from exposure to hazardous substances.

Gloves

Gloves (short cuffs) and gauntlets (long cuffs) can give protection against:

- Chemicals such as acids, alkalis, solvents, oils (e.g. corrosive cement).

- Biological agents such as blood viruses and body fluids.

- Physical agents such as contaminated dusts, and cuts from contaminated blades or syringes.

- Water - even uncontaminated water can soften and damage the skin of someone exposed for long periods.

For protection against chemicals, it is important to ensure the gloves are of the right material impervious to the chemical.

Overalls

'Ordinary' overalls are not regarded as PPE, but 'workwear' - in that they are not commonly intended to do more than keep a person (and their clothing) clean. However, even overalls can offer some level of protection against everyday construction contaminants such as soil, clay, oils and grease.

There are, however, items of PPE intended to protect the construction worker from hazards:

- Flame-retardant overalls.

- Chemical-resistant overalls - protect from acids, alkalis, etc.

- Disposable coveralls (hooded) - worn in asbestos removal and impervious to the passage of extremely fine fibres.

- Aprons - prevent spills and splashes from soaking into normal workwear and the skin.

Eye Protection

Four different types of eye protection are common in construction activities:

- **Spectacles**
  - Offer a degree of front and side protection, but do not completely encase the eyes.
  - Mainly for impact protection from flying objects and debris.

- **Safety Goggles**
  - Completely encase the eyes with protection from impact, chemical gas, liquid splashes and molten metal.

- **Face Shields**
  - Cover the eyes and face, but do not enclose them.
  - Limited protection from impact and splashes.

- **Hoods and Visors**
  - Offer all-round enclosed protection, especially from liquid splashes to the face.

Safety Helmets

Protection from falling or moving objects on a construction site is required, regardless of exposure to hazardous substances.

Safety Footwear

This not only offers protection to the toes, but some may be chemical-resistant where exposure to spillages or contaminated ground may occur. On construction sites, **CDM** specifically recognises that sharp objects where employees walk and stand are a significant risk. Midsole protection should be provided on construction safety footwear to guard against nails projecting from boards and other objects. To meet this standard, the footwear must be able to resist penetration using either a steel, aluminium or Kevlar insert to the midsole.

Personal Hygiene and Protection Regimes

Personal hygiene goes a long way to preventing absorption of hazardous substances into the body, by preventing contact in the simplest of situations. Many chemical and biological agents get into the body from the skin of the hands, into the mouth and eyes from cross-contamination. Likewise, food, drink and cigarettes all offer the same opportunity.

Good hygiene means:

- **Hand-washing** when leaving the work area, and always before eating, drinking or smoking.

- **Careful removal** and disposal of potentially contaminated items of PPE to prevent cross-contamination to normal clothes and the skin.

- **Prohibition** of eating, drinking and smoking in work areas.

All construction sites must have adequate welfare facilities (water, soap and a means for drying). With more serious hazards, showers and nail brushes may be required. Barrier creams may also prove useful.

Hand-washing can prevent the transfer and ingestion of hazardous substances

Facilities should be provided to:

- Change and store clothing and PPE.

- Store, prepare and consume food and drinks.

In some situations **vaccinations** may protect workers from biological agents:

- Vaccination against hepatitis B is often offered to first aiders.

- Those working near water may gain some protection from immunisation against Weil's disease.

Issues to consider before embarking on a vaccination programme:

- Worker consent must be obtained.

- Vaccination does not always grant immunity.

- Vaccination can give workers a false sense of security.

In most cases, vaccination should only be offered when indicated by law or codes of practice.

Health Surveillance and Biological Monitoring

Health surveillance is a system of ongoing health checks and often involves carrying out some form of medical examination or test on employees who are exposed to substances such as solvents, fumes, biological agents and other hazardous substances.

Health surveillance is important to enable early detection of ill-health effects or diseases, and also helps employers to evaluate their control measures and to educate employees. The risk assessment will indicate where health surveillance may be needed, **but it is required where**:

- there is an adverse health effect or disease linked to a workplace exposure, **and**
- it is likely that the health effect or disease may occur, **and**
- there are valid techniques for detecting early signs of the health effect or disease, **and**
- the techniques don't themselves pose a risk to employees.

There are two types of health surveillance commonly carried out:

- **Health monitoring** - where the individual is examined for symptoms and signs of disease that might be associated with the agent in question. For example, those working in the dustiest areas of a site or in cement production may have lung-function tests (spirometry) to check for respiratory disorders.

- **Biological monitoring** - where a blood, urine or breath sample is taken and analysed for the presence of the agent itself or its breakdown products. For example, those working with lead processes might have blood samples taken to check for cumulative levels of lead in the blood.

> **MORE...**
>
> There is a range of industry-specific guidance on health surveillance at:
>
> www.hse.gov.uk/health-surveillance/resources.htm

When necessary, health surveillance should be conducted on first employment, to establish a 'baseline', and then periodically. It can also be done when a person leaves employment as a final check. The need for health surveillance is usually subject to Regulations, ACoP and guidance.

Similar health checks may be required for those exposed to noise, vibration, etc., and are covered in the appropriate section of this course.

Further Controls for Carcinogens, Asthmagens and Mutagens

The **Control of Substances Hazardous to Health Regulations 2002** require that exposure to substances that can cause cancer, asthma or damage to genes that can be passed from one generation to another should be prevented. If this is not possible, specific measures should be adopted, including:

- Total enclosure of the process and handling systems.
- Prohibition of eating, drinking and smoking in contaminated areas.
- Regular cleaning of floors, walls and other surfaces.
- Designation of areas that may be contaminated with warning signs.
- Safe storage, handling and disposal.

STUDY QUESTIONS

17. What principles of control are illustrated by the following measures?

    (a) Using granulated pottery glazes instead of powders.

    (b) Vacuum cleaning rather than sweeping with a broom.

    (c) Job rotation.

    (d) Using water-based adhesives rather than solvent-based ones.

18. What is the difference between local exhaust ventilation and dilution ventilation?

19. What are dead areas, and why are they a problem for dilution ventilation?

20. List four main types of respirator and the three main types of breathing apparatus.

21. What are the key criteria in the selection of the appropriate respirator to use?

22. What is the main purpose of routine health surveillance?

(Suggested Answers are at the end.)

Specific Agents

IN THIS SECTION...

- Specific hazardous agents may be encountered in construction work that can cause ill health to workers exposed, such as blood-borne viruses, organic solvents, carbon dioxide, nitrogen, isocyanates, lead, carbon monoxide, cement, Legionnaires disease, Weil's disease, silica, fibres, hepatitis, tetanus and hydrogen sulphide.

- Construction workers can also be exposed to a number of dusts in their everyday work, e.g. cement dust and wood dust.

- Asbestos, although now banned, can still be found in older buildings. Systems must be in place to:

  - Identify the presence of asbestos.

  - Protect workers.

  - Remove and dispose of asbestos.

Hazards, Risks and Controls Associated with Other Specific Agents

The following are some chemical and biological agents commonly encountered in construction activities, with a description of their health effects and the workplace circumstances in which they might be present.

Blood-Borne Viruses

Blood-borne viruses are carried in the bloodstream of an infected person, but are not easily transmitted to others unless their blood comes into contact with the broken skin of another person. Such viruses include the Human Immunodeficiency Virus (HIV) which causes Acquired Immune Deficiency Syndrome (AIDS) and Serum Hepatitis (hepatitis B - more on this later).

Exposure to blood-borne viruses usually comes from contact with blood from injured persons being treated by a first aider at work, or from unintentional contact with discarded items such as needles ('sharps injuries' and 'needlestick' injuries).

Blood-borne viruses

Typical controls include:

- The use of gloves and eye protection when handling potentially contaminated material.

- Correct collection and disposal of potentially contaminated material.

- Preventing needlestick injuries by correct collection and disposal of sharps in a sharps container.

- Vaccination where appropriate.

- Procedures to deal with accidental exposures (e.g. needlestick injury).

Petrochemicals

Petrol, diesel, oils and greases are used in construction machinery. Skin contact causes defatting and can lead, over a period of time, to dermatitis.

Organic Solvents

These are found in many materials used in construction, e.g. paints, varnishes, adhesives, pesticides, paint removers and cleaning materials. The most common organic solvents used in the construction industry are:

- White spirit - in paints, varnishes and cleaning products.

- 1-Butanol - in paints, lacquers, and natural and synthetic resins.

- Toluene and xylene:

  - Common ingredients in paints.

  - Used as degreasers and cleaners to remove oils, etc. from metal components.

Exposure to them may result in irritation and inflammation of the skin, eyes and lungs, causing dermatitis, burns and breathing difficulties including occupational asthma and sensitisation. Vapours given off are usually flammable, and may be narcotic (e.g. toluene) progressively causing drowsiness, nausea and unconsciousness. Some organic solvents are carcinogenic.

Typical controls include:

- Avoiding inhalation of vapours (e.g. well-ventilated work areas or use of RPE).

- Avoiding skin contact by correct use of gloves and protective clothing.

- Never use solvents to wash the skin.

- Procedures to ensure correct storage and handling of solvents.

- Procedures to deal with spillages and collection and disposal of waste materials.

Carbon Dioxide

A colourless, odourless gas that is heavier than air. When anything organic is burned, carbon dioxide (CO_2) is produced. Road vehicles produce 20% of the UK's CO_2 emissions. CO_2 is used extensively for fire-fighting.

The air that we breathe contains around 0.038% CO_2 (by volume) and 21% oxygen. When we inhale, we absorb some of the oxygen into the blood and carbon dioxide is exhaled. With a higher concentration of CO_2 in the air, the body finds it difficult to get rid of its own CO_2. This can have effects that range from drowsiness (at 1% CO_2) to excessive sweating, muscle tremor and unconsciousness (8% CO_2). At above 10% unconsciousness will occur, followed rapidly by asphyxiation (even with oxygen at 21%).

Typical controls include:

- Avoid burning organic materials on site.

- If unavoidable, ensure well ventilated areas are used.

- Do not leave vehicle engines running unnecessarily.

- Never park vehicles with engines running near excavations or confined spaces.

TOPIC FOCUS

Asphyxiant Gases

Gases described as 'asphyxiant' (e.g. carbon dioxide (CO_2) and carbon monoxide (CO)) do not cause direct injury to the respiratory tract when inhaled, but reduce the oxygen available to the body.

CO_2 is a simple asphyxiant which displaces air, whereas CO is a chemical asphyxiant which combines with haemoglobin to form a compound which prevents oxygen transport by the blood.

Nitrogen

Nitrogen is a gas that takes up 80% of the air we breathe. It is one of a number of gases that can be used for inerting (others are carbon dioxide, argon and helium). The major risk associated with use of inerting is that of asphyxiation, particularly in confined spaces. Nitrogen is also used in pipe-freezing.

Typical controls include:

- Procedures in place for confined space entry.

- Safe systems of work and trained persons to employ inerting processes.

Carbon Monoxide

Carbon monoxide (CO) is a colourless, odourless, tasteless gas. It is found in combustion gases such as coal gas, car exhaust, producer gas, blast-furnace gas and water gas.

CO is toxic. It combines with haemoglobin in the blood, impairing the transportation of oxygen. Concentrations above 5% cause immediate loss of consciousness, but far more people are killed by exposure to much lower concentrations over an extended period, typically when a gas-fired heater is used in a poorly ventilated room, e.g. when used to heat a poorly ventilated site office.

Typical controls include:

- Restrict work on gas systems to competent engineers only.

- Maintenance and testing of boilers and flues.

- Good workplace ventilation.

- LEV for vehicle exhausts in workshops.

- Care in the siting of plant run by internal combustion engines.

- Carbon monoxide alarms.

- Confined space entry controls.

DEFINITION

INERTING

Where an 'inert' gas (e.g. nitrogen) is used to suppress a flammable atmosphere, e.g. in a fuel tank, to prevent explosion.

A carbon monoxide alarm can save lives

Isocyanates

These are organic compounds used to make adhesives, synthetic rubber, foams and paints (particularly 'two-pack' paints). They are liquid at normal temperature but evaporate slowly.

They are hazardous by inhalation and skin contact, possibly leading to sensitisation. Once this has occurred, further exposures may cause severe allergic dermatitis and chronic asthma.

Typical controls include:

- Ensure **COSHH** assessment is carried out and MSDS available.

- Ensure adequate ventilation in all areas of use.

- Ensure hygiene practices prevent skin contact.

Lead

Lead is a soft heavy metal often used in roofing materials and is relatively inert. Lead compounds can be categorised into:

- **Inorganic compounds** such as lead oxide (red lead) and lead chromate (chrome yellow) used as pigments, though because of toxicity no longer in paints for domestic use.

- **Organic lead** which was widely used as an anti-knock agent in petrol (lead tetraethyl), but has now mostly been replaced because of health concerns.

Both can be hazardous by inhalation and ingestion (organic lead is more readily absorbed by both routes). When inhaled or ingested, lead is a cumulative toxin which builds up over time. It has symptoms such as muscle tremors, anaemia (low red blood cell count) and brain damage. It can cause miscarriage and birth defects during pregnancy.

Typical controls include:

- Eliminating or reducing exposure.

- Use of work clothing, and PPE such as gloves and dust masks.

- Good hygiene practices.

- Biological monitoring for lead absorption (blood or urine sampling).

Fibres

Two types of material encountered in construction that are fibrous:

- **Machine-Made** (formerly 'Man-Made') **Mineral Fibres (MMMF)** - classically 'rockwool' and slag wool are used for thermal and acoustical insulation in the construction industry. MMMF products release airborne respirable fibres during production and use.

- **Asbestos** - a group of naturally occurring minerals that have been used extensively as fire-resistant building, lagging and insulating materials. The three main types are blue, brown and white asbestos.

We will look at asbestos in more detail later.

Silica

Silica is a compound present in many rocks and stones, particularly sandstone, quartz and slate, and found in ceramics (e.g. clay pipes) and cement. It is hazardous when inhaled as a dust and can cause numerous chest and respiratory tract diseases. The most common is where silica is deposited deep in the lungs, causing scar tissue to form (silicosis) very similar to asbestosis.

Typical controls include:

- Prevention of exposure by use of alternative work methods.

- Dust suppression by use of water sprays or jets.

- Local exhaust ventilation.

- Respiratory protective equipment.

- Health surveillance (spirometry and chest X-ray).

Cement Dust and Wet Cement

Cement is widely used in construction, e.g. mortar, plaster and concrete, and presents a hazard to health in a number of ways, mainly by skin contact and inhalation of dust.

Contact with wet cement can cause both dermatitis and burns:

- Cement is capable of causing dermatitis by irritancy and allergy.

- Both irritant and allergic dermatitis can affect a person at the same time.

- Wet cement can cause burns due to its alkalinity.

- Serious chemical burns to the eyes can also be caused following a splash of cement.

Cutting concrete creates high levels of cement and silica dust

Typical controls include:

- Eliminating or reducing exposure.

- Use of work clothing, and PPE such as gloves, dust masks and eye protection.

- Removal of contaminated clothing.

- Good hygiene and washing on skin contact.

- Health surveillance of skin condition to control chrome burns and dermatitis.

Leptospirosis (Weil's Disease)

Leptospirosis (Weil's disease) is a zoonotic disease caused by Leptospira bacteria. Rats are the primary cause of the disease (from their urine deposits) but it can also be found in mice, cattle and horses. The primary routes of infection are by swallowing contaminated water or food, and through cuts and grazes. Persons at risk include canal workers, sewer workers, rat catchers and agricultural workers.

Leptospirosis starts with flu-like symptoms - fever, headache and muscle pain - then progresses to a more serious jaundice-like phase. At this stage it can cause liver damage. It can be immunised against and, if diagnosed early, can be successfully treated. If left, it can be fatal.

Typical controls include:

- Preventing rat infestation by good housekeeping and pest control.

- Good personal hygiene (e.g. hand-washing).

- PPE (especially gloves).

> **DEFINITION**
>
> **ZOONOTIC DISEASE (ZOONOSES)**
>
> Diseases which originate in animals and can be passed to humans (e.g. rabies).

Rats are the primary carrier of the Leptospira bacteria

- Covering cuts and grazes.

- Issuing workers with an 'at risk' card to be shown to doctors to assist early diagnosis.

Legionnaires' Disease

Legionnaires' disease is caused by the water-loving soil bacterium Legionella pneumophila, as is Pontiac fever, a shorter, more feverish illness, without the complications of pneumonia. Legionellosis is the generic term used to cover Legionnaires' disease and Pontiac fever.

The bacteria are hazardous when inhaled in a droplet form mixed with water. The most common sources for outbreaks of the disease are outdoor cooling towers associated with air-conditioning systems. Water containing bacteria is sprayed inside the towers to cool, and mists drift out of the top and are inhaled by passers-by.

Legionnaires' disease developing to the pneumonia stage can often prove fatal, especially for the elderly, infirm or immuno-suppressed, and for anyone if not diagnosed early.

Typical controls include:

- **Management Controls**

    - Assessment of the risk from Legionella.

    - A written control scheme (see below).

    - Appointment of a 'responsible person' to carry out risk assessment, and manage and implement the written scheme of controls.

    - Review of control measures.

    - There are also duties placed on those involved in the supply of water systems.

- **Practical Controls**

    - Avoid water temperatures between 20°C and 45°C and conditions that favour bacterial growth.

    - Avoid water stagnation which can encourage biofilm growth.

    - Avoid using material that can harbour bacteria and provide them with nutrients.

    - Control the release of water spray.

    - Keep water, storage systems and equipment clean.

    - Use water (chemical) treatments where necessary.

    - Carry out water sampling and analysis.

    - Ensure correct and safe operation and maintenance of water systems.

- **Written Scheme of Controls**

    With reference to risk assessment, the written scheme should show:

    - An up-to-date plan of the plant or water system layout, including parts temporarily out of use.

    - A description of the correct and safe operation of the system.

    - What checks are required to ensure the written scheme is effective.

    - The frequency of such checks.

    - What remedial actions are to be taken if the written scheme is ineffective.

> **MORE...**
>
> ACoP L8, *Legionnaires' disease - The control of legionella bacteria in water systems,* available at:
>
> www.hse.gov.uk/pubns/books/l8.htm

Hepatitis

Hepatitis is a disease of the liver, caused by viral infection. There are several forms (A, B, C, etc.) caused by different strains of the virus:

- Hepatitis A is contracted orally by cross-contamination with faecal material containing the A virus, putting sewage workers at risk.

- Hepatitis B is transmitted in body fluids such as blood, putting health care workers (and first-aiders) at risk, as well as police, fire-fighters and waste-disposal workers.

The virus survives for long periods outside the body and can survive harsh treatments that would kill other micro-organisms (e.g. boiling water). Contaminated body fluids can cause infection by contact with damaged skin, needlestick injuries and splashing into the eyes and mouth. Symptoms include jaundice and liver damage. Though many people are able to make a complete recovery, some will become long-term sufferers and some continue to carry the virus without displaying any of the symptoms.

Typical controls include:

- The use of gloves and eye protection when handling potentially contaminated material.
- Correct collection and disposal of potentially contaminated material.
- Preventing needlestick injuries by correct collection and disposal of sharps in a sharps container.
- Vaccination where appropriate.
- Procedures to deal with accidental exposures (e.g. needlestick injury).

Tetanus

The organisms causing tetanus (lockjaw) are widespread, usually found in vegetation, contaminated soil and animal excretions. They can gain access to the body through cuts, wounds, splinters, etc. Symptoms include stiffness in the muscles, a stiffening of the jaw until it is in a locked position, and breathing problems. There is a mortality rate of approximately 10%.

Typical controls include:

- Immunisation of workers to help to prevent the disease. Construction workers are susceptible when working on new sites or where there has been any agricultural activity taking place. An immunisation programme should be encouraged for any such workers.
- Use of strong gloves when handling materials that could be contaminated.
- Good hygiene and hand-washing.

Hydrogen Sulphide

Hydrogen sulphide (H_2S) is highly toxic if inhaled, highly flammable and explosive with the classic odour of rotten eggs. It is heavier than air, so will collect in low-lying, poorly ventilated places. It can be detected in very small amounts, but can soon deaden the sense of smell, possibly leading to high levels then going undetected. It is a chemical asphyxiant.

In the construction industry, H_2S sickness and fatalities are most commonly associated with confined spaces (pits, manholes, tunnels and wells) and work in or near sewers or landfills. Work in marshy areas and in hot weather (which accelerates the breakdown of organic material) also heightens the risk of exposure. Other common sources include coal pits, sulphur springs, gas wells and areas where there is accumulation of decaying matter, such as sewage and sewage treatment plants, manure stocks, swamps, ponds and areas of dead water in the sea or rivers.

Typical controls include:

- Monitoring of suspect areas.

- Ensuring good ventilation.

- Suitable work practices.

- Use of air-fed RPE.

Because H_2S is flammable and corrosive, exhaust and ventilation systems are a primary method of reducing H_2S levels. The system must be:

- Explosion-proof.

- Non-sparking.

- Earthed.

- Corrosion-resistant.

- Separate from other exhaust ventilation systems.

When work is being performed in confined spaces, ventilation systems should be operated continuously.

MORE...

Further information on chemicals can be found at:

www.hse.gov.uk/chemicals/index.htm

Generation and Control of Dusts on a Construction Site

Silica

Construction activities such as cutting concrete can create high levels of silica dust. Because silica dust has been identified as a carcinogen and as having a link to Chronic Obstructive Pulmonary Disease (COPD), levels should be as low as reasonably practicable, and at least below the workplace exposure limit of 0.1 mg/m³.

In employing the eight principles of good practice, employers must not exceed the WEL for silica. Specific precautions employed should involve:

- Assessment - including air sampling.

- Eliminate silica - or substitute with other materials.

- Provide PPE - and RPE as necessary.

- Welfare facilities - for washing, changing and storing clothes on site.

- Health surveillance - for levels above mg/m³ 8-hour TWA, a respiratory questionnaire, lung function testing and chest X-rays should be provided.

Fibres

Machine-Made (formerly Man-Made) Mineral Fibres (MMMF) and Refractory Ceramic Fibres (RCF) are often encountered in insulating materials and exposure to inhalation of them should be prevented. LEV is not practicable in many construction activities, so the hierarchy of controls would suggest the following:

- Replace fibrous mineral materials with safer alternatives.

- Suitable RPE is to be provided.

- Fibrous mineral materials will also have a physical irritation hazard, so protective clothing, gloves and suitable eye protection should also be used.

- Good housekeeping regimes and work practices will help to reduce fibres settling that can become airborne dusts.

Asbestos

This is a mineral of fibrous nature, capable of causing asbestosis, lung cancer and mesothelioma from inhalation, as we saw earlier. It has exceptional heat insulating qualities. Its use is banned in the UK, but it may still be found in older properties, where it is required to be managed. The biggest danger in construction is unwittingly locating asbestos during demolition or refurbishment work involving installation and even minor repairs.

We will look at methods for controlling of exposure to asbestos later in this element.

Asbestos in older buildings is required by law to be managed

Cement

Cement is used extensively to make mortar and concrete. In its dry powder form it is an irritant dust easily inhaled or blown into the eyes. Once mixed with water it is corrosive on skin and eye contact.

TOPIC FOCUS

Exposure to Cement

Construction workers can be exposed to cement during:

- **Emptying and disposing of bags** - in dry powder form.

- **Mixing cement** - in both dry powder and mixed wet forms.

- **Brick and block laying** - in the wet form.

- **Pouring** cement into voids and foundations - in the wet form.

- **Concrete pouring and levelling** - in the wet form.

- **Cutting, scabbling, drilling or demolition** - as dust.

Concrete and mortar cutting produces dust which may also contain silica (see earlier) (concrete and mortar contain crystalline silica).

Exposure is controlled by eliminating or reducing it where possible and by use of work clothing and PPE (gloves, dust masks and eye protection). Removal of contaminated clothing, good hygiene and washing after skin contact are also important.

Wood Dust

Wood is classified in two broad categories - hardwood and softwood. The main activities causing problems arise from sawing, routing, sanding and turning. MDF (Medium Density Fibreboard) is a composite of wood dust and resin and particularly causes asthma.

The smaller the particle size and the greater the amount of dust produced, the greater the risk of ill health.

Health problems associated with exposure to wood dust include:

- Skin disorders.

- Obstruction in the nose, rhinitis and asthma.

- A rare type of nasal cancer.

- Wheezing, coughing and breathlessness.

- Stomach disorders due to ingestion.

- Eyes - soreness, watering, conjunctivitis.

Hardwood and softwood dusts both have a WEL of $5mg/m^3$ which must not be exceeded. Because some wood dusts are asthmagens, exposure must be reduced to as low as is reasonably practicable.

Key controls:

- LEV must be provided (maintained and inspected) to extract dust at woodworking machines.

- Wood dust should be vacuum-collected rather than swept or blown with an airline. Such systems should be suitable and have a High-Energy Particle Arrestor (HEPA) filter.

- RPE, as well as LEV, should be used for particularly dusty tasks.

- Health surveillance may be appropriate for respiratory disorders (asthma in particular).

Health Risks and Controls Associated with Asbestos

TOPIC FOCUS

Regulations Governing Asbestos Work

The main regulations governing all work with asbestos on workplace premises are the **Control of Asbestos Regulations 2012**, which:

- Cover everyone who is liable to be exposed to asbestos.

- Maintain an explicit duty on employers and occupiers in non-domestic premises to manage asbestos.

The regulations continue the prohibition on the importation, supply and use of all forms of new asbestos, and allow existing Asbestos-Containing Materials (ACMs) in good condition to be left in place, so long as their condition is monitored and managed to ensure they are not disturbed. The prohibition remains on the use of all second-hand asbestos products.

Work with asbestos cement and similar ACMs remains unlicensed, but under certain conditions notification (not licensing) is still required and medical surveillance necessary as for licensed work.

During construction (in particular demolition), ACMs may be found in roofs (sprayed coatings and asbestos cement sheets), walls (insulation and fire protection), floors and ceilings (tiles), rainwater drainage (asbestos cement gutters, drainpipes and fountain heads) and as pipe lagging.

Three respiratory diseases are associated with asbestos exposure:

- **Asbestosis** - asbestos fibres lodge deep in the lungs and cause scar tissue to form. Extensive scarring leads to breathing difficulties and increases the risk of cancer - can be fatal.

- **Lung cancer** - asbestos fibres in the lung trigger the development of cancerous growths in lung tissue - often fatal.

- **Mesothelioma** - asbestos fibres migrate through the lung tissue and into the cavities around the lung, triggering the development of cancerous growths in the lining tissue around the lungs, the heart and the lining of the abdomen.

The effects of asbestos have a long latency period - it will be a long time after exposure has occurred before symptoms are apparent (10-15 years for asbestosis; 30-40 years for mesothelioma).

Asbestos is now banned in the UK, but it may still be present in older buildings and encountered during maintenance work or demolition.

> **MORE...**
>
> Further information on asbestos can be found at:
>
> www.hse.gov.uk/asbestos/index.htm
>
> www.hse.gov.uk/asbestos/essentials/index.htm

Duty to Manage Asbestos

Identification

Asbestos or ACMs are not easily recognised, so laboratory testing of samples is often required, and it is even more difficult when ACMs are concealed by decorations or coatings. ACMs may be present if the building was constructed or refurbished before blue and brown asbestos were banned in 1985, or asbestos cement in 1999.

The three main types of asbestos that have been used commercially are:

- Crocidolite (blue).

- Amosite (brown).

- Chrysotile (white).

The type of asbestos cannot be identified just by its colour, but requires microscopic examination in a laboratory.

Some products have one type of asbestos in them while others have mixtures of two or more. All types are dangerous, but blue and brown asbestos are known to be more dangerous than white.

Surveys

In order to ascertain if asbestos is present in a building, a survey can be carried out.

If there is doubt as to whether asbestos is present, it should be presumed that it is present and also that it is not restricted to white asbestos, and so the regulations would apply accordingly.

A building survey is carried out to determine the presence of asbestos

TOPIC FOCUS

To establish if asbestos is present in a building, a **survey** should be carried out. The types of surveys are:

- **Management Survey** - to manage ACMs during the normal occupation and use of the premises. In simple and straightforward premises, the duty-holder can do this, otherwise a surveyor is needed. This will establish that:

    - Nobody is harmed by the asbestos remaining in the premises or equipment.

    - The ACMs remain in good condition.

    - Nobody disturbs them accidentally.

    This may require minor intrusion and asbestos disturbance to locate ACMs that could be disturbed or damaged by normal activities, maintenance or equipment installation. It guides the occupier in prioritising remedial work that may be needed.

- **Refurbishment/Demolition Survey** - required where the premises or part of it needs upgrading, refurbishment or demolition. This would not need a record of the ACM condition, and should be done by a surveyor. This will establish that:

    - Nobody is harmed by work on ACMs in the premises or equipment.

    - Such work will be done by the right contractor in the right way.

    This involves destructive inspection and asbestos disturbance to locate ACMs before structural work starts. The area must be vacated and certified 'fit for reoccupation' after the survey.

Where to Look for Asbestos

Some examples of asbestos use include:

- **Insulation board** - contains around 20-45% asbestos - used for fire protection; heat and sound insulation; in ducts; in-fill panels; ceiling tiles; wall linings; bath panels and partitions; and fire doors.

- **Pipe lagging** - contains 55-100% asbestos - used for thermal insulation on boilers and pipes.

- **Fire blankets** - used in homes and commercial catering kitchens.

- **Floor tiles** - very similar in appearance to ordinary vinyl or plastic tiles.

- **Sprayed coatings/loose fill** - inside roofs, lofts, etc.

- **Rope and gaskets** - used as seals around jointed pipe and in joints in boilers.

- **Roof felt** - rolls of felt laid on roofs; roof tiles.

- **Decorative paints and plasters** - lining walls, around and beneath staircases, etc.; 'artex' ceiling coatings.

Asbestos cement products include:

- Corrugated roof sheets.

- Rainwater goods (fountain heads, guttering, drain pipes, etc.).

- Cold water tanks and toilet cisterns.

Procedure for Asbestos Discovery During Construction

A procedure must be in place covering the actions to take on discovering asbestos in unknown locations. This will include stopping work and immediately informing the site supervisor. He/she should arrange for the area to be sealed off until a formal survey can be carried out.

Accidental Exposure to Asbestos

Requirements:

- Stop work immediately.
- Prevent anyone entering the area.
- Arrangements should be made to contain the asbestos - seal the area.
- Put up warning signs - 'possible asbestos contamination'.
- Inform the site supervisor immediately.
- If contaminated, all clothing, equipment, etc. should be decontaminated and disposed of as hazardous waste.
- Undress, shower, wash hair; put on clean clothes.
- Contact a specialist surveyor or asbestos removal contractor.

Requirements for Removal

Provided asbestos is contained and left undisturbed it can be retained, sealed and managed.

Where asbestos is to be removed, then a number of controls apply covering notification, licensing of operators and procedures.

Licensing

Most asbestos removal work must be undertaken by a contractor licensed by the HSE Licensing Unit.

Some work can be carried out without formal licensing (although strict controls will still be required). Such **unlicensed work** is where:

- The work is sporadic and of low intensity.
- Risk assessment shows the exposure will not exceed any limits.
- The work involves:
    - Short, non-continuous maintenance activities.
    - The removal of materials in which asbestos fibres are firmly linked to a matrix (e.g. asbestos cement sheet).
    - Encapsulation or sealing of ACMs in good condition.
    - Air monitoring and sampling.

TOPIC FOCUS

Notification of Licensed Work

If the work is licensable, at least 14 days' notice to the enforcing authority (or such shorter time as the enforcing authority may agree) is to be given. The Notification (as per Schedule 1 of the 2012 Regulations) should contain:

- The name of the notifier and the address and telephone number of their usual place of business.

- The location of the work site.

- A description of the type of asbestos to be removed or handled (crocidolite, amosite, chrysotile, etc.).

- The maximum quantity of asbestos to be held at any one time on the premises at which the work is to take place.

- The activities or processes involved.

- The number of workers involved.

- Any measures taken to limit the exposure of employees to asbestos.

- The date of commencement of the work activity and its expected duration.

Even where work is technically 'non-licensable' work, the relevant authorities must still be notified of the work if:

- it is carried out for more than two hours in any seven days; or

- it takes more than one hour to complete.

Plan of Work

Work with asbestos must not start without a written plan detailing how the work is to be carried out. The plan must be kept at the premises where the work is being carried out for the full duration of the work. For final demolition or major refurbishment, the plan will usually require that asbestos is removed before any other major works begin.

The plan will specify what control measures are required for managing the risk, including:

- Monitoring the condition of any asbestos or ACMs.

- Ensuring asbestos or ACMs are maintained or safely removed.

- Providing information about the location and condition of any asbestos or ACMs to anyone liable to disturb it/ them.

- Making this information available to the emergency services.

The measures specified in the plan must be implemented and recorded.

The plan is to be reviewed and revised:

- At regular intervals.

- If there is reason to suspect that it is no longer valid.

- If there has been a significant change in the premises to which the plan relates.

TOPIC FOCUS

Typical control measures for removing asbestos include:

- Restrict access to the area.

- Enclose the work area and keep it under negative pressure, testing the sealed area for leaks.

- Provide appropriate PPE (coveralls, respirators, etc.) and a decontamination unit.

- Ensure removal operatives are suitably trained.

- Use controlled wet removal methods (e.g. water injection, damping down the surface to be worked on). Dry removal processes are unacceptable.

- Use a wrap-and-cut method or glove bag technique (a method of removing asbestos from pipes, ducts, valves, joints and other non-planar surfaces).

- Where appropriate, use measures which control the fibres at source, e.g. by using vacuuming equipment directly attached to tools. Failing this, a second employee can use a hand-held vacuum right next to the source emitting the fibres (known as 'shadow vacuuming').

- Thoroughly clean the area and obtain a clean air certificate after a successful air test upon completion of the work.

A clearance certificate for reoccupation may only be issued by a body accredited to do so. At the moment, such accreditation can only be provided by the United Kingdom Accreditation Service (UKAS).

Respiratory Equipment

Suitable RPE should always be provided where exposure can be above the control limits.

The RPE provided must be marked with a 'CE' symbol and matched to:

- The exposure concentrations (expected or measured).

- The job.

- The wearer.

- Factors related to the working environment.

RPE must be examined and tested at suitable intervals by a competent person, and a suitable record kept for five years. Respirator testing involves daily checks, monthly checks, and full performance checks every six months. Operator checks would involve fit testing to see that the correct size and model are used to provide an adequate face seal.

Protective Clothing

- **Overalls**

  - **Only** wear **disposable** (hooded) overalls - type 5 (**BS EN ISO 13982-1:2004+A1:2010**) are suitable (cotton not recommended).

  - Wear waterproof overalls for outdoor work.

  - A few tips include:

    - Wear one size too big to avoid splitting the seams.

- If the cuffs are loose, seal with tape.

- Avoid long-sleeved shirts - they are difficult to cover properly.

- Wear the overall legs over footwear, tucking them in lets dust into footwear.

- Wear the hood over the RPE straps.

- Dispose of used overalls as asbestos waste.

- **Caution - never take used overalls home.**

- **Gloves**

  - If worn, use single-use disposable gloves.

  - If latex, choose 'low-protein powder' gloves.

  - Dispose of as asbestos waste.

- **Footwear**

  - Boots are preferable to disposable overshoes which may cause risk of slipping.

  - **Caution - never use laced boots** - they have lace holes to catch asbestos fibres and are difficult to clean.

Information, Instruction and Training

Anyone removing asbestos must have training that includes:

- Properties of asbestos, its effects on health, including its interaction with smoking.

- The types of products or materials likely to contain asbestos.

- The operations which could result in asbestos exposure.

- Safe work practices, preventive control measures, and protective equipment.

- The purpose, choice, limitations, proper use and maintenance of RPE.

- Emergency procedures.

- Hygiene requirements.

- Decontamination procedures.

- Waste handling procedures.

- Medical examination requirements.

- The control limit and the need for air monitoring.

Employees should be made aware of the significant findings of the risk assessment, and the results of any air monitoring carried out, with an explanation of the findings.

Air Monitoring

Sampling for asbestos in the air should be carried out by trained staff, in three situations:

- **Compliance sampling** - within control or action limits.

- **Background sampling** - before starting work (i.e. removal).

- **Clearance sampling** - after removal and cleaning the area.

Medical Surveillance

Requirements for surveillance for persons who are exposed to asbestos:

- A health record is to be kept (for 40 years) and maintained.

- Surveillance for those carrying out licensable work with asbestos requires a doctor to carry out a medical examination every two years; and every three years for those carrying out non-licensable work requiring notification.

- A certificate should be issued to the employer and the employee and kept for four years.

Requirements for Disposal

Asbestos waste is hazardous waste if it contains more than 0.1% asbestos. The **Hazardous Waste (England and Wales) Regulations 2005** apply, and a waste consignment note is required:

- Double wrap and label the waste - standard practice is to use a red (UN) inner bag, and a clear outer bag with **Carriage of Dangerous Goods and Use of Transportable Pressure Equipment Regulations 2009** (**CDG**) warnings and asbestos code visible.

- The waste must be carried in a sealed skip or vehicle with a segregated compartment for asbestos, easily cleanable and lockable.

- It must be transported by a licensed waste carrier and be taken to a licensed disposal site. The waste consignment note is to be kept for three years.

STUDY QUESTIONS

23. Identify six chemical and four biological agents commonly encountered in construction activities.

24. Identify two asphyxiant gases and outline their ill-health effects.

25. Identify three sources of organic solvents used in construction, and describe their ill-health effects.

26. Identify the controls used to avoid or reduce exposure to cement dust and wet cement.

27. Identify the three main types of asbestos.

28. What steps are to be taken if you discover asbestos on site?

29. What are the three air-monitoring sampling methods for asbestos, and when should they be carried out?

(Suggested Answers are at the end.)

Safe Handling and Storage of Waste

IN THIS SECTION...

- Waste must be handled and stored safely prior to disposal.

- Employers must fulfil their duty of care to manage hazardous and non-hazardous waste according to legal standards. This includes keeping different types of waste separate to avoid mixing and contamination.

Duty of Care

The **Environmental Protection Act 1990** creates a duty of care for people concerned with controlled waste.

Controlled waste is any household, commercial or industrial waste as classified in the **Controlled Waste (England and Wales) Regulations 2012**. Certain types of waste, such as radioactive waste, are excluded from this definition of controlled waste.

The duty of care is applicable to all persons involved in the generation, importation, handling, transporting and disposal of controlled waste. It places a responsibility on all of the above to ensure that waste:

- Is managed legally.

- Does not escape from control.

- Is transferred only to an authorised person.

- Is adequately described.

- Is accompanied by appropriate documentation, i.e. a transfer note.

> **DEFINITION**
>
> **WASTE**
>
> Something that is discarded, or is going to be discarded.

Contamination of a fresh water drainage system with waste oil

Hazardous Waste

Hazardous waste is generally waste that is highly flammable, toxic, carcinogenic, corrosive, etc.

Non-hazardous waste generally includes household waste, paper, wood and other biodegradable materials.

Hazardous waste is defined in legislation with additional duties on those involved that are in addition to those assigned to non-hazardous waste.

Safe Handling and Storage

Leaving detailed environmental legislation issues aside, it is important to consider the health and safety issues associated with the management of waste in a workplace. Factors to consider:

- The **hazardous** nature of the waste - the waste may be inherently hazardous to staff involved in handling it. For example, toxic or radioactive. This may require the use of PPE, storage in sealed, labelled containers or bags, or in a separate secure skip, or well-ventilated area. The waste will need to be stored separately from non-hazardous waste.

- The waste may present a **manual handling** risk. This might be overcome by the use of mechanical handling equipment or handling aids.

- Storage equipment such as skips, bins and compactors may be difficult to access and may require steps or platforms to allow safe use.

- Compactors will have **moving parts** that must be effectively guarded to prevent access.

- Collection **vehicles** such as skip lorries present a significant hazard when manoeuvring, especially when reversing (and should be aided by a banksman).

- The waste may present a temptation to scavengers (e.g. waste metals) and to vandals (unlocked storage tank valves) and so must be **secured**.

- Any escape may have the potential to cause **pollution**. Adequately securing the waste might control this risk, but emergency spill or release plans may also be required, along with the necessary personnel, equipment and training to put these plans into effect.

- Waste types (streams) must be **segregated** to prevent the mixing and contamination of one type of waste with another. This usually requires separate secure storage for each type of waste and the clear identification of types.

- Appropriate **documentation** should accompany the waste and the duty of care, to dispose of waste in line with legal requirements, must be fulfilled.

Worker loading a waste compactor. Note the compactor is for cardboard only. Also note the access platform to give safe access to the skip

MORE...

Visit the following sites for further information about handling and storage of waste:

www.gov.uk/government/organisations/environment-agency

www.naturalresourceswales.gov.uk/?lang=en

STUDY QUESTIONS

30. A duty of care is placed on persons who generate, import, handle, transport and dispose of controlled waste. What responsibilities does the duty of care place on such persons?

31. Name six factors to consider when handling and storing waste for disposal.

(Suggested Answers are at the end.)

Summary

This element has dealt with some of the hazards and controls relevant to chemical and biological health hazards in the construction environment.

In particular, this element has:

- Outlined the different forms of chemicals (liquids, gases, vapours, mists, fumes, fibres and dusts) and biological agents (fungi, bacteria and viruses).

- Identified the classification of chemicals (toxic, harmful, corrosive, irritant and carcinogenic) and the meaning of the terms 'acute' and 'chronic' when used to describe their effects.

- Identified the main routes of entry into the body (inhalation, ingestion, absorption through the skin and injection through the skin) and some of the body's defence mechanisms.

- Explained the factors to be considered when undertaking an assessment of the health risks from substances encountered in construction workplaces.

- Outlined the sources of information available about the substances, and the use of safety data sheets and product labels.

- Described some of the equipment that is used when undertaking basic surveys to assess concentrations of substances in the workplace (e.g. stain tube detectors).

- Explained the purpose and principles of workplace exposure limits and their relevance in short-term and long-term exposures.

- Outlined the control measures that should be used to reduce the risk of ill health from exposure to hazardous substances.

- Described the principles of good practice as regards to controlling exposure to hazardous substances: minimising emissions; taking into account routes of exposure; exposure control to be proportional to risk; choosing effective controls; using PPE; regular checks and reviews of controls in place; and provision of information and training. Control measures should not increase the overall risks.

- Described common measures to implement the principles of good practice: eliminate or substitute; change the process; reduce exposure time; enclose or segregate; LEV; dilution ventilation; RPE and PPE; personal hygiene; and health surveillance.

- Outlined the hazards, risks and controls associated with specific hazardous agents.

- Described the generation and control of dusts on a construction site, in particular cement and wood dusts.

- Described the health risks and controls associated with asbestos and the duty to manage asbestos.

- Outlined the basic requirements related to the safe handling and storage of waste on construction sites.

Exam Skills

Approaching the Question

Think now about the steps you would take to answer the question:

Step 1. Read the question carefully. Note that this question asks about substances prevalent to the construction industry. You will need to know that substances can take the form of dusts, fibres, fumes, gases, mists, vapours or liquids.

Step 2. Now highlight the key words. In this case they might look like this:

> **Identify FOUR hazardous substances** prevalent to the construction industry **AND give** the **associated health risk** for **EACH**. **(8)**

Step 3. Next, consider the marks and time available. In this question there are eight marks so it is expected that around eight different pieces of information should be provided. The question is helpfully signposted - four hazardous substances and four associated health risks are wanted, so it's easy to see where marks will be awarded. Remember, you can only gain marks for identifying four substances and associated risks, so don't waste time including more. The question should take around eight minutes in total.

Step 4. Read the question again to make sure you understand it and have a clear understanding of hazardous substances and associated health risks. (Re-read your notes if you need to.)

Step 5. The next stage is to develop a plan - there are various ways to do this. Remind yourself, first of all, that you need to be thinking about 'hazardous substances' and they come in a range of forms. When you see the action word 'identify', you need to select and name the substance and then give the associated health risk, but you must do more than just list the substances.

Your answer must be based on the key words you have highlighted. So, in this case, we need to identify four hazardous substances and give an associated health risk for each.

Now have a go at the question. Draw up an answer plan, and then use it as the basis to write out an answer as you would in the exam.

Remember, you can always contact your tutor if you have any queries or need any further guidance on how to answer this question.

HINTS AND TIPS

- Temperature, sunlight and electricity are not substances.

- Avoid using trade names (e.g. Decothane - the examiner may not know what this substance is) - use generic terms like solvents to introduce your example.

- Make sure you know the health risks associated with the hazardous substances you choose!

Suggested Answer Outline

Substance	Health Risk
• Wood dust.	• Inhalation - respiratory problems, cancer.
• Silica dust.	• Inhalation - silicosis.
• Cement.	• Wet cement can burn, dust causes irritation.
• Organic solvents.	• Inhalation of vapour has narcotic effect.
• Asbestos.	• Inhalation of fibres causes asbestosis and/or mesothelioma.
• Lead.	• Inhalation of fumes from heating of lead paint causes lead poisoning.

Example of How the Question Could be Answered

A hazardous substance that may be released on a construction site is asbestos. Asbestos fibres may become airborne when disturbed and can enter the lungs, causing scarring and tissue damage leading to asbestosis or mesothelioma.

Lead may also be encountered during the refurbishment of old properties, when old, lead-based paints are burnt off to prepare surfaces to be re-finished. Heating the paint may expose the operators to lead fumes. Inhaling lead fume can cause lead poisoning and ultimately the failure of the nervous system.

Solvents are commonly found during construction projects. Solvents may occur as curing agents in flat roof membranes, paint thinners, or some adhesives used to lay flooring, etc. Inhalation of vapours from organic solvents may result in the employee becoming drowsy; or depress the central nervous system; or lead to liver failure.

Wood dust is a hazardous substance, and construction activities are likely to involve cutting, sanding and planing wood in a variety of forms from hardwood through to MDF board. Dust arising from these processes, if inhaled, can cause allergic or non-allergic respiratory symptoms and possibly even cancer.

Reasons for Poor Marks Achieved by Candidates in Exam

• Providing a list instead of identifying hazardous substances.

• Using examples that are not hazardous substances like sunlight, electricity, etc.

• Failing to separate the answers into different parts - structuring your answer to address the different parts of the question is likely to help to gain marks. This question really needed to be addressed by four paragraphs, one for each substance and its effect.

• Illegible handwriting - you need to be aware that examiners cannot award marks if they cannot read what you have written.

Physical and Psychological Health - Hazards and Risk Control

Learning Outcomes

Once you've read this element, you'll understand how to:

1 Outline the health effects associated with exposure to noise and appropriate control measures.

2 Outline the health effects associated with exposure to vibration and appropriate control measures.

3 Outline the health effects associated with ionising and non-ionising radiation and the appropriate control measures.

4 Outline the causes and effects of stress at work and appropriate control measures.

Contents

Noise

IN THIS SECTION...

- Exposure to excessive noise causes Noise-Induced Hearing Loss (NIHL) as well as other physical and psychological effects.

- Noise exposure standards are based on a worker's daily personal noise exposure. A continuous 85 dB(A) over an 8-hour shift is considered the upper limit.

- Noise exposure should be assessed by carrying out a survey using a sound level meter.

- Exposure to noise can be controlled by: eliminating or substituting the source; maintenance; damping of resonating parts; silencing; enclosing the source in an acoustic enclosure; isolating the source; using sound-absorbing materials; providing an acoustic haven for operators; and providing hearing protection.

- Two types of hearing protection are available - ear defenders (muffs) and ear plugs. Both are effective, but have limitations.

- Monitoring and health surveillance will help to reduce the risks of noise-induced hearing loss and maintain adequate control measures.

Introduction to Noise

The **Control of Noise at Work Regulations 2005** provide the framework for addressing the problems of workplace noise, although they are almost exclusively concerned with the risk of damage to hearing.

> **DEFINITION**
>
> **NOISE**
>
> Unwanted sound.

Physical and Psychological Effects on Hearing of Exposure to Noise

In moderation, noise is harmless, but if it is too loud it can permanently damage hearing. The danger depends on how loud the noise is and how long people are exposed to it.

- **Physical Effects of Noise**

  - Temporary reduction in hearing sensitivity as a result of short duration exposure to excessively loud noise. This is known as **temporary threshold shift**.

  - Temporary ringing in the ears as a result of short duration exposure to excessively loud noise.

  - Noise-Induced Hearing Loss (NIHL) - permanent loss of hearing as a result of repeated exposure to excessively loud noise. One cause of **permanent threshold shift** (along with age, infection, etc.)

  - Tinnitus - persistent ringing in the ears as a result of repeated exposure to excessively loud noise.

- **Psychological Effects of Noise**

  - Stress effects:

    - Caused by irritating nuisance/background noise.

    - Due to the inability to clearly hear or define spoken words, and determine sounds (from radio, television, street noises, etc.).

Exposure to loud noise can cause both temporary and permanent hearing loss

- Safety effects:
    - Inability to hear:
        - hazards such as vehicles;
        - alarms and warning sirens; and
        - conversation and spoken instructions;

    as a result of background noise.

- Difficulty concentrating and an increase in errors caused by nuisance/background noise.

The most serious effect is Noise-Induced Hearing Loss (NIHL) (industrial deafness) - this is irreversible and caused by exposure over a long period of time to excessively loud noise. Surgery may reduce the damage in the case of acute injury to the eardrum, but there is no cure for NIHL.

Sound waves travel into the ear canal until they reach the eardrum. The eardrum passes the vibrations through the middle ear bones or ossicles into the inner ear. The inner ear is shaped like a snail and is called the cochlea. Inside the cochlea there are thousands of tiny hair cells which change these vibrations into electrical signals that are sent to the brain through the hearing nerve. The brain tells you that you are hearing a sound and what that sound is. Each hair cell has a small patch of stereocilia sticking up out of the top. Sound makes the stereocilia rock back and forth. If the sound is too loud, the stereocilia can be bent or broken. This will cause the hair cell to die and it can no longer send sound signals to the brain. In humans, once a hair cell dies, it will never grow back. The high frequency hair cells are the most easily damaged, so people with hearing loss from loud sounds often have problems hearing high pitched speech or music.

A quick guide to safe noise levels would be the 'Two-Metre Rule'. If normal conversation can't be heard two metres away from a person talking, the noise level is probably at or above safe limits.

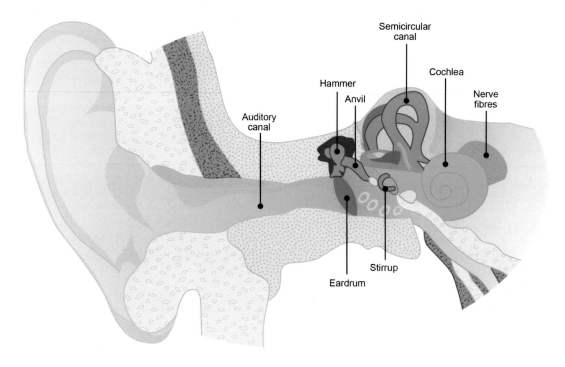

Diagram showing the internal parts of the ear

One-off exposures to high noise levels (e.g. four hours' work in a high-noise area) cause a temporary loss of sensitivity (temporary threshold shift) due to disturbance of the cochlear hairs, and temporary ringing in the ears (tinnitus).

Repeated exposure over a number of years causes permanent damage in the cochlea (**permanent threshold shift**) and this is noise-induced hearing loss. The loss is progressive (it gets gradually worse over time), with earlier periods of damage being unable to repair themselves.

Terms Used in the Measurement of Sound

The following basic terminology is used in the measurement and assessment of sound and noise exposure in the workplace:

- **Sound pressure level** - a measure of the intensity of the sound pressure wave moving through the air. It is normally expressed as decibels (dB).

- **Decibel (dB)** - the unit of sound pressure level (the 'loudness of the noise'). It is a logarithmic scale, which means that relatively small increases (or decreases) actually represent large increases (or decreases) in intensity. For instance, an increase of just 3 dB represents a doubling of sound intensity (i.e. 82 dB is twice as loud as 79 dB).

- **Frequency** - the number of sound pressure waves (e.g. contacting the eardrum) every second. It is measured in hertz (Hz). The human ear is sensitive to noise across a wide range of frequencies, from very low (bass) frequencies at 20 Hz to very high-pitch frequencies at 20,000 Hz.

- **A-weighting** - applied during noise assessment to the decibel scale to give a sound pressure level expressed as **dB(A)**. This A-weighting takes into account the sensitivity of the human ear across a wide range of frequencies. In other words, it is the decibel value corrected for the human ear.

- **C-weighting** - applied during noise assessment to the decibel scale to give a sound pressure level expressed as **dB(C)**. This C-weighting gives a more accurate reading for impulse noise - such as single loud bangs that would not be properly recorded using the dB(A) scale.

- **Daily personal noise exposure ($L_{EP,d}$)** - the dose of noise that a person is exposed to over an 8-hour working period; their 'daily dose' of noise. Sometimes seen as a weekly dose and expressed as $L_{EP,w}$.

Measurement in dB(A)	Sound
0	The faintest audible sounds
20-30	A quiet library
50-60	A conversation
65-75	A loud radio
90-100	A power drill
140	A jet aircraft taking off 25m away

The Need for Assessment of Exposure

Noise exposure limits are set on the basis that the amount of damage done to the ear is directly related to the amount of energy absorbed by the inner ear. This is determined by two factors:

- The noise level (measured in dB(A)).

- The duration of exposure (in hours and minutes).

These two factors determine the '**dose**' of noise absorbed (a similar principle to hazardous substances and workplace exposure limits). It is therefore necessary, when undertaking a noise assessment, to measure a worker's **actual exposure** to noise (which will fluctuate) and then to calculate what the equivalent 8-hour exposure would be. This personal noise exposure is usually written as $L_{EP,d}$ (daily) or $L_{EP,w}$ (weekly).

Equal amounts of noise entering the ear cause the same effect, therefore a short exposure to a high level of noise is considered to cause comparable hearing damage to a longer exposure to a lower level of noise. So, where it may be considered 'safe' to be exposed to 85 dB(A) for 8 hours, exposure to 88 dB(A) would only be 'safe' for four hours. In both cases, the **dose** is the same. This is illustrated in the following table:

Exposure equivalents

Noise Level in the Workplace	Duration of Exposure	Noise 'Dose' ($L_{EP,d}$)
85 dB(A)	8 hours	85 dB(A)
88 dB(A)	4 hours	85 dB(A)
91 dB(A)	2 hours	85 dB(A)
94 dB(A)	1 hour	85 dB(A)
97 dB(A)	30 mins	85 dB(A)
100 dB(A)	15 mins	85 dB(A)
103 dB(A)	7.5 mins	85 dB(A)

As can be seen from the table above, if the sound level is doubled (represented by a 3 dB(A) increase) then the duration of exposure has to be halved for the total dose to remain the same.

To take into account noise dose, the **Control of Noise at Work Regulations 2005** introduced **exposure action values** and **exposure limit values**. These are exposure values at which the employer is required to take particular steps to protect employees and others from the harmful effects of noise.

Lower Exposure Action Values (LEAVs)

These are:

- **80 dB(A)** - a daily or weekly (ambient) noise exposure not taking into account the effects of any hearing protection.

- **135 dB(C)** - a 'one-off' instantaneous noise (one impact) in the 8-hour day, not taking into account the effects of any hearing protection.

Where LEAVs may be exceeded, the employer must:

- Carry out a risk assessment and if this indicates a risk to health then carry out health surveillance.

- Provide information, instruction and training.

- Make hearing protection available.

Upper Exposure Action Values (UEAVs)

These are:

- **85 dB(A)** - as above, a daily, or weekly, personal exposure that does not take into account the effects of any hearing protection.

- **137 dB(C)** - as above, a 'peak sound pressure level' (a 'one-off' instantaneous noise) in the 8-hour day, not taking into account the effects of any hearing protection.

At or above UEAVs the employer must:

- Carry out a noise assessment.

- Reduce noise exposure to the lowest level reasonably practicable.

If noise levels are still above 85 dB(A), the employer must:

- Establish mandatory hearing protection zones.

- Provide information, instruction and training.

- Provide hearing protection and enforce its use.

Exposure Limit Values (ELVs)

These are:

- **87 dB(A)** - daily, or weekly, personal exposure that must not be exceeded. Hearing protection can be taken into account.

- **140 dB(C)** - a 'one-off' 'peak sound pressure level' during the working day. This must not be exceeded. Hearing protection can be taken into account.

If an ELV is exceeded, the employer must investigate the reason for the occurrence and identify and implement actions to ensure that it does not occur again.

Simple Noise Measurement Techniques

Noise assessments are required where there is significant exposure to noise. Some form of noise survey will have to be carried out. Before this is done, some information has to be obtained from the workplace (e.g. about the noise sources in the workplace and shift patterns). This background information can then be used to guide the survey and help to interpret the results. Different types of noise meter can be used, which include:

- **Simple sound-level meter** - measures instantaneous noise levels and can be used for spot-checks and very simple surveys.

- **Integrating sound-level meter** - measures noise over a period of time and gives a time-weighted average over that period; useful for most noise surveys.

- **Dosimeters** - integrating sound-level meters worn by the worker which give a measure of their personal noise exposure; useful for work areas where people move around a lot.

The results of a noise survey need to be interpreted to give an accurate estimate of workers' exposures. These exposures can then be compared to relevant standards and any necessary actions identified.

Basic Noise Control Techniques

In simple terms, noise exposure can be controlled in three ways:

- Reduce the noise at source.

- Interrupt the pathway from source to receiver.

- Protect the receiver.

Source

- **Eliminate the source** - completely remove the noise source; not often achievable.

- **Substitute the source** - change the noise source for something that does the same job, but more quietly (e.g. change a petrol-driven machine for an electric one).

- **Maintenance** - machinery sometimes makes noises because it needs maintenance.

- **Damping** - machine parts (especially metal surfaces) often resonate together, exaggerating the noise generated. Damping can change the resonance characteristics to prevent ringing noises. Change a part, stiffen it or coat one side with a sound absorbent.

- **Silencing** - any machine that produces exhaust air or gases (e.g. a diesel generator or pneumatic control valve) should be fitted with a silencer on the exhaust to suppress noise.

Pathway

- **Insulation** - some noise sources can have an enclosure built around them. Any noise generated inside will remain there, without penetrating the walls into the rest of the workplace. Generators and compressors are often in their own noise-reduction enclosures.

- **Isolation** - noise is often transmitted from a machine into supporting structures by vibration (e.g. a compressor through the floor it stands on). Isolation involves separating the machine from noise-carrying structures using noise-absorbent mats or spring-mounts. This breaks the transmission pathway.

- **Absorption** - once noise has left its source it can go directly through air to a receiver, or be reflected off hard surfaces (e.g. walls and ceilings). Absorption involves putting sound-absorbing materials in the way to absorb the sound waves before they can reach the receiver. Sound-absorbent coatings are often applied to walls to prevent noise reflection.

Receiver

- **Acoustic haven** - if the workplace is generally noisy and the above controls can't be applied, then an acoustic haven can house the operator away from the noise (a 'sound-proof booth').

- **Hearing protection** - where none of the above are practical, or when applied still leave noise above action levels, some form of hearing protection should be used to reduce the noise an operator receives.

Purpose, Application and Limitations of Personal Hearing Protection

Types of Hearing Protection

Hearing protection prevents harmful noise from reaching the ear. Two principal types are available:

- **Ear Defenders (or Muffs)**

    These encase the outer ear in a cup with a sound-absorbent foam or gel-filled cushion to seal against the side of the head.

Advantages	Limitations
Easy to supervise and enforce use.	Uncomfortable when worn for long time.
Less chance of ear infections.	Incompatible with some other items worn (e.g. spectacles).
Higher level of protection possible; bone transmission is reduced.	Must be routinely inspected, cleaned and maintained.

- **Ear Plugs**

  These rigid, semi-rigid or foam plugs fit into the ear canal.

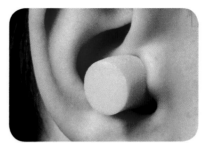

Ear plugs are more difficult to supervise and enforce

Advantages	Limitations
Cheap.	Difficult to see when fitted, so difficult to supervise and enforce.
Disposable.	
Often more comfortable to wear.	Risk of infection if dirty or if cross-contaminated when inserted.
Do not interfere with any other items worn.	Easy to lose or misplace.

Selection

Hearing protection should be chosen taking into account the levels of noise the wearer will be exposed to and the strengths and limitations of each type. It must fit and be comfortable for the wearer.

As with all types of PPE, employers should ensure that only CE-marked hearing protection is purchased and used within their organisation.

Use

To be effective, hearing protection should be worn all the time the wearer is exposed. Much of the protection is lost when earmuffs or plugs are removed, even if only for a short time - removing the protection for only 15 minutes in an 8-hour shift can lose the wearer 80% or more of the protection. Not many users are aware of this fact. For enforcement and supervisory purposes, earmuffs can be seen more easily when worn.

Maintenance

Replacement of earmuffs and ear plugs is required at regular intervals, due to good personal hygiene practices or if the equipment is defective or damaged. Some parts on earmuffs can be changed without replacing the whole thing (e.g. ear cushions or absorbent pads).

Attenuation Factors

Noise received at the ear must be kept below any exposure limits, so information is required on the:

- Noise characteristics of the workplace (from the survey).

- Attenuation characteristics of the available hearing protection (from the manufacturers) - how much noise they remove.

Most forms of hearing protection give better protection against high frequency noises - the high pitched noises. The lower frequency rumbles from machinery are harder to reduce.

There is a general limitation on the level of noise reduction that can be achieved, depending on the quality and type of the ear protection. Ear defenders, because the cup covers the ear and rests on the side of the face, give better attenuation than plugs, as less noise can be transmitted through the bones of the skull.

Protection will be reduced by various factors which reduce the effectiveness of the seal between the ear and the earmuff or plug, e.g. as a result of long hair, thick spectacle frames or jewellery, incorrect fitting of plugs or the wearing of safety helmets or face-shields.

A range of factors can reduce the protection offered by hearing protection

Role of Monitoring and Health Surveillance

This is appropriate for workers exposed to high noise levels, in the form of audiometry - a medical test that quantifies the sensitivity of a person's hearing. It normally involves the worker sitting in a soundproof booth while wearing headphones, listening for a series of beeps and pressing a button when they are heard. This maps the hearing capabilities across the range of frequencies.

Audiometry allows:

- Recognition of existing hearing loss (before starting employment).

- Further damage or hearing loss during employment to be identified.

- The removal or exclusion of workers from high noise areas (to protect from further loss).

- An evaluation of the effectiveness of noise controls.

Audiometry should be conducted by a trained, competent person. Good records must be kept and employees informed of the results of their checks. If any damage is identified, then the affected worker should be examined by a doctor.

STUDY QUESTIONS

1. What does a daily personal exposure of 85 dB(A) mean?

2. What are the general limitations of ear defenders and ear plugs?

3. Identify three benefits that audiometry allows.

(Suggested Answers are at the end.)

Vibration

IN THIS SECTION...

- Exposure of the hands to excessive vibration can lead to hand-arm vibration syndrome. There are also health effects from whole-body vibration.

- Exposure standards exist for both hand-arm vibration and whole-body vibration.

- Exposure to vibration can be controlled by: choosing appropriate equipment; maintenance of equipment; and limitation of exposure (including use of PPE).

- Health surveillance and monitoring can protect workers from the effects of vibration and help to ensure controls are adequate.

Effects on the Body of Exposure to Vibration

Vibration is similar in many respects to noise, both in terms of physical characteristics and preventive measures. The health effects associated with vibration exposure fall into two main categories.

Hand-Arm Vibration Syndrome (HAVS)

Regular and frequent use of vibrating tools and equipment is found in a wide range of construction activities, e.g. building and maintenance of roads and railways; concrete products; construction of mines and quarries; and house building. Any vibrating tool or process which causes tingling or numbness after five to ten minutes of continuous use is suspect. Exposure to such vibration can lead to Hand-Arm Vibration Syndrome (HAVS), the symptoms of which include:

Worker using vibrating tool

- **Vibration White Finger (VWF)** - where the blood supply to the fingers shuts down and the fingers turn white. This is made worse by cold or wet conditions. The blood supply will return after some time, leaving the fingers red and painful. This is the most common form of HAVS.

- **Nerve damage** - the nerves to the fingers stop working properly, resulting in a loss of pressure, heat and pain sensitivity.

- **Muscle weakening** - grip strength and manual dexterity reduce.

- **Joint damage** - abnormal bone growth at the finger joints can occur.

HAVS usually takes many years (five to ten) of exposure to vibrating equipment to manifest itself, but once established it is not curable. Any further exposure to vibration will do further damage. The only effective solution is to stop an affected person from using vibrating tools.

HAVS is a notifiable disease under the **Reporting of Injuries, Diseases and Dangerous Occurrences Regulations 2013**.

TOPIC FOCUS

Vibration Risk Activities

Work equipment that can expose workers to vibration risks includes:

- Chainsaws and circular saws.
- Needle guns and scrabbling machines.
- Road/rock drills, concrete breakers, hammer drills.
- Hand-held grinders, pedestal grinders and hand-held sanders.
- Nut runners.
- Power hammers and chisels, riveting hammers and bolsters.

Operators are particularly at risk if using:

- Hammer action equipment for more than half an hour each day.
- Rotary or other action equipment for more than two hours each day.

Whole-Body Vibration (WBV)

Not yet fully understood, Whole-Body Vibration (WBV) can result from using various construction vehicles or compactors, and can cause other injuries to the knees, hips and back. The damage is caused by vibration from the vehicle or machine passing through the seat into the driver's body through the buttocks. Additionally, standing on the platform of a machine will result in vibration passing through the worker's feet.

Effects will be worse if travelling too fast, through rough terrain, on badly paved surfaces, or if the vehicle itself has poor suspension. The greater the duration and level of vibration, the worse the effect may be. Contributory factors which can cause or increase the effects are poor driving posture, poor design of controls, or lack of visibility making twisting and/or turning necessary when driving.

Construction vehicle drivers or those operating large static compactors, hammering or punching machines and mobile crushers are most at risk from WBV. Young workers may also be susceptible in this respect.

The most significant health effect is back pain as a result of damage to the soft tissues of the spine (such as the intervertebral discs) though other effects have been reported (such as vertigo).

The Need for Assessment of Exposure

The **Control of Vibration at Work Regulations 2005 (CVAWR)** provide the framework for the regulation of exposure of workers to vibration, in order to protect their health.

The employer needs to ascertain (by risk assessment) whether employees are liable to be exposed to vibration levels at or above an exposure action value or above an exposure limit value. These limits are set on the basis that the amount of damage done is dependent on the vibration energy absorbed by the body. This is determined by the:

- Vibration magnitude, measured in m/s^2.
- Duration of the exposure, measured in hours and minutes.

These two factors determine the 'dose' of vibration absorbed (the same principle as applied to noise).

TOPIC FOCUS

A **vibration risk assessment** needs to consider:

- Equipment likely to cause vibration and places of use.
- The employees, and the magnitude, type and duration of exposure.
- The effects of vibration on employees who may be at risk.
- Any effects of vibration on the workplace and equipment.
- Manufacturers' information and vibration data.
- Availability of replacement equipment with reduced vibration.
- Any further exposure at the workplace to whole-body vibration beyond normal working hours.
- Exposure in rest facilities supervised by the employer.
- Specific working conditions, e.g. low temperatures.
- Appropriate information obtained from health surveillance including, where possible, published information.

The assessment should be recorded and reviewed.

Risk assessment should enable the employer to decide whether employees' exposure is likely to be above the **Exposure Action Value (EAV)** or **Exposure Limit Value (ELV)** (see below) and to identify work activities in need of control.

The assessment must be completed by a competent person who must:

- Have had specific training.
- Know:
  - The work processes being used.
  - How to collect and understand relevant information.
- Be able to develop a plan of action based on the findings.
- Ensure the plan is introduced and is effective.

Work activities involving vibrating equipment should be grouped according to the risk they represent: high, medium or low. Action should be planned to control risks for the employees at greatest risk first.

Rough groupings should be based on:

High Risk	Those operating: • Hammer action tools for more than 1 hour per day. • Rotary and other action tools for more than about 2 hours per day.
Medium Risk	Those who regularly operate: • Hammer action tools for more than 15 minutes per day. • Some rotary and other action tools for more than about 1 hour per day.

Exposure Action Value and Exposure Limit Value

CVAWR require employers to take specific action when the daily vibration exposure reaches a certain **action** or **limit** value.

The daily **Exposure Action Value (EAV)** is:

- For hand-arm vibration 2.5 m/s² A(8).

- For whole body vibration 0.5 m/s² A(8).

If these are reached, the employer must:

- Carry out a vibration risk assessment.

- Reduce vibration exposure to the lowest level reasonably practicable.

- Provide information, instruction and training for employees.

- Carry out health surveillance where the assessment indicates a risk to health due to the EAV being exceeded.

The daily **Exposure Limit Value (ELV)** (which must not be exceeded) is:

- For hand-arm vibration 5.0 m/s² A(8).

- For whole body vibration 1.15 m/s² A(8).

If these are reached, the employer must:

- Carry out a vibration risk assessment.

- Immediately reduce exposure below the ELV.

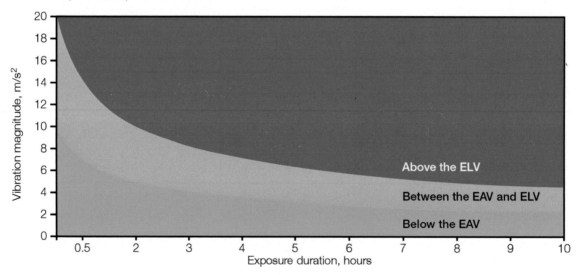

How vibration level and duration affect exposure
(Source: INDG175(rev2) Control the risks from hand-arm vibration, HSE, 2008)

Basic Vibration Control Measures

There is a number of preventive and precautionary measures which can be taken:

- **Choice of Equipment**

    - Mechanise the activity - use a concrete breaker mounted on an excavator arm rather than hand-operated.

- Change the tool or equipment for one with less vibration generation characteristics.

- Use tools that create less vibration, e.g. a diamond-tipped masonry cutter instead of a tungsten hammer drill.

- Support the tools (e.g. tensioners or balancers), allowing the operator to reduce grip and feed force.

- Add anti-vibration mounts to isolate the operator from the vibration source.

- **Maintenance**

  - Keep moving parts properly adjusted and lubricated.

  - Keep cutting tools sharp.

  - Replace vibration mounts before they wear too badly.

  - Ensure rotating parts are checked for balance.

  - Keep all equipment clean - especially look for corrosion.

- **Limit Exposure**

  - Calculate how long a tool/job takes to reach an action level or limit.

  - Operate tools within these known action levels or limits.

  - Avoid gripping too tightly or forcing tools.

  - Use job rotation techniques - share between several workers.

  - Ensure adequate rest breaks during the work.

- **Protective Clothing**

  - PPE (e.g. gloves) may not actually protect against vibration.

  - Gloves will protect from cold and wet - a major contributing factor.

Further measures to minimise whole-body vibration:

- Maintain suspension components adequately.

- Ensure the driver's seat is in good repair and gives adequate support.

- Plan site routes to use the smoothest terrain.

- Fit a suspension seat, correctly adjusted for the driver's weight.

- Make sure correct tyre pressures are used.

- Adjust speed where the terrain is rough.

Role of Monitoring and Health Surveillance

Regulation 7 of **CVAWR** requires that health surveillance should be conducted where appropriate, e.g. in cases where the risk assessment shows a risk of developing vibration-related conditions, or employee exposure reaching action levels. Records of this health surveillance should be kept.

Where an identifiable disease related to vibration exposure is discovered, monitoring is required to minimise the health effects and maintain adequate control. The employer needs to take the following steps:

- Ensure that a qualified person informs the employee accordingly and provides him/her with information and advice.

- Ensure that the employee is informed of any significant findings.

- Review the risk assessment.

- Review any measures taken to control risk from vibration.

- Consider assigning the employee to alternative work where there is no risk from further exposure to vibration.

- Provide for a review of the health of any other employee who has been similarly exposed.

STUDY QUESTIONS

4. State the symptoms of hand-arm vibration syndrome.

5. What control measures can be taken with regard to tools and equipment, to reduce the risk of vibration injuries?

6. When do the Control of Vibration at Work Regulations 2005 require that health surveillance be conducted?

(Suggested Answers are at the end.)

Radiation

IN THIS SECTION...

- Radiation comes in two forms - ionising radiation and non-ionising radiation.

- Ionising radiation includes alpha particles, beta particles, X-rays, gamma rays, radon and neutrons. Exposure to these can cause acute sickness and chronic effects.

- Non-ionising radiation includes ultraviolet (UV), infrared (IR), visible light, microwaves and radio waves. UV, visible light and IR can cause eye and skin damage; microwaves and radio waves can cause internal heating.

- Artificial optical radiation includes sources of non-ionising radiation, and an employer must consider the causes and effects of these in risk assessment.

- Exposure to ionising radiation can be controlled by properly managing time and distance and by providing shielding. Dose limits apply.

- Clothing and PPE can help to control exposure to non-ionising radiation, as can safe distances and isolation, and safe systems of work, including permits-to-work.

- Radiation protection strategies are required where radioactive sources are used in the workplace.

Types of Radiation and their Health Effects

Radiation is energy that is emitted from a radioactive source. The energy emitted is capable of causing considerable harm, depending on its form and the length of exposure. The higher the frequency, the more penetrative its properties.

There are two forms of radiation - **ionising** and **non-ionising**

Ionising and non-ionising radiation can both be divided into several main types:

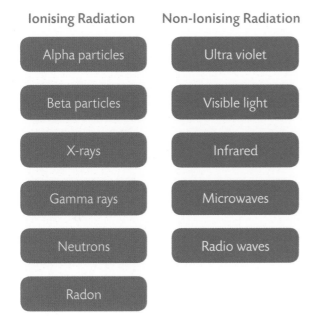

Ionising Radiation	Non-Ionising Radiation
Alpha particles	Ultra violet
Beta particles	Visible light
X-rays	Infrared
Gamma rays	Microwaves
Neutrons	Radio waves
Radon	

> **DEFINITIONS**
>
> **IONISING RADIATION**
>
> Radiation that causes ionisation in the material that absorbs it.
>
> **NON-IONISING RADIATION**
>
> Radiation that does not cause ionisation in the material that absorbs it.

Ionising Radiation

The main types are:

- **Alpha Particles**
    - Sub-atomic particles.
    - Low penetration, stopped by thin barriers such as paper and skin.
    - Low hazard outside the body; higher risk if swallowed or inhaled.

- **Beta Particles**
    - Sub-atomic particles.
    - More penetration and can get through skin to living tissue.
    - Hazardous outside the body.

- **X-rays**
    - High energy electromagnetic light emitted from radioactive substances and generators (X-ray machines).
    - High penetrating power and can shine right through the human body (not through dense bone tissue).
    - Very hazardous.

- **Gamma Rays**
    - Very high electromagnetic energy (light) emitted by some radioactive substances.
    - Very high penetration, can shine right through the human body (even through bones).
    - Can penetrate solid objects such as steel and concrete to a degree.
    - Very hazardous.

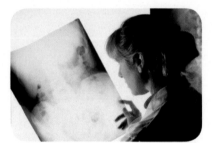

X-rays are a type of ionisng radiation

- **Neutrons**
    - Sub-atomic particles emitted by some radioactive substances.
    - Very high penetrating power, can penetrate through the body.
    - Very hazardous.

- **Radon**
    - Radon 222.
    - A naturally occurring radioactive gas.
    - Decay products of radon are themselves radioactive (alpha particles).
    - Very hazardous.

Health Effects of Ionising Radiation

- **Acute effects** of exposure to high doses include:
    - Sickness and diarrhoea.
    - Hair loss.
    - Anaemia, due to red blood cell damage.

- Reduced immune system due to white blood cell damage.

All of the cells of the body are affected by the radiation, but some more than others. A large enough dose can kill in hours or days.

- **Chronic effects** of exposure include:

  - Cancer.

  - Genetic mutations.

  - Birth defects.

  Chronic effects can arise following exposure to high a low doses of radiation. There is no safe level of exposure below which there will be no chronic effects - instead, there is a clear relationship between dose and risk (i.e. the higher the dose, the higher the risk).

- **Effects of Radon** - most radon gas that is inhaled is immediately exhaled and will cause little harm. However, decay products of radon act more like solid particles and are themselves radioactive. These solid decay products attach to atmospheric dusts and water droplets, which, if inhaled, become lodged in the airways and the lungs. Some emit alpha radioactive particles, which cause significant damage to sensitive lung cells.

  Radon is the second largest cause of lung cancer in the UK (after smoking) accounting for 2,000 fatalities a year.

Non-Ionising Radiation

This form consists of lower-energy electromagnetic waves, whose energy decreases with increasing wavelength. There is a spectrum of types of non-ionising radiation based on the wavelength of the energy transmitted. This spectrum, together with the effects on the body, is as follows:

- **Ultraviolet (UV)**

  High-frequency electromagnetic radiation (light) emitted from white-hot materials (e.g. the arc produced in arc welding).

- **Infrared (IR)**

  Lower-frequency electromagnetic radiation (light) emitted by red-hot material (e.g. molten metal poured into castings).

- **Visible Light**

  Electromagnetic radiation between the UV and IR frequencies and visible to the human eye.

- **Radio Waves**

  Lower-frequency electromagnetic radiation emitted by an antenna.

- **Microwaves**

  Lower-frequency electromagnetic radiation emitted by a microwave generator (can be categorised as a subset of radio waves).

Lasers are sources of non-ionising radiation, and can operate at UV, visible light and IR frequencies. Operating at UV and IR, the rays are not visible to the human eye. Laser light is very coherent - the light waves are all aligned with one another and do not spread out over distance. They can carry power over long distances.

Artificial Optical Radiation

Artificial optical radiation is not a form of radiation in itself, but includes many of the non-ionising sources we have seen above (ultraviolet, infrared, lasers, etc.). The **Control of Artificial Optical Radiation at Work Regulations (AOR) 2010** requires employers to give more consideration to controlling exposure to such artificial sources, to ensure they cause no harm.

Sources of **artificial optical radiation** in the workplace will include:

- Ceiling mounted lights (bulbs or tubes).

- All task lighting such as desk lamps.

- Tungsten-halogen lamps.

- High-pressure mercury floodlights.

- Photocopiers.

- Computer, phone and tablet screens.

- LED remote control devices and LED lamp systems.

- Flash lamps on cameras.

- Gas-fired overhead heaters.

- Lights, indicator lamps and headlights on vehicles.

- Certain classes of lasers.

- Desktop digital projectors.

- Welding and burning (arc and oxy-fuel).

- UV insect traps.

Headlights on vehicles are a source of artificial optical radiation which can often be present in construction activities

The sources identified above are generally considered to be 'safe' - in that, if used correctly, and not positioned in very close proximity to the eyes or skin, they will not cause harm.

Health Effects of Non-Ionising Radiation

These depend on and differ with the types of radiation:

- **UV**

    - Redness and skin burns (e.g. sunburn).

    - Pain and inflammation to the surface of the eye, leading to temporary blindness (often called 'arc-eye' or 'snow-blindness').

    - Increased risk of skin cancer.

    - Premature aging of the skin.

- **Visible Light**

    Can cause temporary blindness if intense (disability glare) and permanent eye damage if very intense (e.g. high-powered laser) and burns to exposed skin tissue.

- **IR**

    - Redness and burns to the skin.

    - Development of eye cataracts over time.

    - Note: sunlight includes UV, visible light and IR - see above for effects.

- Microwaves

  - Absorbed into the body and cause internal heating.

  - High doses cause internal organ damage and could be fatal.

- Radio Waves

  Are absorbed and cause internal heating as microwaves.

Lasers are classified according to intrinsic safety and power output. Class 1 lasers present little risk, but Class 4 lasers can cause instant skin burns and eye damage.

Artificial optical radiation effects:

- Burns or reddening of the skin.

- Burns or reddening of the surface of the eye (photokeratitis).

- Burns to the retina of the eye.

- Blue-light damage to the eye (photoretinitis).

- Damage to the lens of the eye that causes early cataracts.

Typical Occupational Sources of Radiation

Ionising Radiation

This is used to provide energy, take X-rays, detect contaminants (radioactive (sealed) sources are used as portable nuclear density/moisture gauges to measure density and detect moisture in construction materials). Sources include the following:

Alpha particles	Smoke detectors and science labs.
Beta particles	Science labs and thickness gauges.
X-rays	Medical radiography, baggage security scanners, non-destructive testing of equipment and machinery.
Gamma rays	Industrial radiography - employing highly radioactive materials such as cobalt-60 is used commonly on construction sites. The process of gamma radiography - a type of non-destructive testing (NDT) - is used to validate the integrity of poured concrete.
Neutrons	Nuclear power stations.

Radon (Radon 222)

Radon is a naturally occurring radioactive gas originating from uranium, occurring naturally in rocks and soils - radon levels are much higher in certain parts of the UK. The highest levels are found in underground spaces such as basements, caves, mines, utility industry service ducts and in some areas in ground floor buildings, as they are usually at a higher pressure than the surrounding atmosphere. It usually gets into buildings through gaps and cracks in the floor.

All workplaces can be affected in radon-affected areas.

Non-Ionising Radiation

Sources of non-ionising radiation (including artificial optical radiation) include:

UV	Sunlight; arc-welding and oxy-fuel welding/burning; curing of paint in manufacturing and vehicle painting processes; curing of inks in printing.
Visible light	Laser levelling devices; laser pointer.
IR	Red-hot steel in a rolling mill; glass manufacture; ceramics (clay ware) manufacture.
Microwaves	Food processing (ovens); telecommunications equipment (mobile phone masts).
Radio waves	Radio, TV or radar transmitters.

Basic Means of Controlling Exposure to Radiation

The **Ionising Radiations Regulations 2017 (IRR)** provide the framework for controls.

Protection from **ionising radiation** is based on strict adherence to forms of control which limit exposure to the absolute minimum by using time, distance and shielding.

Protection from the effects of **non-ionising radiation** is principally in the form of shields and PPE, although where ultraviolet sources are powerful enough to constitute a hazard, administrative controls may also be necessary.

Controlling Exposure to Ionising Radiation

- **Time** - minimise the duration of exposure. The dose is proportional to time - halve the time, halve the dose.

- **Distance** - the dose will get lower the further away from the source you get.

  - Alpha and beta particles only travel a short distance through air, so short separation distances are often effective.

  - X-rays and gamma rays travel much further, but obey the inverse square law - if the distance from the source to the person is doubled, the radiation dose goes down to a quarter (not a half).

- **Shielding** - relatively thin shields can be used with alpha and beta particles, but X-rays and gamma rays need much thicker, denser shields, such as lead.

Control of Radioactive Substances

Radioactive substances used as a source of ionising radiation should be in the form of a sealed source whenever reasonably practicable. This should be designed, constructed and maintained to prevent leakage. Records of the quantity and location of radioactive substances must be kept.

Controlling Exposure to Radon

A survey should be undertaken to determine if radon levels are acceptable or require action.

Where radon levels are at or above the action level of $400Bq/m^3$ (becquerels per cubic metre), then employee exposure must be reduced. This is often best done by appointing a Radiation Protection Adviser (RPA) to carry out a risk assessment (see later).

Engineering solutions to high radon levels can often be applied, such as:

- Fitting positive pressure air fans to prevent the radon gas from seeping from the ground up into the workplace.

- Installing radon sumps and extraction systems to draw radon out of the ground at low-level before it can seep into buildings.

Controlling Exposure to Non-Ionising Radiation

Control of exposure to non-ionising radiation is generally through the use of barriers and PPE. However, prolonged exposure to ultraviolet radiation may need warning signs, access restrictions and limited exposure times. All require information, instruction and training.

Radiation detector

Engineering controls:

- Restricted access to controlled and supervised areas by interlocked doors.

- Where UV or visible radiation may be generated, reflective surfaces should be avoided and surfaces painted in a dark, matt colour.

- Segregation and containment of unsealed radioactive material.

- Shielding is the best method of protection.

- There should be no unnecessary metal objects near any radiating Radio Frequency (RF) device, as localised high field strengths may result around such items. Care should therefore be taken to remove rings, watches or bracelets when working close to radiating sources.

PPE:

- Gloves and overalls prevent exposure from low-energy beta emitters and prevent skin contact.

- High-density materials are used to provide shielded body protection for persons at risk from penetrating radiation, e.g. radiographers.

- Eye protection, possibly using high-density lenses, may be used to protect the eyes if the head is at risk from exposure to beams of radiation.

- RPE may be needed as an additional precaution to prevent inhalation of radioactive contamination.

Controlling Exposure to Artificial Optical Radiation

A simple hierarchy of control measures should include:

- Use an alternative, safer light source that will achieve the same result.

- Use filters, screens, remote viewing, curtains, safety interlocks, clamping of workpieces, dedicated rooms, remote controls and time delays.

- Train workers in best practice and provide appropriate information.

- Organise work to reduce exposure to workers.

- Restrict access to hazardous areas.

- Issue PPE (as above).

- Display relevant safety signs.

Should harmful over-exposure occur, quick referral to a medical practitioner or occupational health provider will be required. Remember to include AOR in your risk assessment of exposure to non-ionising radiation.

Basic Radiation Protection Strategies

Radiation Protection Adviser

Where controlled areas have been designated, the employer must appoint a qualified Radiation Protection Adviser (RPA). Usually from external organisations, RPAs must have particular experience of the type of work the employer undertakes and be able to provide advice and guidance on the following matters:

- Compliance with current legislation.
- Local rules and systems of work.
- Personnel monitoring, dosimetry and record-keeping.
- Room design, layout and shielding.
- Siting of equipment emitting ionising radiation.
- Siting and transport of radioactive materials.
- Leakage testing of sealed sources.
- Investigation of incidents, including spillage or loss.

Local Rules

Employers must provide local rules to describe the safe systems of working with ionising radiation. These must be prominently displayed and brought to the attention of all relevant employees.

Radiation Protection Supervisor

One or more Radiation Protection Supervisors (RPSs) must be appointed (usually internally) to be responsible for enforcing the local rules. The duties of the RPS include:

- Record-keeping.
- Registration of workers.
- Radiation monitoring.
- Implementation of local rules.

Controlled and Supervised Areas

Areas where there is a radiation hazard must be designated by the RPA and access restricted to classified workers to reduce the radiation dose.

At the entrance to each area, a sign must be posted indicating the:

- Designation of the area.
- Nature of the source and any restriction of activities.
- Names of authorised workers.
- Supervisors of work in the area.

Within the area, all sources of radiation must be clearly marked with the radiation hazard symbol.

Examples of common radiation hazard-warning signs

Two categories of area for radiation work are determined by the likely radiation dose of those working in the area:

- **Controlled Area**

    Exposures exceeding three tenths of a dose limit (see later) may be received. These areas will include where radioactive materials are stored and dispensed.

- **Supervised Area**

    Where a worker could receive between one tenth and three tenths of a dose limit. Most areas in which work with radiation is carried out will normally be supervised areas, including X-ray rooms.

A safe system of work will include rules for handling radioactive source material, action in the event of accidents or other incidents, and procedures on leaving a controlled or supervised area. A formal permit-to-work system may be required to restrict time spent in the radiation area. Areas designated as controlled or supervised areas must have washing and changing facilities.

The Role of Monitoring and Health Surveillance

The International Commission on Radiological Protection (ICRP) has set the following dose limits on exposure to ionising radiation:

- The general public shall not be exposed to more than 1 mSv (millisievert) per year.

- Occupational exposure shall not exceed 20 mSv per year.

These limits exclude exposure due to background and medical radiation.

To give you an idea of what these figures mean, the total natural radiation to which people are likely to be exposed is about 1.5 mSv per year; a chest x-ray involves an exposure of 0.04 mSv.

Three forms of monitoring are used:

- **Personal monitoring** - personal dosimeters used for those in controlled and supervised areas. These may measure whole body dose or partial body dose (i.e. the fingers).

- **Medical examination** - routine examinations conducted before employment and every 12 months, with an immediate special examination after an over-exposure.

- **Area monitoring** - levels of radiation in controlled and supervised areas must be regularly assessed and monitoring equipment properly maintained, examined and tested by a competent person every 14 months.

Records of all forms of monitoring must be kept.

Artificial Optical Radiation

Where any employees may be over-exposed to sources of artificial optical radiation (such as IR, UV, etc.), an employer should provide medical examination and consider whether follow-up health surveillance is appropriate.

STUDY QUESTIONS

7. What type of non-ionising radiation is given off by the following pieces of equipment?

    (a) Radio transmitter.

    (b) Hot plate on a stove.

    (c) Arc welder in operation.

    (d) Laser measuring device.

8. What are the acute health effects of high doses of ionising radiation?

9. What are the health effects of artificial optical radiation?

10. What is radon, and where is it likely to be found?

11. Identify four areas for which a Radiation Protection Adviser (RPA) is responsible, and outline when an employer must appoint one.

(Suggested Answers are at the end.)

Stress

IN THIS SECTION...

- Stress is an adverse reaction to excessive pressure. It can cause various psychological, physical and behavioural effects and serious ill health if prolonged.

- Stress can be caused by: unreasonable demands; lack of control; lack of support; poor working relationships; an ill-defined role; and change.

- To minimise the risk of serious ill health caused by stress, the employer should establish a management framework for: demands, control, support, relationships, role and change.

Introduction to Stress

An employer has a general duty under the **Health and Safety at Work, etc. Act 1974** to ensure the health of employees at work. This includes taking steps to safeguard them against stress-related illnesses arising as a result of their work. The legal obligations on employers under the **Management of Health and Safety at Work Regulations 1999** also require them to take account of the risk of stress-related ill health.

Meaning of Work-Related Stress

Stress is not a disease, but a natural reaction to pressure, and pressure is an inherent part of work, e.g. a deadline to be met or an order to get out on time. Some even say that there are 'good' pressures, that give us strength when needed (the 'fight or flight' response); but never 'good stress'.

If demands are placed on workers which they feel they cannot cope with, they will experience stress, which in turn affects morale and performance. People react differently and some will see certain events as being stressful, while others may not.

> **DEFINITION**
>
> **STRESS**
>
> The adverse reaction people have to excessive pressure or other types of demand placed on them.

Causes, Effects and Control Measures

Causes of Stress

The areas to consider for both causes of stress and prevention are the same: demands, control, support, relationships, role and change.

- **Demands**

    Excessive demands of the job in terms of:

    - Workload (too much or too little).

    - Speed of work and deadlines.

    - Excessively long working hours.

    - Work patterns (changing shift patterns).

    - Also consider the nature of the job:

    - Some are inherently difficult (e.g. air traffic control).

    - Some expose workers to highly emotional situations (e.g. social work).

Excessive workload

- **Control**

  Lack of control over:

  – How work is done.

  – The priorities involved.

  – Simple issues such as the environment (e.g. light levels, temperature, background noise).

- **Support**

  Lack of support in terms of:

  – Information, instruction and training to do the work.

  – Having no-one to turn to for help when pressure increases.

- **Relationships**

  Poor workplace relationships, and, in particular, bullying and harassment (whether by managers, colleagues, subordinates, customers, suppliers or members of the public).

- **Role**

  – Lack of clarity about an individual's role, what the responsibilities and requirements of the job are (role ambiguity).

  – Subject to conflicting demands (role conflict) and how they fit into the larger organisational structure.

- **Change**

  The threat of change and the change process itself, be it a change that affects only one person (e.g. demotion, re-assignment) or the whole organisation (e.g. redundancies, take-over), can create huge anxiety and insecurity.

> **MORE...**
>
> The Management Standards for Work Related Stress can be found at:
>
> www.hse.gov.uk/stress/standards/

There are many things in a person's life outside of work that can cause stress just as badly as work can, and these factors (psycho-social) should also be considered. Even though they are not directly caused by work, they are brought into the workplace, and can therefore affect both the person experiencing the difficulties, and others.

Effects of Stress

Work-related stress has adverse effects on the individual employee and the organisation.

- **Individual**

  For the **employee**, the symptoms of stress may be physical or psychological, including headaches, dizziness, panic attacks, skin rashes, stomach problems, poor concentration, difficulty sleeping and increased alcohol consumption.

  If stress is intense or prolonged, it can lead to the onset of serious physical and mental health conditions, such as high blood pressure, heart disease, gastro-intestinal disturbances, anxiety and depression.

- **Organisation**

  Stress is a major cause of sickness absence and represents a significant cost to **employers**. Losing one employee because of a stress-related illness can have effects on output and costs of a replacement.

  Work-related stress also affects morale and motivation, resulting in lower productivity, reduced performance, tensions between colleagues and increased incidence of industrial relations problems.

  In the long term, it may cause workers to leave, with the consequential costs of recruiting and training replacements.

Control Measures

Case law emphasises the particular need to minimise stress, especially for an employee with a record of stress-related illness. Strategies to tackle work-related stress must be based on a risk assessment and the principles set out in the **Management of Health and Safety at Work Regulations 1999** in the following order:

- Avoiding the risks.

- Combating the risks at source.

- Adapting the work to the individual.

- Developing collective measures.

The basic management framework should be based around the same issues listed by the HSE as causes of stress:

- **Demands**

  - The demands (in terms of workload, speed of work and deadlines) should be reasonable and, where possible, set in consultation with workers.

  - Working hours and shift patterns should be carefully selected and flexible hours allowed where possible.

  - Workers should be selected on their competence, skills and ability to cope with difficult or demanding work.

- **Control**

  Employees should be encouraged to have more say in how their work is carried out, e.g. in planning their work, making decisions about how it is completed and how problems will be tackled.

- **Support**

  - Feedback to employees will improve performance and maintain motivation.

    - All feedback should be positive, with the aim of bringing about improvement, even if this is challenging.

    - Feedback should focus on behaviour, not on personality.

  - Workers should have adequate training, information and instruction.

- **Relationships**

  - Clear standards of conduct should be communicated to employees, with managers leading by example.

  - The organisation should have policies in place to tackle misconduct, harassment and bullying.

- **Role**

  - An employee's role in the organisation should be defined by means of an up-to-date job description and clear work objectives and reporting responsibilities.

  - If employees are uncertain about their job or the nature of the task to be undertaken, they should be encouraged to ask at an early stage.

- **Change**

  - If change has to take place, employees should be consulted about what the organisation wants to achieve and given the opportunity to comment, ask questions and get involved.

  - Employees should be supported before, during and after the change.

TOPIC FOCUS

Reducing levels of occupational stress in construction work:

- Ensure policies and procedures are in place to cover harassment, discrimination, violence and bullying.
- Have managers and supervisors trained to recognise the symptoms of stress.
- Reduce levels of noise on site.
- Ensure adequate lighting in all work areas (especially at night).
- Ensure adequate welfare and rest facilities are available on site.
- Ensure high standards of housekeeping and maintenance of equipment and facilities.
- Discourage long working hours.
- Introduce job rotation and increase work variety as much as possible.
- Ensure competence and ensure people are properly matched to jobs.
- Maintain high levels of communication and involve workers in making decisions.

STUDY QUESTIONS

12. State the six main work-related causes of stress and, for each, give one example of a preventive measure.

13. Identify six potential effects of stress on an employee, and three on an employer and the organisation.

(Suggested Answers are at the end.)

Summary

This element has dealt with some of the health hazards and controls relevant to noise, vibration, ionising and non-ionising radiation and stress.

In particular, this element has:

- Outlined the health effects of exposure to noise, including the physical and psychological effects.

- Defined commonly used terms in noise measurement.

- Outlined the need to assess exposure to noise and the control limits.

- Outlined steps to control noise exposure with reference to the source, the pathway and the receiver, including the use of PPE and the importance of health surveillance.

- Outlined the effects of exposure to excessive vibration and the exposure standards which exist.

- Described the available vibration control measures, with reference to selection of equipment, maintenance and limiting exposure (including PPE).

- Outlined the importance of, and procedure for, health surveillance and monitoring in regards to vibration.

- Described types of ionising and non-ionising radiation, including radon and artificial optical radiation, and their health effects.

- Outlined the methods and control of exposure for ionising and non-ionising radiation, including general radiation protection strategies and the role of health surveillance and monitoring.

- Outlined the workplace causes and effects of stress at work and preventive measures.

Exam Skills

QUESTION

With respect to the **Control of Noise at Work Regulations 2005**:

(a) **Identify** in dB(A), **BOTH** the lower and the upper exposure action values.   **(2)**

(b) **Outline** the measures the employer is required to take when employees are exposed to noise at or above an upper exposure action value.   **(3)**

Approaching the Question

Think now about the steps you would take to answer the question:

Step 1.   Read the question carefully. Note that this question asks for exposure action values in part (a) and the measures an employer must take when persons are exposed to noise at or above the upper action value in part (b).

Step 2.   Now highlight the key words. In this case they might look like this:

With respect to the **Control of Noise at Work Regulations 2005**:

(a) **Identify** in **dB(A)**, **BOTH** the **lower and the upper exposure action values**.   **(2)**

(b) **Outline** the **measures** the employer is required to take when employees are **exposed to noise at or above an upper exposure action value**.   **(6)**

Step 3.   Next, consider the marks and time available. In this question there are eight marks available so it is expected that around eight or nine different pieces of information should be provided. The question is helpfully signposted into two parts. The part (a) command word is 'identify', so express the numbers in dB(A) - no more detail is required. Part (b) has the action word 'outline' and is worth six marks, so this part must have six measures to be taken. It's easy to see where marks will be awarded in these two-part questions. The question should take around eight minutes in total.

Step 4.   Read the question again to make sure you understand it. (Re-read your notes if you need to.)

Step 5.   The next stage is to develop a plan - there are various ways to do this. Remind yourself, first of all, that you need to be thinking about identifying (selecting and naming) and outlining (provide a sentence explaining each measure).

Your answer must be based on the key words you have highlighted. So, in this case, we need to identify the lower and upper exposure action values, and outline the control measures.

Now have a go at the question. Draw up an answer plan, and then use it as the basis to write out an answer as you would in the exam.

Remember, you can always contact your tutor if you have any queries or need any further guidance on how to answer this question.

HINTS AND TIPS

Think about a hierarchy of controls and apply them to noise.

When you have finished, compare your plan and full answer with those that follow.

Suggested Answer Outline

Action Values	Measures to Take
• Lower 80 dB(A). • Upper 85 dB(A).	• Risk assessment. • Eliminate noise at source or reduce so far as reasonably practicable. • Organisational controls. • Engineering controls. • Designate hearing protection zones. • Provide and maintain hearing protection and enforce use. • Inform, instruct and train. • Health surveillance.

Example of How the Question Could be Answered

(a) *The lower exposure action value is 80 dB(A). The upper exposure action value is 85 dB(A).*

(b) *Measures that the employer should take if employees are exposed to noise at or above 85 dB(A) include eliminating the noise at its source. This may be achieved by examination of the process to see if an operation is really necessary. If it is not reasonably practicable to eliminate the noise, the employer should try to reduce the noise. This may be possible by substituting an electric-powered machine for a quieter, petrol-driven machine. It may also be possible to reduce the noise that people are exposed to by implementing organisational controls, such as job rotation. A further measure is to reduce the noise by engineering means, such as using damping or silencing techniques. Areas where noise is still at or above the exposure value must be designated and marked as hearing protection zones to warn those working in the area and those passing through the area of the hazard.*

The employer must provide hearing protection that reduces the noise at the ear to below the exposure value, inform employees of the risks to their hearing from noise and instruct employees on the requirement for wearing hearing defenders and how to wear them. The employer should also consider health surveillance through audiometric testing to ensure measures taken are suitable and sufficient to prevent harm.

Reasons for Poor Marks Achieved by Candidates in Exam

- Providing a list in part (b) instead of outlining measures to take.

- Not answering the question at all - poor time management may cost candidates the opportunity to gain marks on a subject they have some knowledge of.

- Failing to separate the answers into different parts - structuring your answer to address the different parts of the question is necessary in these two-part questions.

- Illegible handwriting - you need to be aware that examiners cannot award marks if they cannot read what you have written.

Working at Height - Hazards and Risk Control

Learning Outcomes

Once you've read this element, you'll understand how to:

1. Explain the hazards of working at height and outline the precautions necessary to control them.

2. Explain safe working practices for access equipment and roof work.

3. Outline the control measures necessary to protect other persons not involved in the work at height.

4. Outline the particular control measures to reduce risk when working over or near to water.

Contents

Working at Height - Hazards and Risk Controls

IN THIS SECTION...

- Work at height accounts for more fatalities than any other construction activity.

- The hazards and factors affecting the risk from working at height include the design of structures, materials and tasks; the vertical distance of a fall; fragile roofs; roof lights; voids; sloping roofs; deteriorating materials; unprotected edges; unstable or poorly maintained access equipment; adverse weather conditions; and falling materials.

- Work at height should be avoided where possible, or engineering methods used to prevent falls and falling materials, including good design; proper planning and supervision of work; and avoiding work in adverse weather conditions.

- Emergency rescue plans should be in place to facilitate the rescue of trapped or fallen workers.

- Equipment, training and instruction are required to minimise the distance and consequences of a fall.

- Head protection is required when working at height.

- All work equipment used to access work at height should be inspected.

Examples of Work Activities Involving a Risk of Injury

Construction work often exposes people to risks from working at height. Examples include:

- Steel workers erecting the steel framework of a building.

- Scaffolders erecting or striking (taking down) a scaffold.

- Roofers cladding the roof of a steel-framed building.

- Demolition workers dismantling machinery on the roof of a building.

- Welders working at the side of a deep excavation.

- Pipe fitters fixing pipework to the ceiling in a factory workshop.

- Painters painting a lamp-post or a steel-span footbridge.

Many of these tasks will involve the use of some form of access equipment (e.g. scaffolding or ladders) and those using this equipment are usually familiar with and used to such work, which can lead to complacency. Other workers may not be so used to these tasks at height, and lack competence.

The main risks associated with work at height are:

- The worker falling from height.

- An object falling from height onto someone below.

Falls from height:

- Account for the largest percentage of annual fatalities in the workplace.

> **DEFINITION**
>
> **WORK AT HEIGHT**
>
> Work at any height (including at or below ground level), from which a fall could cause personal injury.

Cleaning windows on a tower block

- Can result in:
  - Fatalities.
  - Neck or spinal injury leading to permanent disability or paralysis.
  - Multiple fractures.

Falling objects can also cause severe injuries that may result in death, brain damage, paralysis or multiple fractures.

The distance (vertical height) of a fall is not always the deciding factor in the cause of injuries, but is a factor that has to be taken into account, as we will see later.

Basic Hazards and Risk Factors

Design

Good design is important in working at height, not only of the existing structures or materials to be worked on, but design and strength/stability of the access equipment used, and the design of the task itself.

Without good design, access equipment may not be specified correctly, may be poorly erected and positioned, and safety features may be absent or missed. Poor design of the task may permit work by unauthorised or untrained operatives, increasing the risk factor greatly.

Distance of Falls

The vertical distance a person or object can fall will have a direct bearing on the severity of injury or damage it can cause. Where work at height cannot be avoided, the first considerations will be to reduce the distance a person can fall. We will discuss prevention methods later in this element.

Roofs

Roof work includes construction and maintenance of roofs, e.g. replacing tiles, gutter cleaning, chimney repairs and re-pointing. Many accidents occur during small jobs and maintenance work. In addition, maintenance work is often undertaken in a hurry, e.g. storm damage repairs.

Particular dangers arise with three types of roof:

- **Fragile Roofs**

  A fragile roof is any roofing structure which is not:

  - Specifically designed to withstand the weight of a person or a load they may be carrying.

  - Strong enough to withstand adverse weather conditions.

  Roofing materials such as cement, asbestos, glass, reinforced plastics and light tongue and groove wood covered with roofing felt are all liable to collapse under the weight of a worker.

  All fragile roofs except glass should have a large warning notice displayed on them. However, remember that with a multinational workforce, a sign in English does not necessarily provide sufficient warning and must be backed up by verbal warnings.

  The safe method of working on fragile roofs is by the use of roof ladders or crawling boards. These are laid across the surface, supported by underlying and load-bearing roof members, and distribute the load of the worker over a wider area, enabling the roof structure to sustain the load safely. Roof ladders also provide a good foot-and-hand hold for the worker.

Fall arrest equipment should be worn when shown to be required by a risk assessment.

- **Sloping (Pitched) Roofs**

  These are roofs with a pitch greater than 10°. Falls from the edges of sloping roofs generally cause serious injury even when the eaves are low, as on a bungalow. If the person has slipped down the roof from the ridge, considerable acceleration can be generated which tends to project them from the eaves, adding to the force of impact with the ground and hence to the seriousness of the injuries sustained.

- **Flat Roofs**

  Work on flat roofs can lead to falls (usually from unprotected edges). These commonly occur:

  - From a completed roof.

  - From a roof where work is being completed.

  - Through openings or gaps (voids).

  - Through fragile materials making up part of the roof, e.g. roof lights.

Roof Lights

Roof lights are commonly clear sheets built into a roof to allow light through, and are made of fragile materials (such as plastics) and not always easy to see - they may be covered with dirt and grime, moss or algae, or maybe painted over. They are often difficult to visually distinguish from the surrounding roof materials in bright or very dim light. If they are not covered, guarded or fitted with toe boards, it can be easy to fall through and suffer serious (or fatal) injury.

Voids

Voids beneath roofs should be treated as confined spaces because of the close, confined nature of the space. This can restrict movement within the void, perhaps leading to postural problems if prolonged. Since voids often remain undisturbed for long periods, dusts settle and will be disturbed by movement, creating a dusty atmosphere which can cause breathing difficulties and lack of light.

The floor within a void is often the ceiling of a room or space below, so access on fragile surfaces can be a major issue, and crawling boards may be required for safe access within the void.

Deterioration of Materials

The condition of the structure on which people are working should be sound. However, materials deteriorate over time, particularly when exposed to the effects of the weather (heat as well as cold and water) and attack by animals and insects, etc.

Voids beneath roofs are normally closed, confined spaces

Unsound materials represent a hazard in two ways:

- The danger of the material breaking when a person puts his/her weight on it and causing a fall through the surface.

- The danger of materials breaking off and falling to hit people or structures at lower levels. Where they hit lower structures, this may cause a collapse.

It may not always be evident that deterioration has occurred until it is too late, so care needs to be taken to ensure that footholds are sound and secure.

Unprotected Edges

Where the edges of surfaces on which people are working are open, the risk of falls or falling objects is greatly increased. This applies to roofs, elevated walkways, scaffolding and access platforms, etc.

We'll consider the use of guardrails, toe boards, fencing and other protective boarding required to prevent such accidents later.

Unstable or Poorly Maintained Access Equipment

Access equipment includes scaffolding, towers, platforms and ladders. There are inherent risks in using such equipment, but these are compounded if the equipment is unstable, unsecured and not properly maintained.

Any access equipment that is not positioned correctly, is poorly constructed or poorly secured will be unstable. Conditions such as overloading of the equipment, high winds or overreaching can then cause a catastrophic collapse or topple.

Equipment not properly maintained can suffer damage from rust, physical damage, broken or damaged treads and fittings, and platform boards that rot through the timber.

Weather

The weather can increase the risks associated with working at height:

- Rain or freezing conditions can increase the risk of slipping.
- High winds can make access equipment unstable and blow loose materials off (and in extreme conditions, even workers).
- Cold conditions can cause loss of manual dexterity and can lead to an increase in muscle injuries.

Falling Materials

Objects falling from a height are capable of causing considerable damage to both people and other materials that they hit. The objects themselves may be:

- Loose structural material, e.g. tiles, bricks and timber.
- Waste materials, e.g. stone chippings or off-cuts of wood.
- Equipment or tools which are dropped.

Circumstances which contribute to the likelihood of falling materials include the following:

- Deterioration of structures causing crumbling brickwork or loose tiles.
- Bad storage of materials, e.g. at the edges of scaffold platforms, or in unstable stacks.
- Poor housekeeping leading to accumulations of waste and loose materials.
- Gaps in platform surfaces or between access platforms and walls.
- Open, unprotected edges.
- Incorrect methods of getting materials, equipment or tools from ground level to the working area.
- Incorrect methods of getting materials down to ground level, e.g. throwing.

Methods of Avoiding Working at Height

All work at height should be assessed. The best way to manage the risks inherent with working at height is to eliminate the need to work at height altogether. This can be achieved by:

- Modifying a work process, e.g. cleaning windows from the ground by pole cleaning rather than off ladders.

- Good design, e.g. erecting guardrails or steelwork at ground level and then craning the steel and guardrails into place.

However, in most instances in the construction industry, avoidance will not be possible and control measures for working at height will be required.

TOPIC FOCUS

The **Work at Height (WAH) Regulations 2005** impose a **risk prevention hierarchy**:

- **Avoid** work at height.
- Use work equipment or other measures to **prevent falls** where work at height cannot be avoided.
- Use work equipment or other measures to **minimise the distance and consequences** of a fall where the risk of a fall cannot be eliminated.

Main Precautions to Prevent Falls and Falling Materials

A simple hierarchy can be adopted to **prevent falls**:

- Avoid work at height.

- Carry out work from an existing place of work.

- Provide a safe working platform with guardrails, fences, toe boards, etc. that are strong enough to prevent a fall.

- Where this is not possible, provide properly installed personnel equipment such as rope access or boatswain's chairs (see later).

- If this is not possible and a worker can approach an unprotected edge, provide equipment which will restrain or arrest falls, e.g. safety harnesses or safety nets.

A similar hierarchy can help to **prevent falling objects**:

- Not stacking materials near edges, and particularly unprotected edges.

- Close boarding of working platforms to minimise the gaps between scaffold boards, or placing sheeting over the boards so that material cannot fall through.

- Avoiding carrying materials up or down ladders, etc. by using hoists and chutes to move materials.

- Using physical safeguards such as toe boards and brick guards.

- Where a risk remains, use physical safeguards to prevent falling objects hitting people below, e.g. debris netting, fans (wooden shielding angled to catch debris) and covered walkways (tunnels).

Guardrails, toe boards and brick guards are discussed later.

Good Design

Important design factors include the safety features of the access equipment (handrails, toe boards, fall arrest or restraint connections, etc.) and how access equipment is erected and positioned, so as to be stable on secure, firm level ground, away from vehicles and pedestrians. Task design also includes the methods used to lift and lower equipment and materials to and from work at height locations, and the security of the access equipment in inclement weather.

Planning and Supervision of Work

Work at height should be planned in advance, with careful consideration given to the selection and use of work equipment. A safe system of work should be set up which takes account of:

- Levels of supervision of workers required, e.g. fall arrest equipment will require a higher level of supervision than work on a mobile scaffold tower.

- Weather conditions, e.g. carrying out maintenance on an icy roof or working in rainy conditions on a slippery surface.

- Emergency or rescue arrangements that may be required, e.g. if workers fall while using a fall arrest system. It is not acceptable just to rely on the emergency services; this needs to be covered in the risk assessment and planned beforehand.

Avoidance of Work in Adverse Weather

If adverse weather such as icy, rainy or windy conditions greatly increases the risk of working at height (e.g. carrying a wide roof sheet in high wind), the work should be postponed until conditions are satisfactory. Getting a daily weather forecast is a suitable precaution.

This stipulation does not apply for emergency services acting in the event of an emergency.

Emergency Rescue Plans

Emergency procedures should be in place to cover reasonably foreseeable circumstances, e.g. stuck access equipment or deployed fall arrest, so that people can be rescued.

Methods selected need to be proportionate to the risk:

- There should be no reliance on the emergency services.

- Simple systems may suffice (e.g. putting a ladder up to a net and allowing a fallen person to descend).

- More detailed systems may be required (e.g. the use of other work equipment such as Mobile Elevating Work Platforms (MEWPs) or proprietary rescue systems such as a rescue harness, pulleys and clamps.

Employers must ensure that those involved are trained in the procedures and that the equipment required is available.

Measures to Minimise Distance and Consequences of a Fall

Where work at height cannot be avoided, employers must minimise the distance a person can fall, and if not, the consequences of a fall. Equipment such as fall restraint, fall arrest or soft-landing systems such as safety nets or airbags can be used.

In all such cases, operatives must receive adequate training and instruction to appreciate the dangers of working at height, as well as how to service and use the equipment, and the correct methods of use.

Requirements for Head Protection

Construction sites almost always have a risk of someone being struck by falling or moving objects, so should be mandatory hard hat (safety helmet) areas. Hard hats offer protection against small falling objects, e.g. rubble or hand tools, but will not protect against heavy impact from a large object (e.g. a scaffold pole) or something dropped from a great height (e.g. a spanner from ten floors up). Other controls should be used to prevent objects from falling.

Since 6 April 2013, the **PPE Regulations 1992** have applied to the provision and use of hard hats on construction sites. Employers must provide hard hats to employees and ensure hard hats are worn when there is a risk of head injury. Self-employed workers should provide their own hard hats and ensure they wear them.

Hard hats should:

- Be in good condition (if it's damaged it must be thrown away).

- Fit the person wearing it and be worn properly.

- Not stop the wearing of hearing protectors as well (when needed).

- Only be obtained from a reputable supplier (there are fake hard hats on the market).

For head protection from injuries incurred in falls from height, a climbing helmet may be more appropriate as it has:

- Impact strength against:

  - Falling objects.

  - Hitting the head in a fall.

- A four-point chin strap to secure it (a safety helmet usually has only two).

Hard hats offer protection against small falling objects

Inspection Requirements for Work Equipment

The **Work at Height Regulations 2005** require:

- Visual or more rigorous inspection of work equipment by a competent person for safety purposes.

- Testing where appropriate.

Work equipment includes guardrails, toe boards, barriers and similar collective means of protection. It encompasses all working platforms (including scaffolding), nets and airbags, personal fall protection systems, work positioning systems, fall arrest systems and work restraint systems. Ladders are also considered to be work equipment.

Each work at height location must be checked each time it is used, including the surface parapets and permanent rails. An inspection must be made after the equipment has been assembled and as often as is necessary to ensure safety. Pay special attention to potential deterioration of materials.

Inspection is also required for equipment which has come from another business and any equipment leaving the host business.

Any platform used in construction higher than two metres must be inspected in its place of use before being used. The inspection is only valid for seven days. For mobile platforms, inspection at the site is sufficient without inspection again every time it is relocated on that site.

TOPIC FOCUS

An **inspection report** for platforms should be kept for three months after completion, and should contain:

- Name and address of person for whom inspection is carried out.
- Location of equipment inspected.
- Description of equipment inspected.
- Time and date of inspection.
- Details of problems found.
- Details of action taken.
- Future action required.
- Name and position of competent person.

The report must be given to the person responsible for managing the site within 24 hours of completion.

STUDY QUESTIONS

1. What is the hierarchy of risk prevention measures for working at height?
2. What are the safe methods of working on a fragile roof?
3. Where can falls occur from a flat roof?
4. What measures should be taken to prevent materials falling from a height?
5. When should a platform used for construction work where a person could fall more than two metres be inspected?

(Suggested Answers are at the end.)

Safe Working Practices for Access Equipment and Roof Work

IN THIS SECTION...

- Scaffolding provides access to work at height and includes independent tied, putlog, fan, cantilevered and mobile tower scaffolds.

- Safety features of scaffolding include sole boards and base plates for ground support; toe boards and guardrails to prevent falls; and boarding, brick guards and debris netting to retain materials, equipment and debris.

- Scaffold erectors must be properly trained and qualified to erect, maintain and dismantle scaffolding.

- Safe access onto and off scaffolding has to be provided, and loading platforms must be suitable and strong enough to support the work.

- Various equipment and personnel hoists are available to move people and materials on and off scaffolding and building structures.

- Scaffolding must be stable, and its structural integrity must not be affected by loading of people, equipment and materials or adverse weather conditions. It must be protected from impact by vehicles.

- Mobile Elevating Work Platforms (MEWPs) offer a portable alternative to full scaffolding in some situations.

- Other access equipment includes ladders, stepladders, trestles and staging. Where roof work is next to a gap or edge, then further leading edge protection is required.

- Other techniques include boatswain's chairs, cradles and rope access systems.

- Fall arrest systems include harnesses, safety nets, soft landing systems and crash decks. Rescue and emergency procedures should be in place when using these techniques.

- Safe roof work requires safe access, edge and leading edge protection, and crawling boards on fragile materials.

Scaffolding

Features of Different Types of Scaffold

Scaffolding is made up of the following basic components:

- **Standards** - uprights or vertical tubes used to support the load to the ground.

- **Ledgers** - short horizontal tubes tying the structure together longitudinally, usually running parallel to the face of the building.

- **Transoms** - short horizontal tubes spanning across ledgers normally at right angles (90°) to the face of the building. They may also be used to support a working platform.

- **Bracing** - diagonal tubes to give the structure its rigidity.

- **Base plates** - small square metal plates that the standards (uprights) rest on to prevent them sinking into the ground.

Scaffolding

- **Sole boards** - large pieces of timber put under the base plates to spread the load over a wider surface area when the scaffold is erected on soft ground.

- **Work platform** - the fully boarded work area surface.

- **Guardrails** - fixed to the standards (uprights) to fully enclose the work platform.
- **Toe boards** - fixed to the standards (uprights) to provide a lip at the platform edges.

Independent Tied Scaffolds

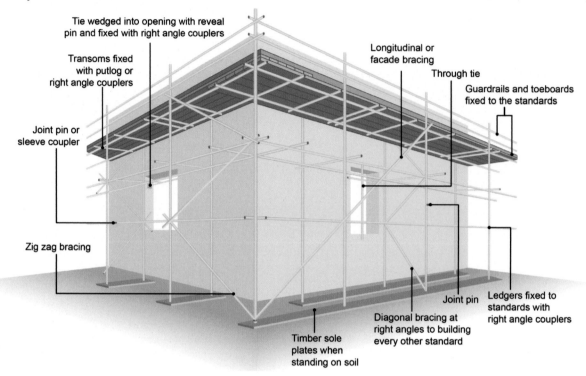

Independent tied scaffold

An independent tied scaffold is designed to carry its own weight and the full load of all materials and workers on the platform. It must be tied to the building where it is sited, to give stability and prevent movement.

As the total weight of the structure is supported by the ground it is very important that the ground conditions are suitable to cope with the load. Base plates and sole boards may be used to spread the weight over a large surface area.

There are a number of ways in which the scaffold can be tied to the building to prevent movement:

- **Anchor bolts** - where one end of a metal bolt is screwed into the wall of the building and the other end is attached to the scaffold tubing.

- **Through ties** - where a scaffold tube extends into the building through an opening (e.g. a doorway or window frame). The end of the tube inside the building is coupled to another tube bridging across the opening.

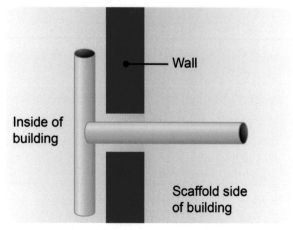

Through tie (as seen from above)

- **Reveal ties** - where a scaffold tube is coupled to a reveal pin that is wedged tightly across an opening such as a window reveal.

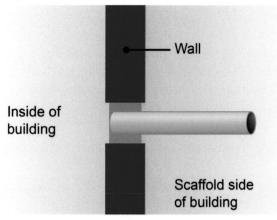

Plan view of a reveal tie

- **Rakers** - supports which push the scaffold onto the building. This system takes up space and may not be suitable in urban environments.

Bracing is another important component of the scaffold and is used to stiffen the scaffold framework to prevent collapse.

The basic forms of bracing are:

- **Facade bracing** - scaffold tubes running diagonally across the face of the scaffold. This is also known as sway and longitudinal bracing.

- **Ledger bracing** - scaffold tubes running diagonally within the framework. Alternate pairs of standards should have ledger bracing.

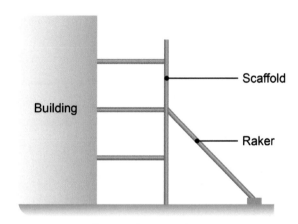

Side view showing rakers

TOPIC FOCUS

Factors that might cause the collapse of an independent tied scaffold:

- Overloaded work platform.
- Scaffold built on soft ground without sole boards.
- Scaffold not adequately tied to building.
- Insufficient bracing incorporated into scaffold.
- Standards not upright.
- Standards bent, buckled or heavily corroded.
- High winds.
- Incorrect couplers used to join tubes together.
- Scaffold struck by mobile plant.
- Scaffold erected by incompetent workers.
- Scaffold not properly inspected.

Putlog Scaffold

A putlog is a tube spanning from the ledger to the wall of a building on a putlog scaffold. It is fixed into the brickwork by a specially formed flattened end (spade end) which may be constructed on a scaffold tube, or by using a detachable fitting (putlog end) with the spade end of the putlog fully home (75mm) in the brickwork (bed joint).

Putlog scaffold showing spade end

Putlog end

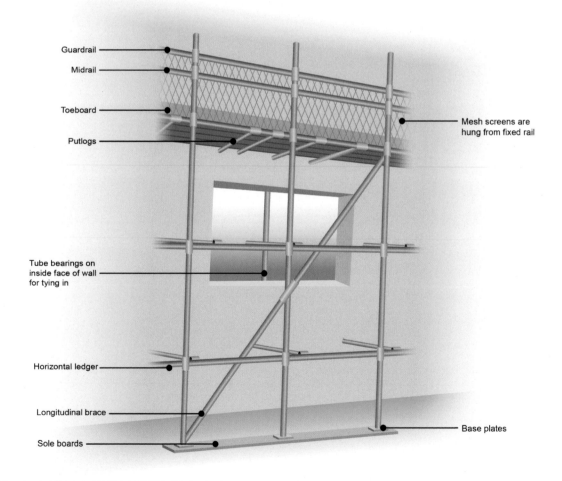

Putlog scaffold

TOPIC FOCUS

Scaffold Inspections

These are carried out:

- After erection and before first use.
- Every seven days.
- After any adverse event, e.g. bad weather, impact from vehicle, or large object falling into it.

The inspector should look for:

- Adequate foundation - level, firm ground (base plates should be central on sole boards).
- Platform - fully boarded, three to five boards wide (depends on use).
- Scaffold boards - each to have at least three supports and be tied down (overhang not more than 150mm).
- All tubes and fittings in good condition.
- Vertical supports - no more than 2 to 2.5m apart.
- Bracing - along diagonals at the faces and at right angles.
- Ties - into the building at least every 4m vertically and 6m horizontally.
- Guardrails and toe boards - secure along outer edges and ends.
- Toe boards - minimum of 150mm high.
- Guardrails - 950mm above the platform; double guardrail at 460mm.
- Appropriate access.
- Ladders - good condition (correctly sited, tied, sufficient length and number, etc.).
- Loading - do not overload; stack any material correctly and securely.

Additionally for a **putlog scaffold**, checks are needed on the spacing of putlogs and to see that the spade end of the putlog is fully home (75mm) in the brickwork (bed joint).

Fan Protection

Fans or protected walkways are often used to protect members of the public from falling materials and debris from work carried out in busy city centres, but can equally be used on construction or refurbishment projects.

Cantilever Scaffold

A cantilever scaffold is an independent scaffold entirely supported by the building. The scaffold has a framework inside the building, wedged between floors and ceilings. The cantilever tubes are fixed to this frame and supported. Rakers bearing on sills or ledges on the face of the building support the outer ends of the tubes. Buildings should be checked to ensure they can support the intended loads.

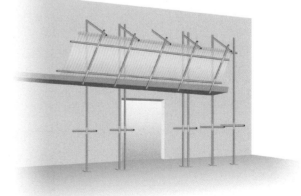

Fan protection

Truss Out Scaffolding

This scaffold has horizontal cantilever tubes passed in through windows and anchored to vertical tubes against wooden packing pieces against an inner wall. Rakers bearing on sills or ledges on the face of the building support the outer ends of the tubes.

It is used:

- Where it is not practical to build scaffolding from ground level.

- For lightweight work, e.g. stone or paintwork cleaning on tall buildings.

Birdcage Scaffolding

This is normally used for working inside factories, cinemas, churches or tall buildings. It can be used to gain access to ceilings and walls for plastering, painting or decorating.

Mobile Tower Scaffolds

Commonly used for painting and simple maintenance jobs inside and outside buildings, they are only light-duty scaffolds. They have one working platform at the top, accessible by fitted internal ladders. They can use scaffold tubes, but most use proprietary-made structures. The assembled tower is mounted on wheels and can be easily moved. They are to be built to manufacturers' instructions by competent persons.

Birdcage scaffolding

Height of a mobile tower should be limited to 12 metres except for special purposes. For internal use, the height should not exceed three and a half times the shortest base dimension (e.g. if the base dimension is 1m × 1m the maximum height will be 3.5 × 1m = 3.5m). For external use, the factor is reduced to three. When a mobile scaffold is used above 9.8 metres, a guy rope, ballast or anchoring device must be used to increase stability. Outriggers will spread the base dimensions and increase stability.

Duties regarding edge protection, overloading and inspections are the same as for other scaffolds/working platforms.

Main hazards associated with mobile tower scaffolds:

- Falls from the work platform.

- Objects falling from the platform.

- Collapse of the structure.

- Overturn (toppling) of the structure.

- Unintended movement of the wheels.

- Contact with live overhead cables or other services.

A worker gains entry to the top of a tower scaffold using internally fixed ladders, through internal trapdoors. This tower has outriggers attached

TOPIC FOCUS

Safety precautions for safe use of mobile tower scaffolds:

- Guardrail fitted to the work platform.
- Tower must not be overloaded.
- Wheels should be locked when tower is in use.
- Tower must be sited on firm, level ground.
- Never move towers with people or materials on them.
- Avoid overhead services during use and movement.
- Use outriggers where necessary to increase stability.
- Never climb up the outside of a tower.
- Towers must be assembled by trained workers.

Mobile scaffold tower

Scaffolding Hazards

Key hazards associated with the use of scaffolds:

- Falls from the work platform.
- Objects falling from the platform.
- Collapse of the structure.

Scaffolds should be erected by trained workers and inspected by competent persons.

Safety Features of Scaffolding

Base Plates

A base plate is a flat, square steel plate with a locating pin that must be inserted into the bottom of a standard to provide a bearing surface for load distribution.

Sole Boards

The sole board is a strong timber plank, wider than a base plate and long enough to be positioned under two base plates (see putlog scaffold diagram earlier). Sole boards spread the load for the scaffold base. They must be used on soft ground (it is good safety practice to use them for all scaffolds).

Base plate

Toe Boards, Guardrails and Brick Guards

Safeguards must be provided for all unprotected edges on scaffolds and platforms. **Guardrails** will prevent people from falling. Toe boards and brick guards are designed to stop materials from falling.

Toe boards are usually scaffold planks laid on their edge at right angles (90°) to the working platform. They are laid at the outer edges and ends of the working platform (sometimes the inner edge - the one nearest the building - may also require them). Toe boards prevent small objects, e.g. rubble and tools, from being kicked off the platform. If material is stored above toe board height then additional boards, **brick guards** (mesh panels) or similar mesh covering are used to prevent material from falling and have a secondary function of helping prevent people from falling as well.

Detailed requirements for edge protection are:

*   Top guardrail to be at least 950mm above the working platform.

*   Intermediate rails so no unprotected gap of more than 470mm between toe board and guardrail.

*   Toe board must extend to at least 150mm above the working platform.

These arrangements are shown in the following figure which also illustrates the use of the scaffold platform in preventing falls from a sloping roof. The same arrangements apply in preventing falls in respect of flat roofs, and also other forms of edge protection such as mobile tower scaffolds, mobile elevating work platforms and elevated walkways.

Boarding

An intermediate guardrail does not have to be used, although there must be no vertical gaps exceeding 470mm. **Boarding**, consisting of several toe boards stacked one on top of the other, could be used instead, or a brick guard hung from the main guardrail and attached to the platform. Providing this could support/

Use of a brickguard

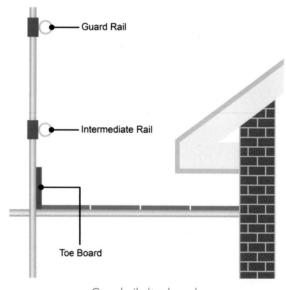

Guardrails/toeboards

contain a person in the event of a slip or fall (in which case it might be possible to do away with the toe board).

Gaps are allowed in edge protection, provided they are the minimum required for reasonable access. Lateral gaps in guardrails are only permitted at a point of access to a ladder or stairway where a gap is necessary.

As an alternative, barriers or fencing can be erected around roof edges using scaffolding tubes and boards. These must extend at least 400mm above the roof surface and the upper guardrail must be at least 910mm above the roof surface.

Debris Netting

Safety nets can also be used to prevent waste material or debris from falling by using them in the shape of a fan to protect those below. In order to achieve this, overlay nets (debris nets) are laid over the safety nets. Care must be taken to ensure that both the size and spacing of the overlay net are in line with the type of material falling on it, e.g. 12-19mm. As with safety nets, overlay nets need to be attached to the supporting framework with tie cords, hooks, rings or thimbles and should be double the strength of the safety net. Such nets should not be allowed to accumulate debris above a certain weight as specially designed nets are required for this purpose. The nets should be cleaned, inspected and stored in accordance with the precautions outlined for safety nets (see later) by a competent person.

Waste Chutes

These are often used to dispose of debris and waste materials from scaffolding and roof work in general, which is then transferred to landfill or waste transfer stations. Precautions must be taken when the skips are removed for disposal and to avoid use of waste chutes by children as a slide (e.g. they should be capped).

Requirements for Scaffold Erectors

Scaffold erection is a skilled and potentially dangerous occupation, and requires the necessary capability and fitness, skill, experience, knowledge and competence to complete scaffolding operations safely.

Anyone engaged in work at height and the use of work equipment for work at height, including organisation, planning and supervision, must be competent to do so. If being trained, they are to be supervised by a competent person.

Scaffold erectors need to be trained in the following:

An independent tied scaffold with guardrails and toeboards, and a debris chute for safe removal of rubble

- Safe systems of work.
- Risks associated with scaffolding and with any particular work involved.
- Assessing site conditions.
- Use of PPE.
- Erecting, adapting and dismantling different types of scaffolding.
- Setting up hoists or lifting appliances.
- Operating mobile access platforms.
- Rigging and inspection of safety nets.
- Application of the **Construction (Design and Management) Regulations 2015** and the **Work at Height Regulations 2005** in the operations above.

Scaffolders are classified as basic (one year of experience) or advanced (two years' experience including one year as a basic scaffolder). New entrants are called trainee scaffolders.

Means of Access

Access onto scaffolding is normally by use of ladders, which should be put in place as early as possible in the erection process and removed as late as possible in the dismantling process. Access to scaffolding for people and materials might also be gained by using hoists and mobile elevating platforms (discussed later in this section).

Design of Loading Platforms

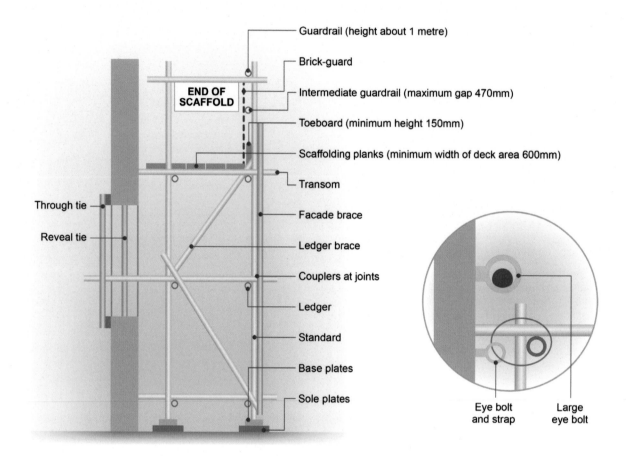

Independent tied scaffold with working platform

Loading/working platforms and any supporting structures must not be overloaded so as to collapse, or be deformed in any way so that they are unsafe to use or give rise to any danger. They should be designed, erected and maintained by a competent person.

Working platforms and decking should be closely boarded to their full width. If boards overlap, bevelled pieces should be used to avoid tripping hazards. The platform must be wide enough for the work being done:

- **Three boards wide** (600mm) - people doing light work without materials (e.g. inspection or painting).

- **Four boards wide** (800mm) - person and materials; jobs like glazing, plastering.

- **Five boards wide** (1,050mm) - a general purpose work platform (general building work and bricklaying). This can carry trestles or similar platforms for work at higher levels.

- **Six boards wide** (1,300mm) - specially designed - for dressing or roughly shaping stone.

- **Seven boards wide** (1,500mm) - heavy duty decking, for dressing stone and to support stone-dressing platforms.

A clear passage 440mm wide should be kept on platforms, and the platform should be no further than 300mm from a wall. Platforms should extend 600mm beyond the end of a wall.

Scaffold Hoists

Manual hoists are used to raise lightweight equipment and materials to a place of work, e.g. block and tackle, hoists, wire ropes, chains or slings.

Different types of **mechanical hoist**, e.g. vertical, swivel and beam, are available to transport materials and people.

All scaffold hoists must be:

- In good repair and well maintained.

- Marked with the safe working load.

- Positioned on stable ground according to the manufacturer's instructions by a competent person.

- Protected at both top and bottom to prevent falls of materials or persons.

- Clearly marked in respect of the control functions.

- Supervised at all times when being used.

Goods hoist

Hazards associated with the use of hoists include:

- Falling down the hoistway:

    - From a landing level, e.g. scaffolding.

    - From a platform or cage.

    - With the platform/cage due to operator error while loading or unloading is taking place, or due to gear failure.

- Being struck by:

    - The moving hoist or cage.

    - Falling materials from the hoist.

    - Landing levels or parts of the enclosure while trying to ride on material/goods hoists.

The safe operation of hoists depends on:

- Routine testing and examination by competent persons.

- Training of operatives.

- Security of the loads.

- Adequate control measures:

    - No riding on a goods hoist.

    - No gaps at the edge of the hoist platform.

- Enclosure of the hoistway.

- Hoist gates at all levels and fencing where people may fall down.

- Landing gates kept closed during loading/unloading from the ground.

- Clear operator visibility to all levels of the installation.

Two types of **passenger hoist** are commonly used:

- Surrounding tower hoist.

- Cantilevered hoist.

Both must be adequately tied at suitable intervals, and only operated within their Safe Working Load (SWL):

- The surrounding tower type has the cage running in the centre of the tower.

- The cantilever type has either one or two cages running on either side of the tower.

These systems have a number of **safety devices**, including:

- Over-run devices.

- High landing gates (minimum two metres).

- Hoist arrester devices.

- Deadman's handle.

- Cage fully enclosed (and enclosure a minimum of 2m in height).

- Hoist tied into building.

- Hoist operated from one position.

- Cage interlocks on gates.

- Landing gate interlocks.

- SWL on hoist.

Ensuring Stability of Scaffolds

- Requirements for scaffold structures:

  - Rigid.

  - Stable.

  - Strong enough to support working platforms and any load that might be placed on them, e.g. bricks, tools, equipment.

  - Erected so that they cannot be displaced and so give rise to any danger.

- Structure must remain stable:

  - Even when being altered or modified.

  - During dismantling operations.

  - In high winds or inclement weather, e.g. slippery, icy surfaces.

Sheeting or netting may also increase the load on structures during high wind conditions.

Scaffolds need to be strong enough to support a working platform

- Care is required to avoid impact from vehicles and possible collapse of the structure.

- There should be proper segregation, marking and lighting of structures.

It is worth noting here that the collapse of a structure such as a scaffold would be a dangerous occurrence, and therefore reportable under **RIDDOR**.

Effects of Materials

An independent tied scaffold is designed to carry its own weight and the full load of all materials and workers on it. The total load is supported by the ground the scaffold is built on. The scaffold is not totally independent and must be tied to the building where it is sited, to prevent movement away from or towards the building.

As the ground supports the total weight of the scaffold when in use, the ground structure must be suitable to cope with the load. Base plates and sole plates will help to spread the load. Overloading the scaffold with excess materials is liable to make the structure unstable.

Weather

The wind strength and adverse weather conditions, e.g. rain, ice or snow, must be taken into account. At ground level, wind may be reduced by the protection given by buildings; at roof level a worker may be exposed to its full force. Footholds at heights are generally not as good as at ground level and balance may be affected. Carrying large items of material, e.g. a roofing sheet or lengths of wide timber, will exaggerate the problem by acting as a 'sail' in the wind. Workers have been blown off a roof while handling large items of materials.

When deciding whether to suspend work it is important to consider:

- The wind speed.

- Measures already taken to prevent falls.

- The positioned height of the roof or work equipment and size of materials being handled.

Sheeting

Two main types of sheeting are commonly employed on scaffolds:

- **Debris netting** - comprised of an open meshwork which reduces the risk of falling debris outside the work area. While not reducing the effects of adverse weather, it may reduce wind loading on the scaffold.

- **Scaffold sheeting** - made of tough reinforced polythene material, often with eyelets to connect sheets together. It has a high tensile strength and is tear and puncture resistant. Sheeting material with strong overlapping joints will reduce the effects of adverse weather conditions within the scaffold, and the effects of very strong winds.

Protection from Impact of Vehicles

- On separated sites, vehicle access areas should be segregated and fenced/coned-off to prevent construction site vehicles impacting with scaffolds.

- In public areas, traffic control measures may need to be used to prevent vehicle impact.

Inspection Requirements

We looked at the inspection requirements for work equipment, which includes scaffolding, earlier in this element.

Mobile Elevating Work Platforms (MEWPs)

Mobile Elevating Work Platforms (MEWPs) are motorised vehicles or trailers with powered extending arms supporting a work cradle. There are many different types of MEWP.

Hazards associated with the use of MEWPs:

- Falls from the working platform.
- Objects falling from the platform.
- Collapse of the MEWP.
- Overturn (toppling) of the MEWP.
- Instability on poor terrain/crossing uneven ground.
- Contact with live cables or overhead services.
- Unauthorised use.

MEWP

TOPIC FOCUS

Safety precautions for use of MEWPs:

- Select the type of MEWP to suit the terrain it will cross/work on.
- Site the MEWP on firm, stable ground.
- Ensure clearance from obstructions around and overhead when operating.
- Place barriers to prevent the MEWP being struck by vehicles or mobile plant.
- Same barriers keep people from beneath the working platform (cradle).
- Cradle to have guardrails; safety harnesses to be worn as additional precaution.
- Controls of the MEWP should be inside the cradle so the operator has some control while at height.
- MEWP should not moved with cradle raised unless designed to do so.
- Must not be overloaded.
- Must be inspected (six-monthly) as item of lifting equipment designed to carry people.
- Restrict use to trained, authorised operators.

Use of Ladders, Stepladders, Trestles, Staging Platforms and Leading Edge Protection Systems

Ladders

Ladders should only be used for low risk activities of short duration (e.g. inspection or painting). Three points of contact should be maintained at all times on ladders. They are also often used to provide access and egress, e.g. into excavations and on and off scaffolds.

Ladders must be regularly inspected and maintained, and should be built to a suitable standard (i.e. **BS EN 131**: duty rated at 115kg).

Main hazards associated with the use of ladders:

- Not being tied or not resting on firm ground, which may cause the ladder to tip or topple sideways.

- Poor storage and maintenance allowing the ladder to rot or warp, which may cause the rungs to break.

- Objects falling from height.

- Contact with live overheads.

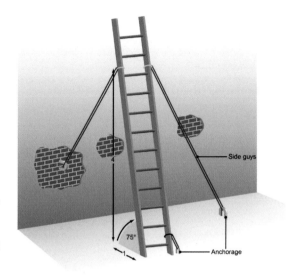

Positioning and securing a ladder

Safety precautions for use of ladders:

- Do not handle or position ladders near live overheads.

- Position on a solid, flat base so the feet do not sink into the ground. Weight should only be supported on the styles, never on the rungs. Tie where necessary.

- Ideal ladder angle is 75° to the horizontal or at a ratio of 1:4 distance away from the wall to height (1 out: 4 up).

- Top of the ladder must rest against a solid support (e.g. not plastic guttering).

- Ideally the ladder should be secured at the top. If this is not possible, then guy ropes should be attached and secured to firm supports. If this is not possible, the ladder should be supported by use of a proprietary ladder stabiliser or 'footed' by someone standing with one foot on the bottom rung while holding both styles.

- Top of the ladder should extend far enough above the level of the working position or the platform onto which it gives access to provide a safe handhold. The stepping-off point should be safe and clear.

- Only one person should climb on the ladder at any one time.

- Nothing should be carried in the hands going up and down the ladder, leaving them free to hold both styles.

- Never over-reach out to the sides of the ladder.

- Wooden ladders should not be painted - this can hide defects.

Ladder used to gain access to a scaffold platform. Note how the ladder extends well above the stepping-off point and how it has been secured to the scaffold

Extension ladders - those that slide up in sections - must have sufficient strength at the overlap. The guide is:

Closed Ladder Length	Overlap
Less than 5m	1.5 rungs
5m to 6m	2.5 rungs
Over 6m	3.5 rungs

Stepladders

Hazards associated with the use of stepladders:

- Falls from height:
    - Falling off the stepladder.
    - Stepladder toppling (not fully opened).
- Falling away from the work (working from the side of the stepladder).
- Objects falling from height.

Safety precautions for stepladders:

- They should be maintained free from defects.
- They should be regularly inspected.
- They should not be painted.
- Retaining chains, ropes or bars (to prevent overspreading) should be of equal length and fully extended.
- Stepladders should be used on a firm, level base and be stable.
- Work should not be carried out from the top step.
- No more than one person at a time should use a stepladder.
- Over-reaching should be avoided.
- Do not work off the side of the stepladder, but facing the steps.

Correct and incorrect positioning of a stepladder

Trestles

A trestle work platform or scaffold is not normally suitable for high level work, and is only used for light work, e.g. painting, decorating. It provides a working platform which can be supported by A-frames, tripods, telescopic frames or split heads. A suitable and sufficient risk assessment is required prior to its use.

Hazards associated with using trestles:

- Falls from height.
- Trestle boards or platforms slipping.
- Equipment and objects falling from height.

Safety precautions for using trestles:

- Trestles should be maintained free from defects, regularly inspected, not be painted and be used on a firm, level base.

- Platforms based on trestles should be fully boarded, adequately supported and be provided with edge protection (toe boards, guardrails).

- Where appropriate, access to platforms should be provided (stepladder or ladder) and only one tier permitted when folding supports are used.

Staging Platforms

These have a number of different uses on access structures, e.g. on scaffolding, wooden trestles and mobile tower access, and are known under the name of Youngman's boards/platforms. They are also adaptable for use with guardrails and are available up to six metres in length for variable loads and situations.

Leading Edge Protection Systems

We discuss these under 'roof work' (see later in this element).

Other Access to Work at Height Techniques

Boatswain's Chair

A boatswain's chair can be used for light, short-term work. The chair consists of a seat, a suspension point and means for carrying tools. The user should be attached to the chair by a harness to prevent falls. Control of descent is by the user, based on the same techniques as abseiling, although there should not be a single suspension point.

Boatswain's chairs being used for painting

TOPIC FOCUS

Installation of a Boatswain's Chair

- To be installed and tested by a competent person.
- Work to be planned and supervised (as required by **WAH Regulations**).
- Chair to have two separate rope systems (main and security).
- Fall arrest harness to be attached to security rope.
- Tools should be secured in pouches or on tool lanyards.
- Means of communication provided for person in chair to ground operatives.
- Safety precautions in place to protect those working below.
- Rescue plan to be in place.
- Consider weather conditions before use.
- Safety equipment to be inspected daily.
- Chair and ropes examined every six months (SWL to be marked).

Cradles

Suspended access equipment (cradles) are lowered into position from above. They can be either a fixed access structure built into the roof of a building, or a cradle designed to be positioned (raised and lowered) by a crane. They should be fully guarded with guardrails and toe boards to provide a safe working platform:

- Cradles must be thoroughly examined every six months by a competent person.
- An exclusion zone should be established below them, and operatives should wear harnesses inside the cradle for extra safety.
- Weather conditions can pose problems in the use of cradles, particularly wind and lightning.
- Cradles may also be used to deliver materials or people to working places, usually suspended by a crane.

Rope Access

Rope access can be used when access is not possible from a working platform.

- Users must be adequately trained and competent, and the equipment must be erected and inspected prior to use by a competent person.
- As such work requires two separately anchored lines (a working line for access, egress and support, and a safety line) both should have separate suspension points so that safe descent is not dependent on one rope.
- The user should wear a harness that is attached to both the working line and safety line, unless the use of a second rope would mean a higher risk to the person using the equipment. In this case, other appropriate safety measures should be used. The safety line should have a mobile fall protection system that is connected to and travels with the user.
- Tools or equipment used should be suspended by suitable ropes or chains to avoid being dropped. The area beneath rope access work must be protected by fans, covered walkways or tunnels to avoid any injuries.

Fall Arrest Equipment

Where all previous preventive methods are not practicable, or where additional safety measures are required, then fall arrest equipment should be used. This is intended to minimise the effect of a fall once it has happened, and is used as part of a safe system of work.

The provision of fall arrest equipment is subject to the **Personal Protective Equipment at Work Regulations 1992** and the **WAH Regulations**.

Fall arrest comes in two main forms:

- **Personal protective systems** - e.g. fall arrest harnesses.
- **Collective protection systems** - e.g. safety nets or air bags.

> **DEFINITIONS**
>
> **FALL RESTRAINT EQUIPMENT**
>
> Designed to prevent falls happening.
>
> **FALL ARREST EQUIPMENT**
>
> Designed to catch you if you do fall.

Harnesses

Personal fall arrest systems consist of a **full-body harness** connected to one or two lanyards, which are connected to a wire rope, fixed anchor point or inertia reel device:

- They should only be used by trained workers.

- All fall arrest equipment should be regularly inspected, maintained and cleaned.

- A higher level of supervision is required when these are used.

- The fall arrest equipment must be suitably anchored (to a suitable point strong enough to withstand the load from a fall), and as high as possible, preferably above the user and never below the level of their feet.

- Adequate clearance is required below the work level for safe operation.

Personal fall arrest equipment

Safety Nets

Safety nets are a **collective protection system**, for arresting falls of persons from height. They can be used on a variety of structures, e.g. towers, piers, bridges, chimneys, over motorways, or even across floor edges or gaps in walls using appropriate anchorage points.

Safety nets should be:

- Fixed to secure anchor points strong enough to support the net and the load of a person (or persons) falling into it.

- Fixed as close below the fall areas as possible, and never more than two metres below.

- Stored under cover in dry, clean conditions and protected from the effects of inclement weather, strong sunlight and contamination from oils, cement and other strong chemicals.

- Inspected before each use and after any fall incident for tears, holes or abrasion, especially at the anchor-attachment points. Such damage may be caused by people walking on the nets, dropped materials, tools or equipment, or friction against parts of the structure.

- Installed, inspected and examined at regular intervals according to manufacturers' specifications by a trained, certificated, competent person.

Soft Landing Systems

Cushioned reusable bags ('bean bags') or inflatable (low pressure) air bags provide a yielding surface onto which to fall.

The bags must be positioned correctly before work commences. They should be clipped together to ensure that they do not separate on impact. The bags should also be checked when re-positioned or after a fall has occurred to ensure that they have not been damaged in any way, and that air bag pressure has been maintained.

It is also important to ensure that other control measures are in place to prevent a fall from occurring in the first place. The bag system is a last resort and should not be relied on as the one and only control measure. It is important to remember that a fall even onto a 'safe' place could be very stressful and traumatic for an individual.

Crash Decks

Horizontal lining forms such as crash decks or tensioned cable netting are erected to protect equipment or items below from damage by objects falling from the work being carried out above. They are often semi-permanent structures erected over machinery to protect it in the event of materials falling, e.g. in the event of a roof collapse.

In public areas, it may be necessary to use pedestrian tunnels or properly constructed false ceilings or crash decks to protect pedestrians below from falling materials during work over occupied areas.

When scaffolding operations are in progress the public must be excluded from both the area of work and a sufficient area around it. It should be possible to incorporate fans, crash decks and tunnels as early as possible into a scaffold in the early stages of construction.

Tunnels can be constructed under scaffolding to protect the public

Emergency and Rescue Procedures

Emergency procedures need to be developed for reasonably foreseeable events where workers might become trapped or suspended in their fall arrest equipment. Workers are placed at considerable risk if they become unconscious while suspended in a harness.

This step is often neglected when work at height is being planned.

Employers should consider the following:

- Suspension trauma and its consequences. There is a general lack of awareness of suspension trauma. Following an evidence based review recently completed by the HSE, the guidelines are now that standard first-aid procedures should be given for suspension trauma once rescue and recovery of the employee has been achieved.

- Rescue provision - the requirement to provide rescue provision.

- Adequate rescue equipment - the requirement to provide suitable and adequate rescue equipment.

The method of rescue may well be simple, such as putting a ladder up to a net and allowing a fallen person to climb down. Where harnesses are used, MEWPs may be required or proprietary rescue equipment employed.

Because rescue operations are often carried out under extreme pressure, consideration should be given to all aspects of the rescue process. It is worth considering the type of equipment required, the demands placed on the rescuer, the training that the rescue persons will require to carry out a rescue and how effectiveness of the system as a whole can be maintained (practice drills, etc.).

TOPIC FOCUS

Suspension Trauma

- Caused by pooling of the body's blood volume into the lower extremities.

- Can lead to changes in blood pressure, an increase in stress on the heart, and a reduction of oxygen supply to the brain.

- The longer a person is suspended in a harness while unconscious (without moving), the greater the chances of trauma and the more serious it is likely to be. It can be fatal after only a short time.

- An unconscious person should be removed from upright suspension within ten minutes.

- A conscious casualty should be encouraged to exercise their legs to circulate the blood - this will reduce the trauma.

- Medical services are to be immediately alerted in trauma cases, especially where the casualty is unconscious (kidney damage may result).

Roof Work

Certain precautions need to be taken during roof work to ensure the protection of:

- **Workers** - those actually working on a roof, such as:
    - Prevention of slips, trips and falls.
    - Safe places to walk.
    - Safe means of access and egress.
- **Occupants of buildings**, such as:
    - Information on the risks and precautions to be observed.
    - Clearance of areas beneath the work, barriers and signs, etc.
- **Members of the public**, such as:
    - Precautions to prevent people being struck by falling materials/objects.
    - Barriers at ground level as well as at height.
    - Children must be protected and prevented from gaining access onto roofs.

Means of Access

Roof access requires careful planning as work progresses. This includes the means of transporting tools and materials to and from the roof, including the removal of waste. A number of methods may be used:

- Independent scaffolding can provide safe access to roofs and to the edges of them, as well as material storage areas.
- Fixed scaffold towers enable safe access to roofs. The use of stairway designs in preference to ladder access allows materials/components/tools to be carried to the roof safely.
- Mobile scaffold towers avoid the risks associated with scaffold erection, but must be suitable for the type of ground conditions present.

- Ladders - important considerations are the:
    - Length of ladder, which may be heavy and awkward to manoeuvre.
    - Need to carry materials or tools to and from the job, remembering that two hands should be free when climbing a ladder.
    - Stability and security of the ladder in use.
    - Type of ladder used.
    - Ladder requires inspection by competent persons.

- Where roof access is achieved by a valley or parapet gutter and the adjacent roof is of fragile material, then suitable covers are required to prevent a fall through the fragile material.

Edge Protection

Edge protection on roofs must be both high and strong enough to withstand a person either rolling or sliding down or falling off a roof structure, whether it is a flat or sloping roof. Protection may be permanent or temporary, e.g. guardrails or toe boards, depending on the roof structure.

Leading Edge Protection Systems

Leading edges are unprotected edges (gaps) that are created and move as work progresses, e.g. where panels have been taken out in preparation for fitting new ones, or the edge of the line of panels as they are fitted (no roof beyond it). Working on a roof at the leading (working) edge gives rise to a number of risks which can be controlled in a number of ways:

- **Safety Nets**

    These need to be installed by a competent person as close as possible to the roof surface (see earlier). They must be securely attached, of sufficient strength to withstand a person falling into the net and suitable for the work taking place. Note that they can also be used on refurbishment operations, e.g. near fragile roof lights.

- **Birdcage Scaffolding**

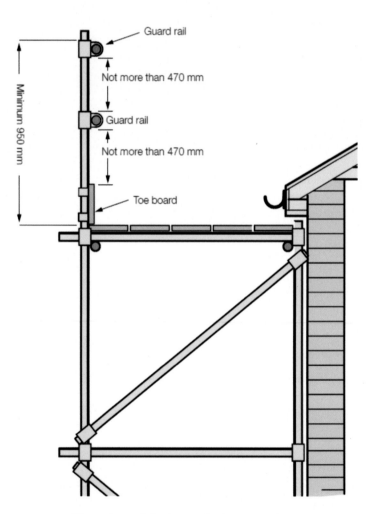

Dimensions of sloping roof edge protection
(Source: HSG33 Health and safety in roof work, HSE, 2012 (www.hse.gov.uk/pubns/priced/hsg33.pdf))

Birdcage scaffolding is normally used for working inside factories, cinemas, churches or tall buildings. It can be used to gain access to ceilings and walls for plastering, painting or decorating, and to provide leading edge protection during roof refurbishments.

- **Safety Harnesses**

  Safety harnesses (as fall arrest systems) can be used which have running lines attached to a suitable anchorage point, mobile or fixed, e.g. a working platform. The harness needs to be fit for purpose, used in accordance with the manufacturer's instructions and the wearer suitably trained in its use (see earlier).

- **Trolley Systems**

  Temporary barriers such as trolley systems may be installed at the leading edge. Such systems require a safe system of work during installation, moving and dismantling, and must be able to be locked in position to prevent overturning. They also require safe access and must be able to move freely within the purlin (horizontal timbers resting on the principal rafters which support the common or subsidiary rafters or boards on which the roof is laid) design. Care is required that during their movement, additional safety is provided by the use of safety nets or harnesses and barriers at the end of the trolley.

  Attempting to free trolleys that have jammed can be dangerous. They are not suitable where design details such as hips, dormers, etc. do not allow adequate support over the full length of the trolley.

  They are not suitable for use where insufficient support is provided for the whole trolley length. Other systems can be protected by trolleys which limit the open area by providing a horizontal barrier attached to the trolley, which does not require a harness and is an alternative to the use of nets.

  Trolley systems are often not practicable and should only be used where there is no safer alternative

- **Other Systems**

  Other leading edge systems consist of soft matting which is used where safety nets are unable to be used (e.g. installation of precast slabs), or air-filled bag systems which are gaining popularity in the house-building sector.

Crawling Boards

These will be required on most sloping roofs and need to be:

- Fit for purpose.
- Of sufficient strength to support workers.
- At least three rafters long.
- Able to be secured or placed in such a way as to prevent any accidental movement.

At least two crawling boards should be used, one to support the worker while the other is moved to a new position.

On larger or more fragile roofs, crawling boards with side rails may be required, which give a worker extra support and anchorage for fall arrest equipment.

Other crawling-board systems include roof ladders that hook over the ridge, and timber battens.

Fall Arrest Equipment

Where all previous preventive methods are not practicable, or where additional safety measures are required, then fall arrest equipment (discussed earlier) should be used. This is intended to minimise the effect of a fall once it has happened, and is used as part of a safe system of work.

STUDY QUESTIONS

6. What safety features are used on scaffolding?

7. What are the main hazards of using ladders?

8. Outline the requirements for edge protection on working platforms.

9. In respect of scaffolding:

    (a) What is the difference between standards, ledgers and transoms?

    (b) What is the difference between tying and bracing?

10. State the safety precautions which need to be taken when mobile elevating work platforms are in use.

11. What is the angle at which ladders should be positioned?

12. What methods of roof access are there?

13. What is fall arrest equipment intended to do?

(Suggested Answers are at the end.)

Protection of Others

IN THIS SECTION...

- Danger areas are to be demarcated; segregated by barriers (fences, tapes, etc.) and tunnels (boarded walkways beneath work areas); and must be adequately signed to warn of the hazards.

- Marking and lighting are required to warn of and protect from the dangers on a construction site; lighting is particularly important for work in poor light and during the night where access is required.

- Sheeting, netting and fans are protective systems to prevent material and debris falling onto members of the public and other persons below work at height areas.

- Head protection should be provided for all persons who could be struck by falling or moving objects.

Introduction to the Protection of Others

Protection from falls from height or falling objects has to be provided for all persons, including site workers, contractors, visitors and members of the public.

Demarcation, Barriers, Tunnels and Signs

Demarcation and Barriers

A suitable barrier a safe distance from the roof edge is used to demarcate between access routes and working areas. Normally, two metres from the edge is an accepted distance to prevent falls from the edge. Such barriers must be adequately supervised and suitably enforced to ensure they are not breached. The barriers themselves should be of sufficient strength and durability, adequately marked and with no visible gaps. The safe area similarly should have no unprotected holes, breaks or fragile material.

The internal area below any roof work and external areas around the edge of a building with roof work being carried out should be clearly segregated from vehicles, members of the public, children and anyone with impaired hearing or sight. This is achieved by the use of barriers - physical demarcation using fencing, mesh panels, cones or hazard tape. The higher the risk area, the more security and strength is required from the barrier.

Tunnels

Tunnels provide a shielded walkway through scaffolding and beneath work at height areas. They are protected on both sides (or just on the building side if along a main street footpath) and from above by boarding, sheeting or netting to prevent falling debris and other objects.

Signs

All demarcation areas, barriers, tunnels, etc. must be suitably signed to indicate the hazards and precautions to be taken, and to enforce their use.

A site safety sign

Marking and Lighting

Marking of safe routes can be achieved by painted zones on the floor, on boarding and sheeting, or by the use of barrier tapes. All approaches (at all levels) to roof work should be signed.

Where demarcated areas are left overnight, adequate lighting is to be provided that illuminates any dim or shadowy areas. Dark areas (e.g. tunnels) may need 24-hour lighting. In addition to illuminating the danger zone, the signs should be highlighted as well.

Marking and lighting on site

Sheeting, Netting and Fans

Sheeting

Sheeting combined with a second layer of scaffold boards or even plywood sheets can help to protect the public from falling objects and materials. For example, hot bitumen can either drip or fall from roofs and so physical barriers below the actual work are required. However, careful consideration of the loading of the scaffolding is essential.

Netting

There are two main types of safety net:

- Personnel nets with 100mm mesh - these are intended to catch a person falling from above. The maximum recommended fall distance of persons is six metres.

- Material or debris protection nets with smaller mesh (12-19mm) - these are intended to protect persons below from falling objects.

Netting should be:

- Properly secured and slung efficiently.

- Higher at the outer edge than at the inner to allow access of any rescue craft.

- Erected as close as possible to the working level.

Scaffold Fans

If there is any risk of pedestrians or vehicles below being hit, then the employer must erect a protective scaffold fan. Suitable and sufficient physical protection measures (of which the scaffold fan is one) need to be provided to prevent objects falling from scaffolding and protect the public if there is a risk of falling objects.

If masonry work is taking place or cradles are being operated, then a scaffold fan is also needed.

Fans or screens must be wide enough to provide complete protection to the public, and to prevent material of any kind from falling onto the public highway. (An illustration of fan protection was included earlier in this element.)

Head Protection

Work at height areas always have a risk of falling or moving objects, so are always safety helmet ('hard hat') areas. This requirement covers not only the construction workers, but all persons who need to be in the areas below work at height, including members of the public where demarcation cannot totally segregate them from the work at height activities.

For supervisory purposes, some larger sites will require different coloured helmets for identification of construction workers, contractors and visitors/members of the public on site.

The issue of hard hats is not a replacement for other controls designed to prevent objects from falling, e.g. toe boards or nets, or to protect people from falling objects, e.g. exclusion zones.

A Sikh who is wearing a turban is exempt from any requirement to wear head protection while working on or visiting a site where construction work is undertaken.

STUDY QUESTION

14. With regard to safety netting:

    (a) What are the two main types of safety netting?

    (b) What are the criteria for installing safety nets?

(Suggested Answer is at the end.)

Working Over or Near Water

IN THIS SECTION...

- There are legal requirements which must be adhered to when working over or near water.

- When working over or near water the most immediate danger is drowning.

- Precautions when working over or near water include warnings; scaffolding and temporary working platforms; buoyancy aids and safety boats (used as a last resort); platforms and gangways; good housekeeping; illumination; first-aid equipment; protective clothing and equipment; life buoys and rescue lines; safe operating procedures; and rescue procedures for use if other protection fails.

- Some specific work environments and equipment require additional controls, e.g. ladders, work in poor weather.

- Anyone falling into water must be kept afloat and recovered from the water as soon as possible.

Prevention of Drowning

Drowning can occur if workers fall from a construction site into water. **Hazardous areas** include:

- Harbours, docks, wharves and piers.

- Lakes, rivers, streams and the sea.

- Swimming pools, ponds (natural and man-made), reservoirs and lagoons.

- Chemical works or factories containing open tanks, vats or water-holding tanks.

- Culverts, sewers, outfalls and other discharge points.

Working over, on or near water presents a risk of people slipping, tripping, falling or being knocked into water. Similarly, loss of balance, failure of ropes or lines or failure or absence of barriers may cause problems. In addition, strong currents and a rapidly rising tide or even passing swell from water traffic may cause a person to be swept off their feet.

The immediate danger to personnel is that of drowning. Other contributing factors include:

- The shock of sudden immersion in cold water (cold shock).

- The weight of waterlogged clothing.

- Incapacity following injury, e.g. by striking an object during the fall or in the water.

- Fatigue or hypothermia where rescue is not immediate.

- The risk of catching Leptospirosis (Weil's disease) caused mainly from the urine of infected rats which can enter the body through unprotected cuts and scratches and can be fatal if not treated.

- In coastal areas, or tidal rivers, the tide may cause problems of drag or undertow making rescue more difficult.

Construction work on Hungerford Bridge (London) requiring work to be carried out near and over water

TOPIC FOCUS

Legislative Requirements When Working Over or Near Water

- A suitable and sufficient risk assessment is required of the work involved, as well as risk prevention and protective measures.

- All craft used to convey persons on water must be safe and be suitably constructed, maintained and operated by a competent person.

- Suitable rescue equipment must be provided nearby and persons trained/instructed in its use.

- Guardrails must be in place if a person can fall from the edge of adjacent land, a structure, scaffolding or a floating stage - these may be removed temporarily to allow materials to be moved but must be replaced as soon as possible.

- Where full scaffolding or gangways (with handrails/toe boards) are not practicable, safety nets can be used.

- Where safety nets are not practicable, safety harnesses can be worn, but need secure anchor points and must be worn and attached at all times.

- Employers must do everything that is reasonably practicable to provide information, instruction, training and supervision.

- Employers must provide a safe place and system of work with safe access/egress and must ensure that provision is made for safe use and handling of materials, etc.

Additional Appropriate Control Measures

There are a number of precautions which can contribute to the safety of individuals and groups of people by preventing them from falling into water, or providing aid if they do fall in.

Warning Notices

These should be erected at all edges and boundaries near water and set so that they are easily seen by anyone approaching.

Scaffolds and Temporary Working Platforms

These should be erected by qualified, competent persons and inspected according to the regulations - prior to work, in inclement weather, and weekly. They provide the best method of ensuring safe working over water. The scaffold should be designed and inspected for the task so that it is stable and of sufficient size for the proposed work, with double height toe boards, double guardrails, and brick guards or nets. Boards should be lashed to prevent damage from high winds.

Buoyancy Aids

Life jackets or buoyancy aids (designed to keep the wearer afloat) must be worn where there is a risk of drowning when working on or near water, and at all times while working on boats:

Life jacket

- A **life jacket** will provide sufficient buoyancy to turn and support even an unconscious person face upwards:

    - Inflation is by means of the mouth or carbon dioxide cartridge.

    - The life jacket supports the head with the mouth and nose well clear of the water.

    - Some people are reluctant to wear life jackets as they find them bulky and restrictive of movement.

- **Buoyancy aids** are worn to provide extra buoyancy to assist a conscious person in keeping afloat:

    - They will **not** turn an unconscious person over from a face-down position.

    - They tend to be less bulky than life jackets.

The selection of either type will depend on an assessment of:

- Water conditions - temperature, current, tides.

- The work being undertaken.

- The protective clothing being worn.

- The proximity of assistance.

- A person's competency as a swimmer.

Safety Boat

The safe transport of any person conveyed by water to or from his/her place of work is a requirement of the **Construction (Design and Management) Regulations 2015 (CDM)**.

Passenger-carrying craft must:

- Not be overcrowded or overloaded.

- Be marked with the number of persons they are intended to carry and, where appropriate, the limits of operation.

- Be suitably constructed and maintained.

- Be inspected if they carry more than 12 passengers at any one time, and a worthiness certificate obtained.

- Carry life-saving and fire-fighting appliances/equipment appropriate to their size.

- Be under the control of a competent person.

Communication is extremely important and should be in place during any work activity on or in the vicinity of water and in the event of an emergency situation arising.

Platforms and Gangways

Where platforms or gangways are erected, these must comply with the requirements of **CDM**. The decking boards should be safely secured with additional handholds. Working platforms, e.g. barges or pontoons, must be properly constructed, sufficiently stable to avoid tipping under loads, and have good anchorage and ballasting.

Ladders

Any ladders used for access must meet all usual requirements and:

- Be of sufficient length.

- Extend at least five rungs above a stepping-off point.

- Be securely lashed to prevent slipping.

Permanently fitted ladders over water are fitted with safety hoops.

Landing places must be provided every nine metres if longer access to the scaffold or platform is required.

Housekeeping

Good housekeeping on scaffolding, platforms and gangways is essential in preventing tripping hazards. All tools, equipment and rubbish should be stored away, stacked safely or disposed of. Any contaminants, e.g. bird droppings, slime, oil or grease, should be cleaned off or treated to prevent slips, injuries and minimise fire hazards.

Illumination

Illumination of the workplace is essential for night work and at all times in shafts, dark corners and stairways to avoid the possibility of shadows and glare. Illumination should always include the immediate water surface. Spotlights may be used to help locate a person in the water. Navigation lights and foghorns may also be required at working places in, on or near water and a check should be made with the appropriate authorities regarding requirements.

Weather Conditions

Rain, wind, fog, sea-mist and inclement weather are potential dangers during any work in the vicinity of water. The local weather forecast should be obtained and employees informed prior to each day's work or shift.

First-Aid Equipment

First-aid facilities, appropriate first aiders and/or an appointed person should always be available (depending on the nature of the construction work).

The facilities/equipment available should:

- Be readily accessible and may be situated on pontoons, barges and near all possible landing places.

- Include portable equipment for resuscitation and transporting any casualties to the main working area over water and to normal landing places.

Protective Clothing and Equipment

- **Safety helmets** must be worn at all times, as anyone struck on the head and then falling into water is at a particular risk of drowning.

- **Footwear** with non-slip soles should be worn, while rubber and/or thigh boots should be avoided due to them filling with water, which could result in the wearer being dragged under water.

- **Safety harnesses** and **safety belts** are permitted under the **WAH Regulations** where it is not possible to provide a standard working platform or safety net, provided that they are always worn and always secured to a safe anchorage.

  Types include chest harness, full-body harness, safety rescue harness, etc. and these must be properly selected for a particular use.

  Operatives must be trained and instructed in their use.

Lifebuoys/Rescue Lines

- **Lifebuoys**

    - Approved lifebuoys, with rescue lines attached, should be set at conspicuous places along or near the water's edge.

    - Lifebuoys are normally 760mm diameter with a 30m lifeline attached.

    - Lifebuoys are made of cork with canvas covering, or of polyurethane foam with a rigid PVC cover, both effective in salt or freshwater.

    - During any night work, self-ignition lights on the lifebuoys should be in use.

- **Rescue Line**

    - A standard rescue line incorporates 25m of line in a canvas bag with a small flotation chamber. The end of this line is held, while the bag is thrown towards the casualty.

    - Another type of rescue line involves a 40m line inside a capsule - sufficiently small to be carried or mounted in a cabinet. The line and the capsule will float, enabling the casualty to grab the line.

Potential users require regular training and instruction in the use of this equipment, and regular checks should ensure that lifebuoys and rescue lines are still in their proper place and that they are intact and not in need of repair, e.g. as a result of vandalism or other interference.

Safe Operating Procedure

To ensure work over or near water is carried out safely, it is vital that:

- A risk assessment and method statement is carried out for the task. This is usually reinforced with the issue of a permit to work.

- Continual checks are made to ensure that no one is missing.

- No lone working occurs.

- Operatives work in pairs so that there is always one to raise the alarm.

- Appropriate training is given to all personnel in emergency procedures.

Rescue Procedure

Rescue procedures should be practised on a regular basis and should have:

- A procedure for raising the alarm (on site and off site).

- A drill to follow to get a rescued person ashore.

- Provision of first aid/resuscitation.

- A routine for getting persons to hospital for check-up following immersion in water (possibly polluted) or for treatment for an injury.

Various circumstances may combine to make a straightforward lifting operation out of the water impossible. Personnel should be trained and instructed in safe rescue procedures, especially if a casualty is injured, too heavy, fully clothed, or in a state of panic.

Regular rescue drills and procedures should take place.

STUDY QUESTIONS

15. Where can drowning occur on construction sites?

16. What legislative requirements apply when working over or in the vicinity of water?

17. What additional precautions may be taken when working over or in the vicinity of water?

18. What protective clothing and equipment is used when working over or in the vicinity of water?

(Suggested Answers are at the end.)

Summary

This element has dealt with some of the hazards and controls associated with working at height.

In particular, this element has:

- Described the hazards and risks associated with working at height, and examples of activities that can cause injury and the significance of such injuries.

- Described the risk factors such as distance of fall, and features such as fragile roofs, roof lights, voids, deterioration of materials, unprotected edges, poorly maintained access equipment, bad weather and falling materials.

- Outlined methods of avoiding working at height, and precautions to prevent falls and falling materials.

- Considered the importance of preparing emergency rescue plans and measures to be taken to reduce the consequences of a fall.

- Outlined the requirements for head protection and the inspection of work equipment, in particular access equipment.

- Described the safe working procedures to be followed when erecting, using and dismantling scaffolding, and the design features of independent tied, putlog, fan and cantilevered scaffold and mobile scaffold towers.

- Described scaffold safety features, including base plates, sole boards, toe boards, guardrails, brick guards, boarding, debris netting and waste chutes.

- Outlined the requirements for gaining access onto scaffolding and the design of loading platforms, and scaffold hoists for persons and materials.

- Described the methods to ensure stability of scaffolding, including the effects of materials and weather; the use of sheeting; protection from vehicle impact; and inspection requirements.

- Outlined the hazards and precautions associated with the use of MEWPs, ladders, stepladders, trestles, staging platforms and leading edge protection systems.

- Outlined other access techniques: boatswain's chairs, suspended cradles and rope access; and the use of fall arrest equipment including harnesses, safety nets, air bags, crash decks and the requirement for rescue procedures (including for workers suffering suspension trauma).

- Described safety in roof work, including means of access, edge and leading edge protection, and the use of crawling boards and fall arrest equipment.

- Outlined the measures required to ensure the protection of other persons, including demarcation of danger areas, barriers, tunnels, signs, marking and lighting, sheeting, netting and fans, and the use of head protection.

- Described the precautions and procedures required when working near or over water, including the prevention of drowning and appropriate control measures such as buoyancy aids and rescue boats.

Exam Skills

> ## QUESTION
> **Outline** the factors that can affect the risk of working at height. **(8)**

Approaching the Question

Think now about the steps you would take to answer the question:

Step 1. Read the question carefully. Note that this question is asking for factors (substitute the word 'things' if you find factors confusing) that affect the risk of work at height. Providing answers on control measures will not win any marks. Working at height continues to be the cause of many deaths in the construction industry and you should be well prepared if this type of question appears on the paper.

Step 2. Now highlight the key words. In this case they might look like this:

Outline the **factors** that can **affect** the **risk of working at height**. **(8)**

Step 3. Next, consider the marks and time available. In this question there are eight marks so it is expected that around eight or nine different pieces of information should be provided. The question should take around eight minutes in total. Try not to overrun that time. Statistically most marks are picked up in the first five to six minutes of attempting a question. It's better to pick up more marks on other questions than run over time perfecting just one. Remember, if you do not attempt a question because you ran out of time, you will get no marks for it!

Step 4. Read the question again to make sure you understand that you need to outline risk factors and not control measures. (Re-read your notes if you need to.) Remember, 'outline' means you will need to give the most important factors in greater detail than a list.

Step 5. The next stage is to develop a plan - there are various ways to do this. You need to be thinking about factors (things) that affect risk when working at height and you need enough information to produce an outline.

Now have a go at the question. Draw up an answer plan, and then use it as the basis to write out an answer as you would in the exam.

Remember, you can always contact your tutor if you have any queries or need any further guidance on how to answer this question.

> ### HINTS AND TIPS
> Read the question with care - you have been asked to 'outline' (not 'list') factors that affect risk.

Suggested Answer Outline

Factors that affect risk	
• Nature of the task to be done.	• Absence of fall protection measures.
• Height.	• Sloping roofs and roof pitch.
• Correct access equipment.	• Falling objects.
• Maintenance of access equipment.	• High winds/bad weather.
• Fragile roofs or surfaces.	• Competence, training, supervision.
• Unguarded edges.	

Example of How the Question Could be Answered

The nature of the task being completed will affect the risk level when working at height; assembling steel structures of a building may be a higher risk activity than installing windows. The height being worked at is also a significant risk factor; whilst falls from a few feet may be fatal or lead to serious injury, falls from a few hundred feet will almost certainly prove fatal. The selection of access equipment will affect the level of risk; employees working at height using fall arrest harnesses will be at a higher risk level than those working from a MEWP. The task may involve roof work where the roof is fragile or where roof lights are present - injuries can occur due to the roof giving way or the operator stepping onto the glass roof light and falling through. The slope or pitch of the roof will also affect risk - highly pitched roofs are more likely to lead to operators sliding off the roof. Work at height should be carefully planned to mitigate against the risk of falls; and working without means to mitigate falls, such as netting, air bags or lanyards, may result in the employee falling a distance sufficient to cause injury. The weather will also play a part in the level of risk; high winds may result in employees being blown off a structure, or the presence of ice may cause slips or a loss of grip that could result in a fall.

Reasons for Poor Marks Achieved by Candidates in Exam

- Providing a list without sufficiently outlining the risk factors.
- Not answering the question and instead outlining control measures.
- Not studying the subject sufficiently.

Excavation Work and Confined Spaces - Hazards and Risk Control

Learning Outcomes

Once you've read this element, you'll understand how to:

1 Explain the hazards and risk assessment of excavation work.

2 Explain the control measures for excavation work.

3 Explain the hazards and risks associated with confined space working.

4 Outline the control measures for confined space working.

Contents

Excavation Work Hazards and Assessment

IN THIS SECTION...

- The hazards of excavations include: striking buried services; people, objects or materials falling in; collapse of sides; collapse of adjacent structures; flooding; use of cofferdams and caissons; contaminated ground; toxic and asphyxiating atmospheres; and mechanical hazards.

- Consideration should be given to overhead hazards, including power lines.

- Risk assessment factors to consider are: depth, type of soil, type of work, use of mechanical equipment, proximity of roadways and structures, the presence of the public and weather conditions.

Excavation Work Hazards

The hazards associated with excavation work include:

- **Striking Buried Services**

    Striking services such as high voltage electricity cables, gas pipes, mains water or other buried services (e.g. telephone and cable TV lines) can lead to electric shock, arcing, burns, fire, gas explosion or rapid flooding of the excavation, as well as major business disruption to service users in the area.

- **People Falling In**

    – Because of an unfenced edge.

    – While climbing in or out from ladders or other access equipment.

- **Objects and Materials Falling In**

    – Tools or materials (bricks, timber, etc.) falling into an excavation onto persons, from an unprotected edge.

    – Vehicles driving too close to the side of an excavation, collapsing the sides or tipping in.

    – Spoil (loose soil) or stacked loose sand piled too close to the sides of an excavation.

    – Adjacent structures (e.g. wall or scaffold) undermined by an excavation and collapsing in.

- **Collapse of Sides**

    When the unsupported sides of an excavation slip and cave in (often due to poor support systems of the excavation sides). Severe crush injuries can result from even relatively small collapses because soil is very heavy, especially when wet. Workers buried or trapped in soil can asphyxiate in minutes, and do not have to be completely buried for this to occur; being buried up to the chest can lock the rib cage and have the same effect.

- **Collapse of Adjacent Structures**

    Digging too close to, or under, the foundations which support nearby buildings or structures may undermine their support and cause collapse of the building or structure into the excavation. This would be even more dangerous if the excavation itself were also to collapse.

- **Water Ingress**

    – From surface water, during heavy rain or snow.

A shallow excavation revealing a collection of buried services

- From groundwater (a high area water table), nearby rivers, streams and watercourses (especially if breached).

- From a burst water main caused by the excavation activities.

- **Use of Cofferdams and Caissons**

   Structures (usually watertight enclosures) which are pumped dry to allow work to be carried out inside them below the waterline on bridge building, etc.

   They must be suitably designed and constructed to prevent the ingress of water (or other materials), or appropriately equipped to pump out water and provide shelter and escape should water or materials enter it.

Cofferdams or caissons constructed to prevent the ingress of water

- **Contaminated Ground**

   - On sites that previously housed chemical works or storage areas.

   - Containing methane or hydrogen sulphide gas (both from microbial decay).

   Contaminants can be varied in range and include:

Industry	Possible Contaminant
Petrochemicals	Hydrocarbons, benzene, phenol, acids, alkalis
Steel/iron works	Iron, copper, zinc, asbestos
Gasworks/power stations	Coal, sulphur, phenol, asbestos, cyanides
Pits/quarries	Leachates, copper, zinc, lead, methane
Tanneries	Anthrax
Miscellaneous industries	Polychlorinated biphenyls, sulphates, metals, micro-organisms

- **Toxic and Asphyxiating Atmospheres**

    From industries mentioned above, and from gases used on site:

    - Heavier than air, gas such as LPG and carbon dioxide, can infiltrate an excavation.

    - The combustion gases from nearby construction equipment, such as diesel generators and motor vehicles, can seep into excavations with the same effect.

- **Mechanical Hazards**

    Mainly from the use of plant and equipment around or in the excavation:

    - Vibration from plant operation may cause collapse.

    - Excavating machinery itself may create hazards, such as striking persons in or around excavations.

Overhead Hazards Including Power Lines

Work beneath overhead services and power lines in particular should be avoided.

Before excavation work starts, all overhead services should be identified and any diversions or disconnections ensured before excavation work begins. Service providers should be contacted to obtain accurate plans of supplies.

Three situations arise in construction work at overhead power lines:

- No scheduled excavation work or passage of plant to take place under the lines.

- Excavation plant and equipment will pass beneath the power lines.

- Excavation work will take place beneath the power lines.

These situations, and appropriate controls, were discussed in detail earlier in the material.

Risk Assessment

Risk assessments should be carried out in accordance with the **Management of Health and Safety at Work Regulations 1999**, with due consideration to the excavation under the **Construction (Design and Management) Regulations 2015**.

TOPIC FOCUS

Risk assessment - factors to consider:

- Depth of the excavation.

- Soil type - this may vary from fine sand which can flow easily, to heavy clay which is much more cohesive.

  Three broad classes of ground exist:

  - Non-cohesive ground or light soil, e.g. sand or gravel, whose natural angle of repose (see later) when dry is usually 45° or less.

  - Cohesive ground or heavy soil, e.g. stiff clay, whose natural angle of repose is about 60°.

  - Rock, whose natural angle of repose varies from about 80° for loosely bonded or light rock, to 90° for tightly bonded heavy rock. Rock may, however, have steeply sloping clay planes which may fail, with resultant collapse.

- Type of work involved, e.g. at the side of a road; in a housing development; laying pipes/cables; trenches; pits.

- Use of mechanical equipment - the types being used.

- Proximity of the excavation to roadways, watercourses, structures, schools and hospitals.

- Presence of the public/children.

- Weather.

STUDY QUESTIONS

1. What hazards are associated with work in and around excavations?

2. What factors should be taken into account with regard to risk assessments for excavations?

(Suggested Answers are at the end.)

Control Measures for Excavation Work

IN THIS SECTION...

- Precautions must be taken to prevent persons falling into, or being injured while working in, excavations. General precautions include:

    - Identifying buried services and using safe digging methods to avoid contact with them.

    - Supporting the sides of excavations to prevent collapse, and providing workers with suitable access and egress, and crossing points to pass over excavations.

    - Barriers, lights and signs used to demarcate danger areas.

    - Spoil (the ground dug from an excavation) to be removed to and stored at a safe distance from the excavation to prevent it collapsing back in.

    - De-watering methods used to remove water from excavations.

    - Vehicles and materials on site kept away from excavations to prevent them falling into or collapsing the excavation.

    - Workers in excavations to wear items of PPE - safety helmets, safety footwear, respirators or breathing apparatus, and hearing protection.

- When working in the vicinity of contaminated ground, testing is essential and extra welfare facilities should be provided to accommodate workers (separate from normal site facilities). Health surveillance may be appropriate for contaminants such as asbestos, lead or radioactive materials.

- Excavation supports, cofferdams and caissons are to be inspected before each shift, and after any event that could affect the integrity of the excavation, and reports to be made and kept.

Control Measures

In common with other construction activities, control of the risks involved in excavation is based on effective management. The **CDM Regulations** apply in this respect, and excavations must be carried out under the supervision of a competent person.

Identification, Detection and Marking of Buried Services

The location and configuration of underground services should be identified prior to work commencing. It may well be possible to avoid cable routes at the planning stage of work. Before work starts, the following action should be taken:

- Check any available plans.

- Contact local service providers and owners, such as electricity, gas, water, telecommunications or TV companies.

- Survey the site and surrounding areas to identify indicators of the existence of cables, etc., e.g. streetlights or junction boxes.

Use of a cable detector
(Source: HSG47 Avoiding Danger from Underground Services, HSE, 2014
(www.hse.gov.uk/pubns/priced/hsg47.pdf))

- Use cable locators with trained operators. Plastic and non-metallic underground services cannot be identified by conventional locators, but could be identified by the use of metallic tracer wire laid with the pipe or by using a signal transmitter inserted and pushed along the pipe itself.

The positions of known services should be marked on plans and also on the ground itself. All employees must receive adequate information and instruction about the nature of the risks.

Where appropriate, arrangements must be made with the service providers to isolate the cables/pipes and ensure that it is safe to work in the vicinity of them.

Safe Digging Methods

Safe digging methods include:

- Use locators to determine the position and route of pipes or cables (frequently using them during the course of the work).

- Keep a careful watch for evidence of pipes or cables. Remember that plastic pipes cannot be detected by normal locating equipment.

- If contact is made with any unidentified service pipe or cable, stop work until it is safe to proceed.

- Regard all buried cables as live until disconnected and proven - pot-ended cables cannot be assumed to be dead or disused.

- Do not use excavators and power tools within 0.5m of the indicated line of a cable/pipe.

- Use hand digging when nearing the assumed line of the cable/pipe.

- Use spades and shovels (preferably with curved edges) rather than other tools, e.g. forks and picks.

- Report any damage to the appropriate services and keep personnel clear until it is repaired.

- Have an emergency plan to deal with such damage to pipes or cables.

- Support exposed cables and pipes and protect against damage by backfilling. They should never be used as hand- and foot-holds.

Methods of Supporting Excavations

Excavation supports will prevent the collapse of the side walls of the excavation and allow work to continue uninterrupted inside the workings. The type of support structure used will vary, depending on:

- Type of ground being excavated.

- Length of time the excavation will be open and in use.

- Type of work being carried out.

- Groundwater conditions and potential for flooding.

- Depth of the excavation.

- Number of people in the excavation.

Types of **excavation supports** include:

- **Battering**

  This allows almost any excavation to be dug without the need for a support system. It relies on the properties of the soil into which the excavation is being dug to form a stable, sloping pile when allowed to form naturally into heaps. The sloping surfaces of the heap form an angle with the horizontal called the angle of repose. Each material has its own particular **angle of repose** which will differ according to the amount of moisture it contains (discussed earlier).

  As the excavation is dug out, the sides are sloped back to less than the angle of repose (which has to be determined first) so that the soil will support itself without the need for extra support. This method requires considerable space to construct an excavation and is normally impractical in built-up areas.

Angle of repose

- **Shoring**

  Steel sheets are laid across the faces of the excavation walls, secured together by clamps and braced by expandable steel struts or wooden beams. The steel sheets should be toed in at the bottom and rise above the tops of the trench sides.

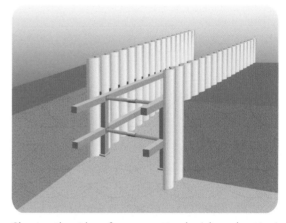

Shoring the sides of an excavation by 'close sheeting'

  Trench boxes (support boxes) are ready-constructed units which can be easily and quickly installed into an excavation using an excavator or similar machine, to provide strong, reliable shoring for most ground conditions while giving full protection for operatives. They can be moved along as the work progresses.

  Where necessary, both types should have edge protection and a means of access via a protected area.

Support of Surrounding Areas

Where there are structures (walls, bridges, roads, etc.) or buildings next to where excavations will be dug, it may be necessary to prop and/or underpin these structures to prevent the excavation causing their collapse.

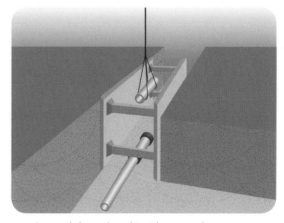

A trench box placed inside a trench creates a protected area for workers

Means of Access

Ladders provide the main method for access to and egress from an excavation. They must be suitably secured to prevent undue movement and extend above the excavation to give the necessary height required for a safe handhold (at least 1.05m).

There must be adequate means of escape in an emergency: one ladder every 15m is an average to work to (more may be required depending on the number of workers and the potential risk, e.g. where there might be a possibility of flooding from a rising water table).

Ladders must be kept in good condition, be fit for the purpose and of adequate strength. Climbing in and out of the excavation using other means should be prohibited.

Crossing Points

Excavations should only be crossed at designated points. The crossing point should be of sound construction and suitable to support all the types of vehicle and equipment likely to use it. Gangways across excavations should have guardrails and toe boards.

Barriers

These should consist of guardrails (as for a scaffold work platform) to prevent people falling in, and toe boards to prevent objects being kicked down into the excavation. In addition:

Crossing point

- To prevent vehicles from falling in, logs or concrete blocks are laid some distance from the edge, to act as a buffer.

- Excavations may need to be covered, particularly at night. Such covers need to be capable of bearing a person's weight and be held securely in place.

- Fencing or hoarding may be required to protect members of the public as well as construction employees.

Lighting and Warning Signs

Signs should be used to warn people of the excavation hazards, and any special precautions required. They should be placed in clearly visible spots at all potential access points.

Appropriate lighting should be installed to ensure that there is an adequate level of illumination, without distracting shadows, to ensure the safety of work activities both within the excavation and on the surface. High-powered electric lights or those which operate from Liquid Petroleum Gas (LPG) will be required for general workplace illumination, and consideration may need to be given to smaller, personal lights for individual workers. These should be battery-operated to avoid the risks associated with trailing electrical leads.

When working on a roadway, the police or local authority need to be consulted about traffic lights or stop/go signs. There are rules for the placing of cones to warn motorists of the hazard.

Safe Storage of Spoil

If spoil is to be left in spoil heaps near the excavation, there must be space to stack it without interfering with other operations, leaving a clear area of 0.6m between the spoil and the edge of the excavation. The officially recognised depth of the excavation depends on **the distance of the spoil heap from its edge**. For excavations up to 6m deep, the following rules apply in the UK:

- If the spoil heap is within 1.5m of the edge of the excavation, the depth of the excavation should be measured **from the top of the spoil heap**.

- If the spoil heap is more than 1.5m from the edge (but less than the actual depth of the excavation), the official depth should be taken as the actual depth plus half the height of the spoil heap.

De-Watering

Preventing Water Entering Excavations

Water can fall as rain, snow and sleet directly into excavations, especially if they are uncovered. The run-off following these downpours can also run in. Water can enter through the sides depending on the height of the surrounding water table, and close proximity to watercourses (rivers, streams, lakes, etc.) can cause excess water.

Accidental damage to nearby tanks, water mains or other supply pipework in the vicinity of the excavation can also lead to an ingress of water. All exposed pipes should be identified and supported.

To protect the stability of the sides of the excavation, drainage channels can be cut around the excavation and the water can be channelled away to sump points where it can be pumped away. The water table is then lowered below the level of the excavation. In extreme cases, watercourses might be redirected.

Excavation sides can be strengthened by using higher shoring and sandbagging the outside. However, the continued flow of water from the area surrounding the excavation may cause settlement problems.

Well pointing or deep wells can be considered where sandy or silty soil exists. Ground freezing or providing an impermeable barrier by injecting cement, bentonite or a chemical is an option, but can be expensive and cause disruption to the ground.

The disposal of any water should be discussed with the appropriate environmental agency.

Positioning and Routing of Vehicles, Plant and Equipment

To prevent vehicles and objects falling into excavations, and collapse of sides, the following precautions should be observed:

- Machinery and vehicles should only be operated in specially designated areas strong enough to withstand the effects of vibration without causing a collapse. Specially built routes to allow access to the floor of the site for vehicles and plant may have to be constructed.

- Where vehicles have to pass close to excavations, barriers and signs should be in place to keep them a safe distance away.

- Where vehicles have to approach the edges of the excavation (e.g. to receive or tip materials), there should be stop blocks to prevent them overrunning.

Personal Protective Equipment

Hard hats and safety footwear are a likely requirement at all times. The need for other PPE will be determined by the nature of the work carried out in the excavation, for example:

- Fumes and dust may require the use of masks and respirators.
- Excessive noise levels will require the wearing of hearing protection.
- Where welding work is carried out, face shields and protective clothing will be necessary.
- Breathing apparatus and safety harnesses may be required for working in tunnels and shafts.

Particular Requirements for Contaminated Ground

Soil Testing

Soil testing to show the presence of any contaminants must be carried out by competent persons from an accredited laboratory.

Once the nature of contaminants is established, measures can be put in place to limit the risk that might be present, e.g. PPE, hygiene facilities, safe systems of work and medical surveillance.

Soil testing

Great care must be taken as:

- Digging will uncover buried materials or contaminants within the ground which are hazardous to health.
- The contaminants themselves can change over time due to bacterial or chemical action, which may also alter their properties. This may be the result of the decomposition of organic matter or from the dumping or spillage of hazardous substances.
- Certain contaminants are subject to specific legislation, namely asbestos, lead, anthrax, radioactive materials and buried explosives, and well established procedures need to be followed to deal with each of these situations.
- There may be radioactive hazards from the ground itself (probably as a result of previous occupancy).
- Toxic and asphyxiating atmospheres may be present, for example:
    - Flammable gases such as methane (marsh gas) and carbon monoxide from plant and machinery used in connection with excavation, including pumps involved in de-watering operations.
    - Toxic gases such as hydrogen sulphide.
    - Chemicals and metal compounds, either in containers or within the soil.

Welfare Facilities

Where work involves contaminated ground, the welfare requirements include:

- Separate facilities (e.g. toilets, washrooms and showers, rest and eating facilities) from the main facilities will be required for all work involving contaminated sites.
- Specialist facilities may be required where work involves asbestos, lead or radioactive materials.
- Separate changing rooms and clothing accommodation may be required to prevent cross-contamination.
- These facilities must have adequate heating, lighting and ventilation.

Health Surveillance

Medical practitioners can screen the workforce involved (e.g. blood/urine testing) and provide continued monitoring to ensure that no serious medical conditions arise. The effect of screening can also alleviate any anxiety caused to either the workforce or the public as to whether the measures in place are adequate.

Inspection Requirements for Excavations, Excavation Supports Systems, Cofferdams and Caissons

No person is allowed to work in an excavation, cofferdam or caisson (other than to examine it) until it has been examined by a competent person.

The inspection of excavations, their supports, cofferdams and caissons is required:

- At the start of each shift.

- After any event likely to have affected the strength or stability of the excavation (e.g. flooding).

- After any material unintentionally falls or is dislodged.

An **inspection report** must be made and kept (**CDM** Regulation 24):

- The report must be completed before the end of the shift in which the excavation was inspected.

- A copy of the report must be given to the person in charge of the worksite within 24 hours of completing the inspection.

- Reports must be retained at the site until the excavation work is completed and, after that, for three months.

Though excavations must be routinely inspected prior to each shift, no more than one written report is needed in seven days unless the strength or stability of the excavation is affected, e.g. after accidental falls of material.

TOPIC FOCUS

An **excavation inspection report** must contain:

- The date, time, location and a description of the workplace inspected.

- The name and position of the person inspecting/making the report.

- The name of the person on whose behalf the inspection was carried out (i.e. the person in charge of the worksite).

- Details of any matters identified that could give rise to health and safety risks, and any actions taken to control them.

- Details of any further actions considered necessary.

When work in the excavation is completed, support materials (timber, sheeting, etc.) should be safely removed by experienced workers and a competent person should inspect the site to ensure that all dangerous materials and equipment have been removed. Water may have to be pumped out of the excavation before it is filled.

Filling should use only appropriate materials and be conducted in a controlled manner under the direction of a competent person.

STUDY QUESTIONS

3. What controls may be necessary during excavation work?

4. What particular hazards may arise during the excavation of contaminated ground?

5. What inspection requirements are there for excavations?

(Suggested Answers are at the end.)

Confined Space Working Hazards and Risks

IN THIS SECTION...

- A confined space is any enclosed space with a specified risk of injury associated with it, including trenches, sewers, chambers tanks, pits and cellars.

- Hazards include toxic, explosive and oxygen-deficient atmospheres; heat; water; free-flowing solids; and restricted space.

Meaning of the Term 'Confined Space'

Examples of confined spaces include: chambers, tanks, vats, silos, pits, reaction vessels, trenches, pipes, sewers, enclosed drains, flues, wells, open-topped chambers, combustion chambers in furnaces, ductwork or other similar spaces.

Other places can become confined spaces:

- Due to the type of work undertaken, e.g. spray painting a room.

- As a result of a change in conditions inside the space, e.g. overheating in a plant-room or electricity sub-station.

- Due to a change in confinement or the degree of enclosure, e.g. inside an item of moving plant or machinery (such as a compactor or baling machine).

> **DEFINITION**
>
> **CONFINED SPACE**
>
> Any enclosed space where there is a reasonably foreseeable specified risk of any serious injury associated with it.

> **TOPIC FOCUS**
>
> **'Specified risks'** associated with work in confined spaces are risks of:
>
> - Serious injury arising from fire or explosion.
> - Loss of consciousness arising from an increase in body temperature.
> - Loss of consciousness arising from asphyxiation due to gas, fume, vapour or lack of oxygen.
> - Drowning as a result of an increase in the level of liquids.
> - Inability to reach a respirable environment due to entrapment by free-flowing solid, e.g. flour, grain, sand, sugar, etc.

Typical Confined Spaces in Construction

Typical confined spaces found in construction work include trenches, sewers, manholes, tunnels, excavations, chambers, tanks, pits, cellars and unventilated rooms. Cofferdams and caissons by their enclosed nature may also be included.

The **Confined Spaces Regulations 1997** lay down the legal requirements for work in confined spaces. These Regulations contain the following key duties:

- Avoid entry to confined spaces, e.g. by doing the work from outside.

- If entry to a confined space is unavoidable, follow a safe system of work and put in place adequate emergency arrangements before the work starts.

Due to the nature of the work itself, i.e. where there are risks from machinery, electricity or hazardous substances, other legislation may be involved as discussed in earlier elements.

Hazards and Risks Associated with Confined Spaces

Toxic Atmospheres

Poisonous gas, fumes or vapour can:

Poisonous gases, fumes and vapours can build up in sewers

- Build up in sewers, manholes and pits.

- Enter tanks or vessels from connecting pipes.

- Leak into trenches and pits in contaminated land, e.g. old refuse tips and old gas works.

Certain toxic gases may be present:

- Hydrogen sulphide from sewers or decaying material.

- Carbon monoxide from internal combustion engines (petrol/diesel) or the incomplete combustion of LPG.

- Carbon dioxide:

  - From fermentation processes.

  - Naturally from the rocks/soil.

  - From combustion processes.

- Certain fumes/vapours could be present from chemicals, e.g. ammonia, chlorine or petrol/solvents.

Explosive or Flammable Atmospheres

Certain gases, even in small concentrations, can pose a hazard and produce either a fire or an explosion depending on their explosive range in the atmosphere. Examples include LPG, acetylene, propane, butane, methane, hydrogen sulphide, acetone, toluene, alcohol, white spirit, thinners, solvents and hydrogen.

Confined spaces that need to be entered for cleaning or maintenance may have been used to store hazardous substances, e.g. toxic, flammable or explosive liquid or dust.

Oxygen-Deficient Atmospheres

Oxygen-deficient atmospheres can occur:

- Through displacement (the addition of a gas or vapour to the space displaces the oxygen), for example:

  - Purge gas.

  - Pipe freezing.

  - Gas leaking from elsewhere.

- Through consumption (oxygen in the atmosphere is depleted by a chemical reaction or biological process occurring in the space), e.g. oxidation, rusting, bacterial growth.

- Through welding operations.

- By people working.

- By any process of combustion.

- Where there is a reaction between some soils and the oxygen in the atmosphere.
- Following the action of groundwater on chalk and limestone - this can produce carbon dioxide and displace normal air.

Heat

Hot conditions can lead to a dangerous increase in body temperature and may result in:

- Heat stress, fatigue or exhaustion.
- Dehydration/loss of fluids.
- Loss of consciousness.

Water

Work in confined spaces such as trenches, pits or sewers that contain standing water can lead to gastroenteritis, Weil's disease and hepatitis A or B. There is also a risk of water ingress and being drowned or swept away.

Free-Flowing Solids

Free-flowing solids are substances consisting of solid particles that, because of their small size and numerous quantity, have a flowing or running consistency. Examples include cement, sand, grain and coal dust.

A person can drown or asphyxiate if immersed in a free-flowing solid. The solid acts as a liquid and so presents the same hazards as a liquid. If breathed in, the solid could clog the respiratory tract and enter the lungs, depriving the person of oxygen.

Restricted Space

Where a confined space imposes exceptional constraints as a result of its physical layout. It may be further restricted by the equipment it contains and the tools and PPE used by the person entering.

Liquids or solids can suddenly fill the space, or release gases into it, when disturbed. Free-flowing solids, such as cement, can also partially solidify or 'bridge' in silos, causing blockages which can collapse unexpectedly. If access to the space is through a restricted entrance, e.g. a manhole, escape or rescue in an emergency will be more difficult.

Some of the above conditions may be present in the confined space, some may arise from the work being carried out, or because of ineffective isolation of plant nearby, e.g. leakage from a pipe connected to the confined space.

The enclosure and working space may increase other dangers arising through the work being carried out, such as:

- Machinery being used may present addition hazards, such as:
  - Dust, e.g. from a portable grinder.
  - Electric shock.
- Gas, fume or vapour can arise from welding, or by use of volatile and often flammable solvents or adhesives.

STUDY QUESTIONS

6. (a) What is the definition of a confined space?

    (b) Where are confined spaces found on construction sites?

7. What hazards are associated with confined spaces?

(Suggested Answers are at the end.)

Control Measures for Confined Space Working

IN THIS SECTION...

- Ideally, persons should not enter confined spaces at all, but where they must, precautions must be taken to protect them.

- Risk assessment and planning will determine what precautions are appropriate.

- Precautions will include the use of a permit to work, training of competent personnel and testing the atmosphere for contaminants.

- There must be a safe way in and out of a confined space, usable by persons wearing PPE, including rescue crews.

- Monitoring arrangements and procedures to deal with rescue and any other emergencies must be in place.

Precautions for Safe Entry

Avoidance Where Possible

Persons should not enter a confined space to carry out work unless it is not reasonably practicable to do it any other way. Better planning of work or using a different approach can reduce the need for confined space working, for example:

Avoid entry where possible

- Modify the confined space itself so that entry is not necessary.

- Do the work from outside, e.g. blockages can be cleared in underground chambers by use of remotely operated rotating flail devices, vibrators or air purgers.

- Inspection, sampling and cleaning operations can often be done from outside the space using appropriate equipment and tools.

- Remote cameras can be used for internal inspection of vessels.

A safe system of work is always required to enter, carry out work in, and leave a confined space (other than in an emergency).

Risk Assessment

The **Management of Health and Safety at Work Regulations 1999** require a risk assessment to be carried out to identify the hazards present, assess the risks and determine what precautions to take. The **Confined Spaces Regulations 1997** apply, and the assessment will help to identify the precautions to be planned and included in the safe systems of work required. Appropriate health surveillance must be offered where required.

TOPIC FOCUS

Confined space risk assessment will consider:

- Whether confined space entry can be avoided.
- Work needing to be done, e.g. routine or breakdown.
- Methods of working - tools and equipment to use.
- Entry with or without breathing apparatus.
- Hazard identification in the plant.
- Hazards from neighbouring plant/vessels.
- Suitability of those carrying out the work.
- Steps necessary to make the job safe, i.e. a safe system of work.
- Arrangements for emergencies and rescue facilities.

Planning

Preliminary planning of confined space entry is important to establish whether entry:

- Can be avoided or an alternative method used.
- Is required with or without breathing apparatus.

Proper planning will also help to establish effective lines of authority and communication so that the procedures put in place are clear and free from any misunderstanding or conflict of interest. The precautions necessary for each entry will vary with the nature, size, location, risks involved and number of people working, however, the basis of the safe system of work will depend on the risk assessment carried out.

Permit-to-Work Procedures

An employer must establish a permit system for controlling confined space entry, using competent personnel to ensure formal checks are undertaken, and putting in place a safe system of work before people are allowed to enter the confined space. A permit system is also a means of communication between site management, supervisors and those carrying out the hazardous work.

TOPIC FOCUS

Essential features of a permit-to-work system are:

- Clear identification of who may authorise particular jobs (and any limits to their authority).
- Who is responsible for specifying the necessary precautions (e.g. isolation, gas testing, emergency arrangements, etc.).
- The inclusion of contractors engaged to carry out work.
- Training and instruction in the issue and use of permits.
- Monitoring and auditing to ensure that the system works as intended.

Permit-to-Work Requirements

The safe system of work based on the risk assessment should consider:

- Adequate, competent supervision.

- Experienced and competent workers.

- Proper isolation of plant and equipment.

- Pre-cleaning and correct disposal of debris and sludge.

- Adequate lighting (intrinsically safe) and ventilation.

- Atmospheric testing.

- Provision of specialist, non-sparking tools; breathing apparatus; and rescue harnesses.

- Emergency arrangements/plans.

The **permit to work** incorporates the requirements laid out in the safe system of work, including:

- **Hazard Identification**

  Each permit requires the confined space to be evaluated for its potential hazards and their severity, including surrounding plant and buildings.

- **Hazard Control**

  - Safe entry procedures and practices must be put in place.

  - The equipment or area may need to be withdrawn from service.

  - Warning notices should be displayed and all plant operators notified.

  - The person in charge of the process should be competent and sign the permit.

- **Isolation and/or Locking Off**

  - Plant should be physically disconnected from other items of plant.

  - Mechanical and electrical isolation of equipment is essential if it could otherwise operate, or be operated, inadvertently.

  - Lock-off systems should be used.

  - If gas, fume or vapour could enter the confined space, physical isolation of pipework, etc. needs to be carried out.

  - In all cases, a check should be made to ensure isolation is effective.

- **Permit System**

  A written system for preparing, issuing and implementing permits for entry must be established. A separate and additional 'hot-work permit' is required for operations which could provide a source of ignition, such as riveting, welding, cutting, burning or heating.

- **Employee Information**

  Signs that warn of the hazards and prohibit unauthorised entry must be posted on or near confined spaces.

- **Prevention of Unauthorised Entry**

  A combination of worker training, posting of signs, and utilisation of barriers must be employed as necessary.

> **DEFINITION**
>
> **LOCK-OFF SYSTEM**
>
> This involves securing an electrical isolator (or other energy control handle, lever, pipe-valve, etc.) with a padlock so it cannot be switched on or operated. Each operative will apply their own separate padlock, and a safety sign ('tag') will be put on the locks.

- **Employee Training**

  Personnel directly involved with confined space entry, issuing permits to work, or entry supervision must receive specialised training.

- **Equipment**

  Testing, monitoring and communication equipment and PPE necessary for safe entry and rescue must be provided, maintained and used.

- **Rescue**

  Procedures, plans and equipment necessary for rescue must be in place. An employer must have a trained, in-plant rescue team or an arrangement with an outside team to respond upon request. Rescuers must have the same entry training as employees working in confined spaces. In addition to specific rescue training, they should attend a simulated rescue operation at least once every 12 months. If an outside rescue organisation is used then they must be made aware of the specific hazards they may encounter when responding to an emergency.

- **Protection from External Hazards**

  Steps must be taken to protect the entrant(s) from external dangers, e.g. placing vehicle barriers when the operation is adjacent to traffic areas.

- **Duty to Other Employers**

  Contractors hired to perform confined space entry must be provided with all relevant health and safety information they need to protect their employees' safety.

Procedures, plans and rescue equipment must be in place

TOPIC FOCUS

A **sentry** (someone keeping watch) must be present at all times during entry operations, maintain continuous contact with those inside, and order them to evacuate the confined space if one of the following occurs:

- A condition is observed that is not allowed in the entry permit (e.g. the development of a hazardous atmosphere caused by changing conditions or as a result of the work activity in the confined space).

- The sentry detects behavioural changes in the entrants that could be the result of harmful exposure.

- The sentry detects a situation outside the space which could endanger those inside.

- The sentry is monitoring more than one permit space and must focus attention on the rescue of the entrants from one of those spaces.

- The sentry must leave the workstation for any reason.

Training and Use of Competent Persons

All persons involved with supervising or carrying out confined space work must have adequate training, which should be repeated regularly.

The training should involve the permit to work, respiratory equipment, gas-testing equipment, rescue procedures, first-aid treatment including artificial respiration, evacuation and emergency procedures, fire-fighting, and communication procedures. No person should be allowed to enter a confined space unless they are trained and competent to do so and records should be kept of all types of training carried out.

Atmospheric Testing

It is necessary to check that the atmosphere within a confined space contains sufficient oxygen, is free from both toxic and flammable vapours and is fit to breathe. Testing should be carried out by a competent person using a suitable gas detector which is correctly calibrated. Breathing apparatus should be worn to enter a confined space for testing. Gas testing involves testing the atmosphere at all locations, drain points, instrument bridles, orifices, and at a high and low level, as some denser gases do lie in low positions, e.g. hydrogen sulphide.

Where the risk assessment indicates that conditions may change, or as a further precaution, continuous monitoring of the air may be necessary.

TOPIC FOCUS

Atmospheric testing should detect:

- A flammable gas, vapour or mist in excess of 10% of its Lower Explosive Limit (LEL).

- An atmospheric oxygen concentration below 19.5% or above 22%.

- An atmospheric concentration of any substance for which a Workplace Exposure Limit (WEL) is published in EH40 by the HSE and which could result in employee exposure in excess of the permissible limits.

- An airborne combustible dust at a concentration that obscures vision at a distance of 5 feet (1.52m) or less.

- Any atmospheric condition recognised as immediately dangerous to life or health.

Flammable

Explosive

Testing the atmosphere in confined spaces is essential. It is particularly important to be aware of any flammable or explosive substance that may be/have been present

Means of Access

Safe access/egress must be provided. No one may enter or remain in a confined space unless the following requirements are met:

- They are wearing approved breathing apparatus if dangerous fumes are present or in an oxygen-deficient atmosphere. The minimum space required in this case is 575mm. Smaller openings must be assessed for safe access and egress.

- Depending on the work being done, a number of access and egress points may be required.

- They have been authorised to enter by a responsible person, i.e. through a permit-to-work system.

- Where practicable, they are wearing a belt or harness with a rope securely attached.

- A person keeping watch (sentry) outside and capable of pulling them out is holding the free end of the rope.

A person may enter or work in a confined space without breathing apparatus, provided that:

- Effective steps have been taken to avoid ingress of dangerous fumes.

- Sludge or other deposits liable to give off dangerous fumes have been removed/cleaned.

- The space contains no other material liable to give off such fumes.

- The space has been adequately ventilated and tested for toxic, flammable and explosive gases/fumes.

- There is a supply of breathable air.

- The space has been certified by a responsible person as being safe for entry for a specified period without breathing apparatus.

Personal Protective Equipment

Appropriate PPE needs to be worn which:

- is fit for purpose;

- fits correctly; and

- is compatible with any other equipment worn.

In confined spaces this might include hard hats, coveralls, boots, Wellingtons, breathing apparatus sets, gloves and/or safety spectacles, and radios.

Monitoring Arrangements

Monitoring should be carried out by competent, trained personnel with individual detector tubes which are available for specific substances.

Gas monitoring can be carried out using appropriately calibrated portable gas detection equipment. The gas meters can be used to detect individual gases or to sample a range of gases.

Personal monitors may also be used by individuals working in confined spaces.

> ### TOPIC FOCUS
>
> **Monitoring may be required:**
>
> - Before the first entry.
> - At the start of each shift.
> - At each entry.
> - After each break.
> - At a specified time limit, as set out in the permit.
> - Continuously.

Emergency Arrangements

The **Confined Spaces Regulations 1997** require arrangements for emergency rescue to be in place when working in a confined space. The rescue plan must be communicated to all personnel involved before commencing work:

- Arrangements for raising the alarm and carrying out rescue operations must be in place.

- Rescue team members and equipment should be readily available for emergencies.

- Team members must be:

    - Properly trained in rescue techniques and use of all equipment.

    - Physically fit enough to carry out their task.

- Rescuers must be aware of and protected against the cause of the emergency.

Rescue equipment should consist of:

- Breathing apparatus sets.

- Rescue and resuscitation equipment - harnesses, lifting tripods and winch, stretchers, first-aid equipment.

- Fire-fighting equipment.

- Means of communication and summoning help:

    - A tug-rope is commonly used when personnel are not visible.

    - If radio is to be used it must immediately be tested on entry.

- Lifelines.

- Oxygen - for resuscitation, not for 'sweetening' (increasing the oxygen content in the atmosphere).

Rescue teams must not enter without breathing apparatus. They must be thoroughly trained in rescue techniques, first aid and use of resuscitators.

An essential part of such a rescue plan might include:

- Shutting down adjacent plant before attempting emergency rescue.

- Communication with local emergency services (e.g. the fire service), remembering to pass on information about the particular dangers in the confined space.

STUDY QUESTIONS

8. What precautions are necessary for safe entry into a confined space?

9. What factors might be involved in a safe system of work for confined space entry?

(Suggested Answers are at the end.)

Summary

This element has introduced you to the hazards and precautions required to ensure safe work at or in excavations and confined spaces.

In particular, this element has:

- Described the hazards and risks associated with working in excavations, including buried services; falls into excavations; collapse of sides; collapse of adjacent structures; water ingress; use of cofferdams and caissons; contaminated ground; toxic and asphyxiating atmospheres; mechanical hazards; and power lines.

- Described measures that will adequately control risks associated with excavations, such as marking of buried services; safe digging methods; methods of supporting excavations; means of access and crossing points; barriers, lighting and signs; safe storage of spoil and removal of water; safe routing and positioning of vehicles; and appropriate PPE.

- Described particular requirements for ensuring safety when working in contaminated ground, and inspection requirements for excavations and excavation supports.

- Defined what a confined space is and identified typical confined spaces found in construction activities.

- Described the hazards and risks associated with confined space working, including toxic, flammable and explosive atmospheres; heat, water and free-flowing solids; and work in restricted space.

- Described the appropriate measures to control the risks associated with work in confined spaces, including avoidance where possible; risk assessment and planning; permit-to-work procedures; training and competence; atmospheric testing and monitoring; means of access; appropriate PPE; and monitoring and emergency arrangements.

Exam Skills

Approaching the Question

Think now about the steps you would take to answer the question:

Step 1. Read the question carefully. Note that this question asks for control measures to reduce risks, so the examiner is not looking for risks. It's a good question though, because you need to understand the risks associated with excavation (collapse of sides, falls of persons, material or vehicles, contact with buried services, build-up of fume, ingress of water, etc.) to be able to outline control measures. Just make sure you don't waste time writing about the risks in your answer!

Step 2. Now highlight the key words. In this case they might look like this:

Outline the **control measures** needed to **reduce** the **risks** during **excavation work** on a construction site. **(8)**

Step 3. Next, consider the marks and time available. In this question there are eight marks so it is expected that around eight or nine different pieces of information should be provided. The question should take around eight minutes in total. Try not to overrun that time. Statistically most marks are picked up in the first five to six minutes of attempting a question. It's better to pick up more marks on other questions than run over time perfecting just one. Remember, if you do not attempt a question because you ran out of time, you will get no marks for it!

Step 4. Read the question again to make sure you understand the question. (Re-read your notes if you need to.)

Step 5. The next stage is to develop a plan - there are various ways to do this. You need to be thinking about control measures in excavation work in enough detail to produce an outline (cover the most important features in more depth than just listing them).

Your answer must be based on the key words you have highlighted. So, in this case, we need to outline control measures to reduce risks in excavation work.

Now have a go at the question. Draw up an answer plan, and then use it as the basis to write out an answer as you would in the exam.

Remember, you can always contact your tutor if you have any queries or need any further guidance on how to answer this question.

HINTS AND TIPS

Read the question with care - you have been asked to supply control measures; and take a broad view - do not focus simply on one factor.

Suggested Answer Outline

Control Measures
• Detection of underground services (plans, surveys, detectors, etc.) - use hand digging around these areas.
• Support for sides, shoring, trench boxes, battering.
• Store material and spoil heap away from excavation
• Guardrails and safe access and egress.
• Stop blocks for vehicles.
• Underpin/support adjacent buildings to prevent collapse.
• Pump out water, test ground conditions.
• Testing atmosphere inside excavation.
• Means of ventilating the excavation.
• Adequate lighting.
• Inspections by competent person.
• PPE to protect against any biological or chemical contaminants.

Example of How the Question Could be Answered

The control measures associated with excavation work on construction sites include the following:

- *Conducting surveys or using maps of underground services to locate electric cables, gas mains or water mains to allow hand digging operations and prevent breaking into the service pipes/cables.*

- *It may be necessary to support the sides of the excavation by shoring to the sides of the excavation to prevent collapse, or by using a trench box.*

- *Barriers or guardrails should be used around the excavation, possibly with lighting points on the railings to ensure people can see the excavation and are prevented from falling in.*

- *Stop blocks should be used to prevent vehicles reversing into the excavation.*

- *Materials should not be stored near to the excavation, including the spoil from the excavation, to prevent material falling back into the excavation.*

- *If the excavation is adjacent to a building, a competent person must ensure the structure is underpinned or supported to ensure it does not collapse due to its foundations being disturbed.*

- *Ground conditions can be tested to ensure no underground water systems will be broken into and that the excavation will not become filled with rain or flood water; provision must be on hand to pump water out from the excavation.*

- *The atmosphere within the excavation should be checked by using gas detectors to ensure that there are no noxious gases, and to ensure an adequate supply of oxygen.*

- *PPE should be provided to protect workers from possible biological materials or any chemical contamination present due to the land being contaminated.*

- *In order to ensure ongoing safety the excavation should be inspected before the start of every shift, after any fall of earth and after any event likely to affect stability.*

Reasons for Poor Marks Achieved by Candidates in Exam

- Providing a list without sufficiently outlining the control measures.

- Failing to read the question and spending time outlining risks.

- Taking too narrow a view and writing several sentences on how to shore the excavation. This shows you have a great deal of knowledge but have not answered the question set.

Demolition and Deconstruction - Hazards and Risk Control

Learning Outcomes

Once you've read this element, you'll understand how to:

1 Identify the main hazards of demolition and deconstruction work.

2 Outline the control measures for demolition and deconstruction work.

3 Identify the purpose and scope of a pre-demolition/refurbishment survey.

4 Outline the main control measures that a demolition/refurbishment method statement should include.

Contents

Demolition and Deconstruction Hazards and Risks

IN THIS SECTION...

- Demolition and deconstruction methods include piecemeal demolition, deliberate controlled collapse, pre-weakening, progressive demolition and wire rope pulling. It is important to select the appropriate method.

- There are many hazards associated with demolition and deconstruction work, including the premature collapse of buildings; falls and falling materials; and plant and other vehicles overturning.

- Many demolition tasks involve manual handling and expose workers to dust, fumes, noise and vibration.

- Other hazards include:

  - The existence of services, often buried, such as gas, water, electricity, etc.

  - The presence of hazardous substances.

  - Dilapidation.

Introduction to Planning and Managing Demolition Projects

Decommissioning

Where structures, plant or services are to be decommissioned before demolition or deconstruction, planning should be carried out in order to bring the structure (plant or services) from fully operational to a 'dead' state, with all operational systems discharged. The decommissioning action plan is the responsibility of the client and should set target dates for the programmed shutdown.

Decommissioning activities will include:

- Isolation, earthing, spiking and cutting of (high, medium and low voltage) electrical cables.

- Disconnection of supplies crossing demolition areas.

- Disconnection or separation of DC battery systems.

- Removal of bulk process or other chemicals.

- Draining and purging of process chemicals from pipelines and systems.

- Draining, purging and venting of storage vessels.

- Draining all substantial heads of water.

- Isolation of water and gas services and supplies.

- Controlled release of any stored energy in systems or processes.

- Removal or elimination of all 'substance hazards'.

- Removal of asbestos.

Clearing a site after demolition work

Planning Demolition Work

An assessment and survey of the site should be carried out (see later) at the planning stage to identify:

- The extent of decommissioning required (see above).

- Details of isolation or removal of services and details of temporary supplies.

- Details and history of the structure.

- Isolation and protection of adjacent structures.
- Hazardous materials.
- Previous use of the site.

Managing the Demolition Project

A detailed programme and timetable of events should be produced that covers:

- The scheme, sequence and method(s) of demolition to be used.
- The plant and equipment required and its usage.
- Traffic management on and off site.
- Management of 'arisings' (debris, waste, materials, etc.).
- Contingency arrangements to cover 'mishaps'.
- Agreed start and completion dates.
- Limitations such as night working, seasonal issues, tides, etc.

Environmental Management

Issues of wastes will be looked at later, but an assessment should be made at the planning stage to determine environmental issues, such as:

- Control of noise at the site boundaries.
- Control of all dust emissions.
- Waste management (see later).
- Minimisation of materials haulage.
- Bunding arrangements for fuel and oil storage and dispensing facilities.
- Wheel washing and road cleaning arrangements.
- Skip or truck sheeting.
- Arrangements for dealing with hazardous materials.
- Anticipated values of air over-pressure and ground vibration.
- Areas of conservation.
- Minimising landfill.
- Carbon consumption/agendas.

Landfill needs to be minimised

Definitions

Piecemeal Demolition

> **DEFINITIONS**
>
> **DEMOLITION**
>
> The deliberate pulling down, destruction or taking apart of a structure, or a substantial part of a structure (usually not for re-use).
>
> **DECONSTRUCTION**
>
> Often also referred to as 'dismantling', is the taking down of all, or a substantial part, of a structure (often for re-use).

The piecemeal method of demolition uses hand-held tools or machines to gradually reduce the building to ground level. It is sometimes a preliminary to other methods. It can be begun or completed by the use of machines.

Techniques available for piecemeal demolition include:

- Pneumatic hammer.
- Hydraulic (pecker) or electric hammer.
- Tooth grapples.
- Ball and chain.
- Non-explosive blasting, using a liquid CO_2 cartridge which expands to a gas creating high pressure.
- Hydraulic bursters - these can be inserted into concrete to create bursting forces.
- Thermic lance method of melting concrete - the presence of reinforcement aids the process.
- Flame jet piercing - a melting process using a flame jet by burning kerosene in oxygen.
- Water jet - cement grouts can be cut with high water pressure.

For example, with a tall stack in an area where there are occupied buildings nearby, the task may be begun by slow methodical hand dismantling until the structure has been reduced to about 10m before heavy dismantling plant can be used.

Deliberate Controlled Collapse

This is carried out using explosives or pre-weakening of the structure followed by remote mechanical demolition or pulling using a wire rope. The use of explosives requires a competent and fully qualified explosives engineer, and work must be properly documented and notified to various bodies (e.g. gas, electricity, rail, police, airports, local authorities). The process must be properly carried out using appropriate techniques regulated by the construction industry.

Selection of the Appropriate Method

Whether demolishing or deconstructing a building or structure, it is vital that the pre-demolition survey (more detail later) identifies the correct method to be used.

Pre-Weakening

This is the removal of key structural members to cause complete collapse of the whole or part of the building or structure. Where controlled collapse demolition is adopted, the key structural members to be removed should be clearly indicated, together with the sequence of removal, in the method statement.

Certain problems can arise during this procedure, for example:

- The structure may collapse more than expected.

- Only partial collapse may occur leaving a dangerous structure to deal with.

- Considerable debris may be projected long distances, hitting unprotected people.

- The condition/state of the debris created may make it difficult to remove.

Progressive Demolition

This is the controlled removal of sections of the structure, while retaining the stability of the remainder and avoiding collapse of the whole or part of the building to be demolished. Progressive demolition should be considered for the majority of sites and is particularly useful in confined and restricted areas.

Overturning by Wire Rope Pulling

This may also be used, except on brick or masonry buildings over 21m. The wire ropes are attached to winches or vehicles. The ropes should be attached prior to pre-weakening taking place and must be fit for purpose and not less than 38mm in circumference.

Equipment to be Used

Progressive demolition: remove part of a structure, leave the rest intact

Hand Tools

Demolition using hand tools can be efficient, requiring far less set-up time. Workers are required to work along the weaknesses of the section to be demolished, cutting along the mortar joints rather than through brick.

Where masonry/brickwork is involved, lifting operations may be necessary when cutting large structural members, and the debris needs to be disposed of using chutes or hoppers. Partial removal of floors may assist in the removal of debris, taking care to ensure the structural stability is maintained, and guardrails and toeboards are fitted for safety. Debris must be frequently disposed of and any debris that contains asbestos, radioactive materials or chemical contamination must be treated with all the necessary precautions. Services that may be needed must be identified and protected; and temporarily disconnected and reconnected by a competent person if required.

Certain precautions need to be in place:

- Access scaffolding should be progressively removed, ensuring no scaffold tubes project more than 3m above the demolition work.

- Scaffold towers, if in use, should not project above the work by more than one lift.

- The working platform should not be more than 6m above the highest row of ties (if in use).

- For roof work, crawling boards may be required which should span the purlins (horizontal timbers resting on the principal rafters, which support the common or subsidiary rafters or boards on which the roof is laid).

- Harnesses and/or edge protection are needed if recovery of materials is involved, e.g. slates, tiles.

- Strict observation of access/egress should be followed during the demolition phase.

- A safe place of work must be provided, e.g. not the top of an unprotected wall.

In the case of steel-framed buildings:

- All non-structural material should normally be removed before any dismantling takes place.

- Main structural members should be supported while the ends are either cut or unbolted. Care is needed as the members might spring away from the structure. The area below should be protected and sealed off if falling material is allowed to drop. On completion, members and/or trusses should be lowered carefully to the ground. The cutting or unbolting operation should be carried out from appropriate work platforms, with operatives wearing appropriate safety harnesses.

Use of Machines

Piecemeal demolition can also take place using machines. Certain precautions are needed:

- Where two structures are attached, they should be separated by a minimum of 1m prior to using a machine.

- Only the machine operator and banksman should be allowed within the restricted area around the demolition site.

- The machine should be adequately protected by being of robust and suitable construction and containing shatterproof material and appropriate strong mesh steel bars/grille.

- The operators must be protected by respirators when asbestos dust or other health hazards may be present.

Machine demolition techniques include:

- **Demolition ball** - 'wrecking ball' - a pear-shaped ball of around one tonne, suspended from a crane, fitted with an anti-spin device, i.e. a dragline. The ball is allowed to fall vertically onto the structure or by swinging it forward or sideways into the structure. Buildings should be less than 30m high before this technique is used.

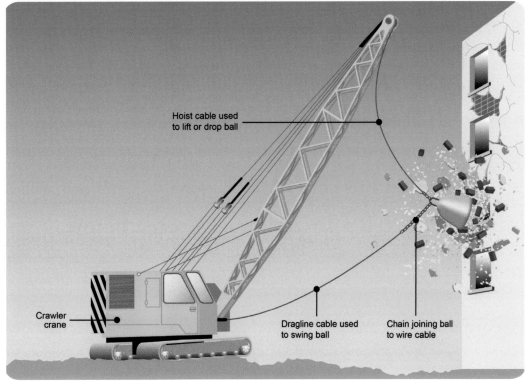

Demolition ball

- **Impact hammers**, which have a heavy duty pick which is incorporated within a track- or wheel-mounted chassis, with an articulated boom. The pick is vibrated using either pneumatic or hydraulic power, and is usually used to remove material from the top of columns or walls (usually limited to 600mm thickness) after removing any steel reinforcement which may be in place.

- A **360° excavator** with multi-functional attachments - these machines have a reach of between 15m and 35m plus the length of the fitted attachment.

A 360° excavator with protective cage

- **Remote control** demolition of a high level concrete floor - achieved using radio control from a safe distance away.

- Use of a **hydraulic pusher arm**, which is normally mounted on a tracked or wheel chassis and has a toothed plate or hook. The pusher arm pushes into the structure that is being demolished. The equipment does, however, have a limited reach.

- Use of **shears** in cutting steel structures.

Chimneys, pre-stressed concrete, brick and masonry viaducts require more specific precautions to remove the structures in smaller sections, not only to contain the materials during a fall but to retain the fall within a tightly controlled area, such as an exclusion zone (due to the height and length of such structures).

Hazards Relating to Demolition and Deconstruction

Demolition is one of the most dangerous activities undertaken in the construction industry. It involves a number of legislative requirements including the **Health and Safety at Work, etc. Act 1974**, and the **Environmental Protection Act 1990**. The **Construction (Design and Management) Regulations 2015** apply to all demolition and dismantling work, however, a project is only notifiable to HSE if it will last longer than 30 days or involve more than 500 person-days of work.

Special requirements need to be applied where appropriate, e.g. demolition may be subject to the **Control of Major Accident Hazards (COMAH) Regulations 2015** or the **Work at Height Regulations 2005**.

Premature Collapse

This is a main cause of accidents in demolition, a common factor being failure to plan the operation at an early stage. Lack of planning can lead to workers devising their own means of access and methods of work, both of which are inherently dangerous. In addition, other works which fall outside the scope of demolition can also threaten the stability of structures.

Buildings and structures can become unsafe during the demolition process and temporary scaffolding/support may be required, e.g. for heavy overhanging cornices. All temporary structures must support the loads required to ensure overloading does not occur. Similarly, structures within buildings may become unsafe, e.g. staircases.

The removal of certain parts of the building or structure during demolition can result in other parts becoming unsafe for persons in, on or near the building being demolished.

Falls and Falling Materials

Falls are often due to poor access and egress, unsuitable pedestrian and traffic routes, and unsafe structures. Work at height is also a major contributor.

Causes of falling materials include:

- Deliberate dropping.

- Materials falling or being ejected from the apertures.

- Inadvertent falls of dislodged material.

- Materials acting as a projectile.

- Falling loads or equipment.

- Lifting loads over areas of public access.

- Unplanned falls of material, including accidental falls of tools and materials.

Falling materials may also be a risk to operators of vehicles and plant being used on site.

> **DEFINITION**
>
> **DELIBERATE DROPPING**
>
> In demolition, deliberate dropping refers to deliberate pulling down or knocking over of a structure (e.g. knocking a wall over with a digger bucket).

Plant, Vehicles and Other Equipment Overturning

Transport-related accidents in demolition work are due to:

- Poor, unstable and uneven ground.

- Poor control of vehicle movements.

- Use of unsuitable plant or vehicles.

- Unauthorised use of vehicles and plant by untrained operators.

- The potential proximity of private or road-going trade vehicles to heavy demolition plant.

- Vehicles left in unplanned areas, causing obstructions and obscuring sight lines.

Manual Handling

Damaging work postures are likely in demolition work, involving stooping, kneeling and working in postures with the arms raised above shoulder height. Because of this, the industry has a high incidence of Musculoskeletal Disorders (MSDs) affecting the lower back, knees, shoulders and neck. In each case, long-term disability is common.

Many of the manual handling risks can be reduced through better planning, control and management. At the practical level this will involve better co-operation between designers and contractors.

A hierarchy of control measures includes:

- Mechanical means, such as hoists and chutes rather than manual methods.

- Lifting and handling aids such as forklifts, trolleys or barrows rather than carrying.

- Correct choice of job-specific equipment which is well maintained.

- The use of lighter bags and loads.

- The avoidance of repetitive handling and awkward movements.

In Element 10 we discussed **inclined hoists** - these and other scaffold hoists are good examples of equipment which can be used to avoid excessive manual handling in demolition work.

CASE STUDY

A Manual Handling Case Study in Demolition Work

A multi-storey office block was being partly demolished and the concrete skeleton was to be incorporated into the new office block. Labourers used wheelbarrows to move waste materials and tip them down an open lift shaft. The HSE served a Prohibition Notice on the unguarded open lift shaft edge and an Improvement Notice for the manual handling tasks.

The site management guarded the lift shaft and installed a conveyor system to take materials to the shaft for disposal.

This solution removed the risk of:

- falling down the shaft;

- being struck by falling debris;

- MSDs;

while increasing productivity.

Dust and Fume

Dust is a common hazard during demolition. The dust may be irritant, toxic, corrosive, cause eye injuries or carry fungal or bacterial matter:

- Dusts are produced mechanically by grinding or similar actions and are divided into two categories dependent on the size (inhalable and respirable - discussed earlier).

- Those dusts causing damaging health effects are below 10µ in diameter.

- In particular, the respirable dusts of below 7µ are the most damaging to the lungs and are likely to cause chronic respiratory disease.

The dusts generated during active demolition work often contain silica compounds, waste cement, plaster products and possibly Asbestos-Containing Materials (ACMs).

Vehicle movements on dry soil surfaces may also create dusts. Such dust becomes a visible nuisance to local residents. It can prevent people from opening windows or using their gardens. Regular damping of traffic routes can reduce the risk.

Fumes are generated by heating and melting metals from demolition methods that involve welding and burning in the dismantling of steelwork. Techniques generating fumes include the use of plasma arc torches, arc cutters and oxy-acetylene torches.

Noise and Vibration

Demolition is inherently noisy, and uses equipment that can create vibration. As well as causing hearing loss and vibration-related injuries to workers, noise and vibration can be a nuisance to the surrounding community. In such cases, the local authority environmental health department can intervene to reduce it. They should be informed of the progress of the demolition and the dates and times of any particularly disruptive activities and try to address complaints before any formal action is taken.

Existence of Services

Before any demolition work can commence, all services must be identified and the corresponding disconnections built into the demolition plan (see later).

All underground and overhead services (electricity, gas, water, etc.) must be located, as well as services within buildings (intrusion into unpurged pipework for some services may carry risks of explosion):

- Service providers (electricity suppliers, lighting companies, etc.) should be contacted to obtain accurate plans of supplies. Other tell-tale signs, such as junction boxes, should be observed. Cables should be avoided at the planning stage.

- Similarly, water, gas and telecommunications companies should be able to provide plans of their respective buried services.

- Demolition supervisors must be supplied with this information, and should in turn ensure it is passed on to the employee or contractor carrying out the work. Information given by the owner of the site should only be taken as a guide.

- Cable locating devices, in conjunction with cable plans, can subsequently be used to trace the position of cables (but, even where cables carry live current, the detector may still be confused by other close services).

- Suitable pipe locating devices should also be used, but care should be exercised as these devices will not detect plastic pipes.

- Operators of detection devices must be:

  - Fully conversant with the instruments.

  - Trained in their use.

Hazardous Substances

Hazardous substances can often be found in buildings which are to be demolished or deconstructed. The ground may also carry risks from contamination by hazardous substances. The presence of dangerous substances such as asbestos, polychlorinated biphenyls (PCBs), lead paint, flammable liquids, any unidentified materials, drums, packages, radioactive materials and residual material in pipelines or tanks can pose serious hazards to workers. There can be serious health hazards associated with these, e.g. toxic, carcinogenic, pathogenic (causing disease), sensitising, corrosive or irritant, or radioactive.

Drums of hazardous substances and contaminated ground are often found on demolition sites

The method statement and demolition plan should outline:

- How the presence of hazardous substances is to be identified.
- The means of disposing of such substances.
- The requirements for any protective equipment.

Where existing plant has contained flammable materials, special precautions must be observed to avoid fire and explosion. It may be necessary to engage the services of a competent analyst to identify any residues, carry out monitoring and assess whether any pockets of contamination remain.

Where it is necessary to enter plant for cleaning or to carry out an assessment, breathing apparatus may be required and a permit-to-work system used.

Dilapidation

Some buildings and structures, by the nature of their age and periods left empty and unused, will be in a state of dilapidation (i.e. a state of disrepair or ruin). Dilapidation can add to the hazards of the demolition work by leaving services exposed or hidden by debris and rubbish. Such debris also hides holes and voids, adding danger to the already long list of hazards. The effects of dilapidation will be looked at in the pre-demolition survey (see later).

STUDY QUESTIONS

1. In addition to piecemeal demolition and deliberately controlled collapse, identify three other methods of demolition.

2. Identify three common causes of transport-related accidents in demolition work.

3. With regard to hazardous substances, what three significant areas should be outlined in the method statement and demolition plan?

(Suggested Answers are at the end.)

Control Measures

IN THIS SECTION...

- The hazards associated with demolition work must be controlled to prevent harm to workers. Such control measures include:
    - Avoiding premature collapse; protection from falls and falling materials; safe siting of plant, vehicles and other demolition equipment.
    - Measures to control exposure to dust, fumes, noise and vibration, and protection of the environment.
    - Having a well trained, competent workforce.
    - Carrying out pre-demolition investigations and surveys.
- Other factors to take into account when considering control measures include:
    - The condition, type of structure and method of construction of buildings about to be demolished.
    - The presence of cellars and identification of services that could be discovered during the work, together with the presence of hazardous substances.
    - Waste management and access and egress to and from the site.
    - The proximity and condition of nearby structures and roadways, etc.

General Control Measures for Demolition Work

While it is the direct duty of the contractor to control the hazards on site, designers should give consideration to measures which remove the hazards altogether or reduce the likelihood of them occurring.

Avoidance of Premature Collapse

Designers should consider structural stability and include relevant information with their designs in order to avoid premature collapse of structures and maintain structural stability throughout demolition work.

- **Temporary structural supports** should be used in accordance with the appropriate standards and should be suitable for the work required. These include temporary structural support for shoring, propping and facade retention, including standard scaffolding support systems and screw-jack propping (commonly called 'acros'); shoring systems; facade retention systems; and buttresses.

    Temporary structural supports should be:

    - In position before disturbance or removal of the existing supports.
    - Founded on secure and effective footings.
    - Adequately laced and braced.
    - If appropriate, capable of resisting dynamic loadings.
    - Checked both prior to and during demolition for effectiveness, including for the effects of vibration.

    Where scaffolding is required, it should normally be an independent tied scaffold. It must conform to the usual construction standards and, as work progresses, be removed in a progressive and planned manner to ensure its integrity.

> **DEFINITION**
>
> **BUTTRESS**
>
> An inclined tube assembly anchored at one end (on the ground or other suitable point) and fitted to the scaffold at the other, to widen the structure base and increase stability.

Any shoring and propping should be placed in position at the appropriate time and designed not to interfere with subsequent work. Shoring should be checked for effectiveness as the demolition proceeds and should never be loaded in excess of the design limits.

- **Facade retention systems** should be installed as demolition progresses, to ensure that stability is always maintained. Structural engineering advice should be obtained for the design of temporary facade supports, taking account of the stability of the facade and of the shorings as the demolition proceeds.

    - The method of fixing the facade retention system should not damage the facade.

    - Account should be taken of movement of the facade that could occur before, during or after demolition operations.

    - All fixings should be regularly checked throughout the period of the contract.

    - Demolition work should be carried out so as not to damage the facade.

    - Elements to be removed which are built into the facade structure should be carefully cut away.

    - The temporary support system should not be weakened by removal of components until the facade in that location is fully supported either by the new structure or by an alternative temporary structure.

Protection from Falls and Falling Material

Exclusion zones (see later) should be applied to all demolition operations, keeping people away from areas of deliberate dropping, the potential for falling materials, or inadvertent falls of dislodged material. A safe place of work and safe access in the workplace are to be maintained at all times, including access by roads, gangways, passageways, passenger hoists, staircases and ladders. Scaffolds, permanent access stairs or catwalks (narrow bridges) used by demolition personnel should be maintained in a safe condition, for as long as possible.

TOPIC FOCUS

To **prevent falls**, safe access routes and working places should include:

- Removal of obstructions, including trip hazards such as debris, materials and tools.

- No nails projecting from timbers (remove or hammer flat to remove trip hazard).

- Walkways and working platforms that are not overloaded.

- Pedestrian routes that are segregated from routes used by vehicles and plant.

- Erection of adequate barriers or other edge protection, to prevent falls from the open edges of roofs, buildings, gangways, staircases and lift shafts.

- Holes and openings that are securely fenced off or provided with adequate, fixed, clearly marked and properly secured covers.

- Adequate artificial lighting when work is carried out in the absence of sufficient natural light.

When work at an open edge is the only option (e.g. not using remote machine methods) a safe, independent working platform, or anchored fall restraint or fall arrest equipment, should be used.

Persons can be protected from **falling materials** by:

- Walkways made of fully sheeted scaffolding with debris netting or reinforced plastic sheeting.

- Use of other temporary structures (e.g. tunnels, protective gantries, fans and crash decks).

Such structures should be designed to take account of the loads (including wind loads) imposed when sheeting and/or netting material are used.

Further protective measures:

Protecting the public

- Fire exit routes must not be obstructed, and possibly be protected with fire-retardant sheeting and netting.

- Where appropriate, windows should be boarded up to prevent materials falling or being ejected from the apertures.

- PPE (hard hats, boots, specialised clothing, goggles, etc.) is to be worn at all times.

- Avoid lifting loads over areas of public access (if unavoidable, temporary closure of the access and the provision of a safe alternative is required).

- Restrict or prohibit access beneath the demolition work at times when safety cannot be guaranteed.

- Remove occupants from a building undergoing major demolition work. If part is to remain occupied, a safe system of work is required.

The locations of temporary supports must be identified before demolition starts, and this should be clearly shown in the demolition method statement (see later). No part of the structure should be so overloaded that any part of it becomes unstable during demolition work.

Protective fans, crash decks and gantries are temporary structures that should be of adequate strength to safely prevent premature collapse, including accidental falls of tools and materials. If necessary, they should be waterproofed to protect persons below from drips and should not be used for storage or access.

Where there is a risk of falling materials striking vehicle and plant operators, e.g. excavators used in demolition work, vehicles should be fitted with Falling-Object Protective Structures (FOPS).

Siting and Use of Plant, Vehicles and Other Equipment

Various items of plant and equipment may be used in demolition. The following measures can be taken to avoid creating additional hazards:

- An inventory of the plant and equipment intended to be used on site should be kept, along with any appropriate test certificates.

- Appropriate, up-to-date training certificates for vehicle and plant operators should be kept.

- The plant and machinery should be properly sited within a compound and isolated at the end of each shift.

- Sufficient and suitable parking areas should be provided for all vehicles using the site - including employees' and visitors' private vehicles.

- Vehicles should not be left in unplanned areas, otherwise the safe operation of the site may be jeopardised - for example, by obscuring sight lines.

- Safe areas for loading and unloading skips and collection vehicles should be provided.

- Prevent parking of vehicles near any scaffolding, stacks of materials or compressed gases, or storage compounds containing toxic or flammable substances, especially transport carrying LPG.

- Where the risk of vehicles overturning is significant, e.g. dumpers used on sloping ground, vehicles should be fitted with Roll-Over Protective Structures (ROPS).

Dust and Fume

Protection against dust and fume from demolition activities may include the following:

- A **COSHH** risk assessment.

- Maintaining a high standard of housekeeping, regularly cleaning and sweeping the site roads.

- Using techniques that produce low levels of dust; damping down.

- Designating vehicle routes to and from the site to limit the problem.

- Maintaining plant and equipment to a high standard, so that it is less likely to break down and will emit fewer pollutants, and to prevent spillage of oil and fuel to the environment.

- Using wheel-washing facilities at exits onto public traffic routes.

- Using water sprays as a dust suppressant, taking care as to the potential consequences of environmental contaminants in the resultant run-off, and the proximity to electrical services.

- Using air movers or LEV where possible.

- Using covered wagons and skips and restricting the speed of vehicles.

- Using PPE as a last line of defence.

- Where asbestos might be present, take samples to verify its presence and carry out the necessary precautions, actions and required notification.

- Put precautions in place if lead is found to be present.

Noise and Vibration

Precautions are required to avoid noise and vibration and provide protection from them for people working in or living near demolition sites:

Workers need to be protected from noise

- A noise assessment may be required, in accordance with the **Control of Noise at Work Regulations 2005**, which will identify all potentially noise-sensitive areas on the site.

- Background noise should be monitored prior to work beginning at any noise-sensitive areas.

- Actions should be taken to reduce noise levels (in the demolition method statement).

- The following should be used:

  - Plant and equipment with low operating noise levels.

  - Mains-generated electricity in preference to diesel generators.

  - Solid-panelled fencing around the site instead of wire fences.

- Deliveries should be restricted to daytime working hours, i.e. not early morning or late at night.

- Project contact details should be prominently displayed in residential areas, to allow any nuisance issues to be addressed quickly.

- Warning notices should be posted to warn people to keep away from the danger area.

- Appropriate silencing/soundproofing should be fitted to all machinery and plant on site.

- Personnel working within the noise zone should be provided with, and use, adequate hearing protection.

- Continuous vibration levels must not exceed 10mm/sec at any nearby buildings (e.g. tower blocks, office blocks, steel framed factories, warehouse units and structures related to transport, power and water services) and 2.5mm/sec for nearby houses (including houses converted into flats), listed buildings or ancient monuments.

Protection of the Environment

Contaminants from construction work must be closely controlled to prevent damaging releases into the environment (onto land, or into air or water) during both demolition and transportation for disposal.

Environmental information relating to any underground tanks or potential chemical/biological hazards or the presence of contaminated land, along with the building's former use, should be supplied to the contractor prior to demolition. Environmentally damaging releases can occur from:

- Waste disposal sites; gasworks; power stations; sewage treatment works.

- Railway land including sidings and depots; coal-yards (contaminated by phenols).

- Oil refineries, petrol stations and associated sites; metal mines, smelters, electroplating works, refineries and foundries.

- Chemical works.

- Industrial Revolution era workshops and warehouses.

- Slaughter yards and abattoirs; fish and meat markets; tanneries.

- Paper and printing works; wood preservative treatment sites.

- Hospitals, including isolation and quarantine premises.

- Buildings with animal hair used as insulation in roofs, etc. (anthrax).

Protection is also required from noise, dust and site waste, and suitable controls should be identified in the risk assessment and included in the health and safety plan for the demolition project.

Competence of the Workforce

The **CDM Regulations 2015** require that competent persons are employed in demolition work. Management should ensure workers have the necessary levels of competence, developed by appropriate training as required, e.g. health and safety. In the case of a subcontractor, the presence of a health and safety policy, the suitability of method statements, previous work and accident history, quality of risk assessments and the level of training of staff would be a guide to such competence.

The certificate of competence of demolition operatives is administered by the Construction Industry Training Board (CITB) and issued at various grades, e.g. labourer, etc. following successful completion of training. The training and competence of workers can be further enhanced by site induction training, or other training covering the hazards and legislation involved in the demolition process, e.g. NVQs.

Pre-Demolition Investigation and Survey

The purpose of a pre-demolition investigation and survey is to collect all relevant safety, health and environmental information relevant to the site, to establish a safe system of work and a demolition plan.

The survey is performed by an initial desktop study followed by an on-site survey, taking into account any off-site features that can affect work on site.

The investigation and survey should consider a number of issues:

- The **type of structure and method of construction** of the building and **the condition** of structural members, roofs, walls, floors; variations in building construction where old and newer buildings may be present; and the general stability features of the structures and buildings.

- The **presence of cellars**, basements, vaults, underground tanks, confined spaces, etc. Many of these features can remain hidden by the debris of dilapidation and age.

- The **identification of services**, above and below ground (electricity, gas, water). Again, dilapidation can hide the presence of services, or expose them in critical locations.

- The **presence of hazardous substances** or contaminated land (see earlier).

  As discussed previously, where asbestos might be present, samples need to be taken to verify its presence and the necessary precautions, actions and required notification should be carried out; and precautions need to be put in place if lead is found to be present.

- **Waste management** should ensure that wastes are separated on site into their different waste streams and controlled separately. Licensed waste removal contractors will have to dispose of the waste at licensed sites. Some of the waste, such as asbestos, will be controlled waste which is required to be kept in locked skips until disposal off site.

- **Safe access** onto and around the site must be maintained at all times, together with safe egress, for vehicles and pedestrian traffic. Access must always be maintained for emergency vehicles.

- The **proximity and condition of other structures**, e.g. hospitals, schools, care homes, industrial premises, roadways, waterways, bridges, etc.

Other useful information that would complement the demolition plan could include:

- The site's physical features and hydrology.

- The systems (shoring or other supports) necessary during demolition.

- The method of bonding of the main load-bearing walls.

- The possibility of making the adjacent buildings watertight.

- The effects of removing superstructure (an upward extension of an existing structure), stabilising loads, additional props or support during the demolition.

- The actual sequence of demolition operations (reverse of erection of the structure if possible, i.e. the preferred demolition work method is by reducing the height of the building initially and then carrying out a controlled collapse so that work can be completed at ground level).

- Site storage facilities, compounds for machinery, fuels, oils, etc.

- Waste disposal; removal and storage of rubble from the immediate area during demolition and its eventual removal off site (possible reuse of rubble for building up towpaths, etc.).

- The proximity of people to the site, e.g. access/egress for vehicles, noise, vibration, dust problems, protection of the public.

- Timescale of the demolition job to minimise interference for other jobs on site and the public.

- Establishment of site safety following demolition, e.g. safety of the remaining structure, control and disposal of debris, preventing unauthorised access, safety relating to gravity chutes used.

Safe Working Spaces and Exclusion Zones

Demolition, deconstruction and refurbishment projects should have exclusion zones set up to prevent exposing persons outside those zones to physical, chemical or biological hazards, noise, vibration and dust associated with the work in the zone.

Safe working spaces and exclusion zones should be included in the method statement and will be set up when determined by risk assessment. Each demolition activity should be assessed separately, ensuring each is adequately covered.

Operatives who must work inside these zones must be in a position of safety appropriate to the stage of demolition work being carried out. The zones will, therefore, change according to the activity and its rate of progress.

Exclusion zones can be set up to cover a wide area of site (or a complete site at some stages) or a small operating area for single plant and machines. For example, an excavator can have a **safe working space** around it that keeps the operator safe within that space, and keeps pedestrians and other vehicles outside that space and its safe operating parameters (extent of reach, etc.). Safe working spaces can also be established in or on machines for operators of that machine, such as in the covered cab of a crane.

Exclusion zones can be determined by the extent of the demolition works:

- Plan area - the area to be demolished.

- Designed drop area - immediate hazard area where most of the collapsing structure will fall.

- Predicted debris area - the predicted limit where debris from the collapse will travel and come to rest.

- Buffer area - an area planned to allow for unpredictable events. Outside this should be safe for all persons.

STUDY QUESTIONS

4. How is the premature collapse of a building/structure avoided during demolition?

5. What protection measures are used for noise during demolition?

6. What protection measures are used for dust control on demolition sites?

7. What precautions are put in place to ensure the safe siting of plant and machinery on a demolition site?

8. How is the environment protected during the demolition process?

9. How do you ensure the competence of the workforce for demolition purposes?

(Suggested Answers are at the end.)

Purpose and Scope of Pre-Demolition, Deconstruction or Refurbishment Survey

IN THIS SECTION...

- Owners of property and controllers of premises have duties for carrying out pre-demolition surveys.
- Only competent persons can conduct pre-demolition surveys.
- Structural elements and location of services must be identified, as well as effects of dilapidation on the structure.
- Drawings, calculations and the health and safety file should be reviewed as part of the survey.
- All previous alterations to the structure are to be taken into account.

Duties

The **property owner** or person in control of the premises has a duty to ensure that a pre-demolition survey is carried out on non-domestic premises, whether the project is CDM notifiable or non CDM notifiable. In the case of refurbishment or deconstruction, the local authority building department should be consulted before any structural alterations are made.

Major refurbishment/pre-demolition survey is also the name commonly given to the **MDHS 100 Type 3 asbestos survey**, which is often included in a full survey.

Carrying Out the Survey

Pre-demolition, deconstruction or refurbishment surveys should be carried out by **competent persons**, usually being structural engineers, asbestos surveyors, etc.

The expertise of a structural engineer must be used in the following cases:

- In the design of a facade retention scheme.
- Where there is doubt:
    - Over the building's stability.
    - About the proposed method of demolition.
    - About the capacity of the building to take loadings.

It is good practice to consult a structural engineer at the planning stage of demolition to avoid uncontrolled collapse.

A pre-demolition survey

The **purpose of the survey** is to carry out a thorough structural investigation and assessment before any potentially load-bearing parts of a structure are altered, and this survey, as well as determining the presence (or absence) of asbestos (what types and in what locations), will consider:

- **Key Structural Elements**

    Structural collapse is to be prevented, so all key structural elements of the building are to be identified, such as pre- and post-tensioned components. The competent person will decide on the suitable method of demolition (see earlier) and the design and nature of any temporary structural supports that may be required - they are to withstand foreseeable loads. During the work, structures are never to be overloaded.

- **Services**

  The location and identification of any services are to be determined, such as electricity, water, gas, etc. Either integral, underground or overhead services are likely to be encountered in demolition, refurbishment or deconstruction projects.

- **Dilapidation**

  The extent of any dilapidation is to be determined, identifying the locations and significance of its effects on the structures involved in the work.

- **Review**

  A review should be made of the existing health and safety file for the project, together with any drawings and structural calculations that may be relevant to the work in hand. This will give an indication of the effects that the demolition, deconstruction or refurbishment may have on the structures and nearby structures.

- **Structural Alterations**

  All previous alterations to the structure should also be reviewed and compared with the health and safety file, calculations, drawings, etc., to ensure the significance of any change does not adversely affect the current project work.

STUDY QUESTION

10. What information is to be considered in a pre-demolition survey?

(Suggested Answer is at the end.)

Control Measures Included in a Method Statement

IN THIS SECTION...

- A method statement should be in place for demolition, deconstruction and refurbishment projects. This will determine the control measures required to ensure safe working.

- Controls include: identification and isolation of services; temporary services; soft strip requirements; appropriate work at height access; protection of the public; emergency arrangements; and waste management.

- Competence of the workforce will be assured, together with communications between all parties involved in the project.

- Controls for asbestos and other hazards will be specified.

- The safe use of plant and equipment and safe access onto and egress from the site will be controlled, and training and welfare provisions will be in place.

- A responsible person will be named who has duties to ensure safety during the project.

- Co-ordination, co-operation and planning of the work activities on site is essential.

The Method Statement

The information from the pre-demolition investigation and survey can be incorporated into a demolition method statement. This is a safe system of work which sets out the sequence of work and the methods to be employed for each type of work.

The method statement should:

- Be drawn up before work starts.

- Be communicated to all involved.

- Identify the work procedure, associated problems and their solutions.

- Be easy to understand.

- Be agreed by all and known to all (of whatever level).

- Form a reference for site supervision.

The method statement should be drawn up before work starts and communicated to all involved

TOPIC FOCUS

The **demolition method statement** should include:

- Name and address of the demolition contractor and site.

- Sequence and method of demolition.

- Details of personnel access, working platforms and machinery.

- Details of any pre-weakening of structures which are to be pulled down or demolished using explosives, and temporary propping required.

- Arrangements for protecting workers and the public, and the exclusion of unauthorised people from the work area.

- Site security, including: fencing and/or barriers; controlling of spectators and/or site visitors; use of exclusion zones; and containment of demolition materials.

- Details of the removal or isolation of electrical, gas and other services.

- Details of temporary services required and welfare services provided.

- Arrangements for the disposal of waste.

- Details of environmental considerations (dust, noise, pollution of water, contaminated ground, etc.).

- Details of controls covering substances hazardous to health and flammable substances, e.g. asbestos, LPG and compressed gases, and any permit-to-work system.

- Arrangements for the control and co-ordination of the site, e.g. transport, contractors, storage.

- Training requirements and competencies of personnel involved in the demolition process.

- Identification of people with special responsibilities for the co-ordination and control of safety and emergency procedures/arrangements.

Isolation or Diversion of Services

Before any work commences, all utility companies should be contacted and sent a plan of the work to be carried out. A request should be made for the disconnection or isolation of their services. This should be done in good time and confirmation in writing should be obtained that such services are either disconnected or isolated. Where this is not possible, clear identification of the pipes and cables is required. Particular care needs to be exercised near overhead power lines, especially when high reach cranes or excavators are used.

Temporary Services

Temporary electrical systems and the provision of other temporary services (water, air, etc.) should be selected to ensure they are suitable for use on the site and are robust enough to withstand the demolition conditions.

Such equipment should have flexibility in application for repeated use on different sites, and must have ease of transport and storage.

In particular, temporary services **must** be marked so that they can all be positively identified to ensure they are not disturbed, damaged or inadvertently removed during the demolition work.

They should undergo regular visual examination and test by a competent person.

Soft-Strip Requirements

Particularly in deconstruction and refurbishment projects, where demolition to destruction is not the object, soft strip may be required. This is a planned, progressive removal of products and services from the structure, causing as little damage as possible to the infrastructure.

Often in soft-strip work, fixtures removed are stripped of all items such as nails, screws and fittings, and are packed away for re-use or transport to another location or storage.

Working at Height

Once the nature of the work and the safety of existing structures have been determined, means of access for personnel to work at height will be specified. These will have to be means that can be extended or reduced as the demolition or deconstruction work progresses.

Scaffolding must be of a suitable type, as often tied scaffold is not suitable on buildings that are being demolished, or cannot be used due to dilapidation or incomplete structures, so portable units may be more appropriate.

Protection of the Public and Others

A fence should be erected enclosing all the demolition operations. It should:

- Not be less than 2m high.

- Not be capable of being easily climbed.

Access gates should be secured outside working hours and danger notices should be displayed. Where perimeter fencing is not practicable, excavations should be fenced. Lighting may be required in high-risk areas.

Debris fans and facade netting may be required to prevent people being accidentally struck by falling objects. These must be cleared of debris regularly, and checked for damage. Any ladders in use must be regularly checked to ensure they remain tied after each time they are moved.

Emergency Arrangements

Emergencies can take many forms and can occur on different scales, and organisations need procedures in place to cope with them. Typical emergency arrangements that a demolition contractor might need to consider include:

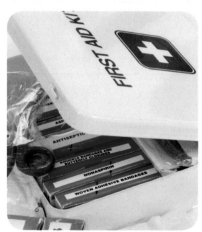

First aid

- Containing a localised chemical spillage or gas/vapour release.

- Dealing with emergencies caused by damage to utility supplies that have not been isolated, particularly gas explosion.

- Fire evacuation.

- Plans to deal with premature or unplanned collapse of structures.

- Rescue of persons trapped under collapsed structures.

- Recovery of persons fallen from height (perhaps from collapsing structure).

- Rescue of persons fallen into cellars, pits, voids, etc.

- First-aid treatment.

The requirement for emergency planning is included in many pieces of health and safety legislation, including:

- **Management of Health and Safety at Work Regulations 1999**.
- **Control of Substances Hazardous to Health Regulations 2002**.
- **Dangerous Substances and Explosive Atmospheres Regulations 2002**.
- **Control of Major Accident Hazards Regulations 2015**.

Emergency Plans

It is the duty of the contractor or principal contractor to prepare and provide a current Emergency Contacts Set of Procedures for each demolition site. The procedures should be followed in any site emergency situation (see above) and should contain emergency telephone numbers and the method of notifying services for action.

The emergency plan is a formal, written document designed to assist the demolition contractor with the control of emergency situations, so that minimum disruption to normal work activities will occur. Individual emergency plans will then cover the following main points with regard to each of the identified emergency situations:

- Nature of the emergency situation.
- Location (site and area of site).
- Potential for harm (consequences of the emergency).
- Existing instructions for dealing with the problem.
- Immediate actions to be taken.
- Control of the emergency situation.
- Assessment of the emergency situation.
- Emergency response and safety equipment required.
- Damage limitation action.
- Recovery plan.

Such a plan must operate smoothly and efficiently, so it is important that responsibilities are set out and understood. Non-company personnel may be involved in both the development and implementation, such as:

- Emergency services: police, fire and rescue services, ambulance service.
- Local authority.
- HSE, Environment Agency/Natural Resources Wales, DEFRA.
- Local companies, local transport.
- Local utilities: electricity supplier, gas company, water company.

Someone within the company (e.g. the safety officer for the contractor) should be trained in dealing with the media, as this can have a profound effect on company image.

On sites where contaminated material is encountered, the contractor's safety officer should ensure that a Worker's Safety Information sheet is prepared and displayed in rest rooms and washrooms covering hygiene, work practices, clothing requirements, etc.

Waste Management - Segregation and Disposal of Waste

Waste can take the form of solid waste, liquid waste or waste water from the demolition process itself and should be dealt with accordingly. The main regulatory requirements and methods of control are outlined below.

Solid Waste

- All waste must be stored, segregated, labelled correctly and disposed of correctly in accordance with the **Environmental Protection Act 1990** and associated regulations, which is the responsibility of the main contractor and subcontractors.

- Only licensed contractors can transfer waste to a permitted landfill site or transfer station.

- Records must be kept of all wastes received or transferred through a system of signed Waste Transfer Notes.

- Registration as a waste carrier with the environmental regulator is required (e.g. for building or demolition waste).

- An environmental permit may be required to burn waste, chip trees or cut down scrub on site, but certain exemptions are available.

- A Part B permit is required under the **Environmental Permitting (England and Wales) Regulations 2016** if concrete, etc. is to be crushed at a processing plant on site (a Part B permit is obtained from the local authority (SEPA in Scotland)).

- Materials with hazardous properties (e.g. oil, diesel, asbestos) may need to be dealt with as 'hazardous waste'.

- Empty containers, the original contents of which were hazardous waste, must be treated as hazardous waste.

- Storage compounds and waste skips should be located away from environmentally-sensitive areas on site, e.g. drains, water bodies and site boundaries close to housing/offices.

- Recycling outlets should be used, e.g. timber, metals, bricks and tiles. Note that material requiring treatment or recycling may be classed as waste.

> **DEFINITION**
>
> **WASTE**
>
> Any substance or object that is discarded, intended to be discarded or required to be discarded (including for recycling or in-house treatment).

Liquid Waste

Liquid waste produced or obtained during the demolition process should be dealt with as follows:

- While awaiting disposal, it should be clearly labelled, stored and contained within a bunded area to prevent contamination.

- Bunded areas may contain contaminated rainwater which may need to be treated as hazardous waste.

- Disposal must be in accordance with current environmental legislation (which regulates, for example, who can carry or handle waste, the available ultimate disposal routes and whether pre-treatment of waste is required).

- Liquid waste should be disposed of using a permitted facility.

- Disposal of liquid wastes or effluents into the foul sewer or directly/indirectly to a ditch, watercourse or land requires prior written authorisation.

- Additional precautions are required where Protection Zones exist to avoid a pollution incident.

Waste water treatment plant

- All surface water drains and watercourses require protection, e.g. ditches or earth bunds.

- The location, discharge point and identity of all drains and sewers on and off site are required (accurate and up-to-date drawings and information are required).

- Colour co-ordinate drainage grilles on site:

  - Surface water drains are often coloured blue.

  - Foul water drains are often coloured red and effluents must be prevented from entering drains and/or watercourses.

- Spillage procedures/plans are required and absorbent materials, e.g. mats, pads or granules must be available for use on site.

- Drip trays should be used for all plant and equipment on site, especially in the vicinity of watercourses or drains.

- Rainwater within drip trays used for storing chemicals may be contaminated and should be tested and removed from the site as hazardous waste if appropriate.

Competence of the Workforce

The method statement should reflect that workers have the necessary levels of competence and health and safety training. As we saw earlier, in the case of a subcontractor, the presence of a health and safety policy, the suitability of method statements, previous work and accident history, quality of risk assessments and the level of training of staff would be a guide to such competence.

Communications

Throughout the demolition project, good communications must remain in place, both internally and externally. The method statement should show what internal means of communication are available, and how regular communication between all parties involved in the project will be achieved. Externally, essential contacts will be maintained, such as the emergency services. The statement will also list all key site personnel.

Asbestos

The method statement will show that before work starts, the owner or controller of the site is required to provide an asbestos management plan. It will detail the steps that will be taken to avoid exposure to asbestos, and where it cannot be totally avoided, how co-ordination with licensed asbestos removal contractors (where necessary) will take place. Control of waste and disposal will be detailed.

Communication is essential at all levels to ensure a project is carried out correctly and safely

Control Measures for Identified Hazards

Where hazards are identified in the risk assessment, the control measures will be detailed in the method statement, together with notification of who is responsible for ensuring they are put in place and followed.

Plant and Equipment

All plant and equipment will be indicated, together with details of authorised and competent operators.

Access and Egress from Site

Vehicle and pedestrian access routes must be under constant review. Where scaffolding is used, platforms and gangways must be kept free from debris and tripping hazards. The security of scaffolds is important and monitoring is required to see that when the structure is demolished, sufficient ties are maintained with the building.

Some operations require the demolition worker to occupy precarious positions where it is not possible to provide an adequate safety structure. Here it becomes crucial that safety harnesses are used and attached to a secure part of the structure. Where floors have been removed, some boards should be left so there remains a skeleton floor structure to allow work to proceed in relative safety.

Training and Welfare Arrangements

Training

Safe demolition depends largely on the knowledge and experience of the foreman or supervisor and the skill of the operatives. Foremen and supervisors in immediate control of demolition work must:

- Be able to recognise hazards.
- Know correct methods of demolition.
- Be able to enforce safe practices.

Where there is a potential for sudden collapse, a competent foreman or supervisor should be in constant attendance. Some unsound structures will need the supervision of a qualified engineer.

Training for demolition foremen, supervisors and operatives is available through the National Demolition Training Group of the Construction Industry Training Board:

- Initial training for all operatives should relate to basic safety, familiarity with everyday hazards and requirements for a safe place of work.
- At foreman and supervisor level, training should cover all the implications of the demolition method statement and the significance of legal requirements.

Written records should be kept of training and copies of such records should be supplied to employees.

General training in demolition work should be in accordance with the recommendations in **BS 6187:2011** *Code of practice for full and partial demolition.*

TOPIC FOCUS

Specialised training may be necessary for work involving unusual or special hazards, for example:

- Controlled collapses.
- Working places and access to them (including scaffolding, fans, chutes and hoardings).
- Plant - characteristics and correct utilisation (including hazards due to speed and scale of operation).
- Services (gas, water, electricity, telephones).
- Shoring.
- Flame-cutting equipment or use of special tools and equipment.
- RPE.
- Entry into confined spaces or tank demolition.
- Fume tests - use of instruments and breathing apparatus.
- Asbestos and other health hazards.
- Storage, conveyance and use of explosives.

Welfare Arrangements

Welfare arrangements should include the basic requirements for washing (hot and cold running water, soap and towel), adequate toilets (separate for men and women where possible and appropriate), rest and changing facilities (separate clean and dirty clothes storage if contaminated land) and drying rooms, as well as somewhere clean to eat, drink and take breaks, with drinking water provided. Showers should be provided where risk assessment requires it (e.g. the removal of asbestos, or if the site is on contaminated land).

Named Responsible Persons

All construction and demolition activities are covered by the **CDM Regulations 2015**. This places duties on responsible persons.

The Client

Clients must make suitable arrangements for managing a project, including the allocation of sufficient time and other resources, and ensure that these arrangements are maintained and reviewed throughout the project.

Contractors

The principal contractor is the main contractor involved and is normally a specialist in managing demolition projects. Significant to this role is the planning, managing and monitoring of the demolition activity and co-ordinating matters relating to health and safety to ensure that the work is carried out without risks to health or safety.

The principal contractor must also consult and engage with the workforce to ensure that measures for their health, safety and welfare are developed, promoted and checked for effectiveness.

Co-ordination of Work Activities On Site

Demolition projects require a more rigorous approach to co-ordination, co-operation and planning than general construction work. Those undertaking the work must understand the risks involved and how to control them.

The demolition plan details the arrangements of how the demolition work will be carried out and must be prepared before demolition or dismantling starts. This requirement applies to all demolition work:

- The **principal contractor** is responsible for preparing and reviewing the demolition plan and co-ordinating the activities of all contractors to ensure compliance with health and safety legislation and the demolition plan. The principal contractor may give information, instruction and site induction to other contractors and arrange for their training where appropriate.

- All other demolition contractors must:

  - Plan, manage and monitor their own work so that risks to health and safety are minimised.

  - Take reasonable steps to ensure that work is carried out in accordance with the demolition plan.

  The principal contractor must be kept informed of the appointment of any other contractors.

STUDY QUESTIONS

11. What type of information is contained in a demolition method statement?

12. List the typical emergency arrangements that a demolition contractor may need to consider.

(Suggested Answers are at the end.)

Summary

This element has dealt with safety in demolition activities.

In particular, this element has:

- Introduced basic terminology and methods used in construction.

- Identified the main hazards associated with demolition and deconstruction work: premature collapse; falls and falling materials; plant, vehicles and other equipment overturning; manual handling; dust and fumes; noise and vibration; existence of services (buried, overhead and in buildings); hazardous substances; and dilapidation.

- Outlined the control measures for demolition and deconstruction: avoiding premature collapse; protection from falls and falling material; siting and use of plant; manual handling; how to control dusts, fumes, noise and vibration; protection of the environment; maintaining a competent workforce; and carrying out a pre-demolition investigation and survey.

- Identified the purpose and scope of pre-demolition/refurbishment surveys, including: the duties of owners of properties and competent persons to carry out investigations; identification of key structural elements, identification of services and the significance of dilapidation of structures; the need to review drawings, calculations and the health and safety file, and all structural alterations carried out prior to the current project.

- Outlined the appropriate control measures that a demolition/refurbishment method statement should consider:

  - Isolation or diversion of services and the use of temporary services; soft strip requirements; working at height and protection of the public and others, and adjacent structures.

  - Emergency arrangements to be in place; management of waste on site and correct disposal off site; the importance of a competent workforce and good communication; controls that will ensure safety with asbestos and other site hazards identified; safe use of plant and equipment and safe access and egress; training and welfare arrangements; named responsible persons; and co-ordination of work on site.

Exam Skills

Approaching the Question

Think now about the steps you would take to answer the question:

Step 1. Read the question carefully. Note that this question asks you to identify (select and name) the main areas to be covered in a demolition method statement. Do not be overly concerned about how the scene has been set for this question by using a steel-framed building; nearly all modern office blocks are constructed using this method; you have probably seen many examples of such construction.

Step 2. Now highlight the key words. In this case, they might look like this:

A steel-framed building is to be demolished.

Identify the **main areas** to be included in a **demolition method statement**. **(8)**

Step 3. Next, consider the marks and time available. In this question there are eight marks so it is expected that around eight or nine different pieces of information should be provided. The question should take around eight minutes in total.

Step 4. Read the question again to make sure you understand it and have a clear understanding of demolition method statements. (Re-read your notes if you need to.)

Step 5. The next stage is to develop a plan - there are various ways to do this. Remind yourself, first of all, that you need to be thinking about 'demolition method statements'. You need to provide an acceptable definition, so you can choose your own words to describe each area covered by the statement.

Your answer must be based on the key words you have highlighted. So, in this case, we need to state the main areas of a demolition method statement. A method statement essentially sets out the sequence of work and the method employed for each part of the work.

Now have a go at the question. Draw up an answer plan, and then use it as the basis to write out an answer as you would in the exam.

Remember, you can always contact your tutor if you have any queries or need any further guidance on how to answer this question.

HINTS AND TIPS

Think about the breadth of factors to be covered.

Suggested Answer Outline

Method Statement	
• Sequence of work.	• Work at height precautions.
• Temporary shoring to prevent collapse.	• Hazardous substances, asbestos and solvents.
• Stability of adjacent structures.	• Noise/dust control.
• Isolation of existing services.	• Waste control.
• Temporary services required.	• Emergency situations.
• Protection of employees and the public.	

Example of How the Question Could be Answered

A method statement will include the sequence of work and the method employed to do that work. Areas to be included would be the stability of the structure during demolition to prevent premature collapse and consideration of the stability of adjacent structures. Included would be details of any temporary propping or shoring of the structure and the isolation of any services to the structure. The statement needs to cover how employees and members of the public will be protected, which may mean identification of any exclusion zones or the use of perimeter fencing. Details of access for working at height and the use of working platforms need to be included. The method statement would detail the provision of temporary services to the site/building and would also address environmental hazards such as the control of noise and dust. The method statement would have a section on hazardous substances such as asbestos, lead (possibly in paint work), and any solvents that may have been used on the site. Details of the arrangements for the disposal of waste would be a part of the statement. In the event of an emergency situation the method statement would identify those employees with special responsibilities for the co-ordination of emergency procedures.

Reasons for Poor Marks Achieved by Candidates in Exam

- Providing extravagant details on one particular aspect, e.g. work at height, where various approaches are covered, instead of covering the breadth of factors in a demolition method statement that will gain marks.

- Using expressions such as 'PPE' or 'information, instruction and training' to try to attract marks. There are many factors to be considered in a demolition method statement to demonstrate the knowledge that is being tested. These catch-all phrases are unlikely to attract marks in this case.

- Being distracted by the scene-setting description and spending too long on removal of steel structures and **LOLER** to load vehicles. While these may be pertinent, the question requires candidates to demonstrate a breadth of knowledge to attract the full marks available.

The Last Hurdle

Now that you have worked your way through the course material, this section will help you prepare for your NEBOSH examination. This guide contains useful advice on how to approach your revision and the exam itself.

Your NEBOSH Examination

The NEBOSH examination will consist of one question paper which contains one 20-mark question and ten 8-mark questions. You are allowed two hours in which to complete the exam paper and you should answer all the questions.

To pass the exam, you must obtain a minimum of 45% of the total marks available.

If your performance is less than the pass mark then you will be "referred". This means you may resit the examination provided you do so within five years of the original sitting. You may resit as many times as you want within that five-year timescale.

Be Prepared

It may be some time since you last took an exam. Remember, success in an exam depends mainly on:

- **revision** - you have to be able to remember, recall and apply the information contained in your course material; and

- **exam technique** - you have to be able to understand the questions and write good answers in the time available.

Revision and exam technique are skills that can be learnt. We will now look at both of these skills so that you can prepare yourself for the exam. There is a saying that "proper planning and preparation prevents a poor performance". This was never truer than in an exam.

Revision Tips

Using the RRC Course Material

You should read through all of the topics at least once before beginning your revision in earnest. This first read-through should be done slowly and carefully.

Having completed this first revision reading of the course materials, consider briefly reviewing all of it again to check that you understand all of the elements and the important principles that they contain. At this stage, you are not trying to memorise information but simply checking your understanding of the concepts. Make sure that you resolve any outstanding queries with your tutor.

Remember that understanding the information and being able to remember and recall it are two different things. As you read the course material you should **understand** it; in the exam, you have to be able to **remember**, **recall** and **apply** it. To do this successfully, most people have to go back over the material repeatedly.

Re-read the course material and make notes that summarise important information from each element. **You could use index cards** and create a portable, quick and easy revision aid.

Check your basic knowledge of the content of each element by reading the Summary. The Summary should help you recall the ideas contained in the text. If it does not, then you may need to re-visit the appropriate sections of the element.

Using the Syllabus Guide

We recommend that you download a copy of the NEBOSH Guide to this course, which contains the syllabus for your exam. If a topic is in the syllabus then it is possible that there will be an examination question on that topic.

Map your level of knowledge and recall against the syllabus guide. Look at the **content** listed for each element in the syllabus guide. Ask yourself the following question:

If there is a question in the exam about that topic, could I answer it?

You can even score your current level of knowledge for each topic in each element of the syllabus guide and then use your scores as an indication of your personal strengths and weaknesses. For example, if you scored yourself 5 out of 5 for a topic in Element 1, then obviously you don't have much work to do on that subject as you approach the exam. But if you scored yourself 2 out of 5 for a topic in Element 3, then you have identified an area of weakness. Having identified your strengths and weaknesses in this way, you can use this information to decide on the topic areas that you need to concentrate on as you revise for the exam.

You could also annotate or highlight sections of the text that you think are important.

Another way of using the syllabus guide is as an active revision aid:

- Pick a topic at random from any of the elements.

- Write down as many facts and ideas that you can recall that are relevant to that particular topic. Go back to your course material and see what you missed, and fill in the missing areas.

Exam Hints

Success in the exam depends on scoring approximately half of the available marks for the entire exam paper. You can score very poorly, or even zero, on some questions and, as long as you score well enough on other questions to bring the overall score up to 45%, still pass.

Marks are awarded for setting down ideas that are relevant **to the question asked** and demonstrating that you understand what you are talking about. If you have studied your course material thoroughly, then this should not be a problem.

One common mistake in answering questions is to go into too much detail on specific topics and fail to deal with the wider issues. If you only cover half the relevant issues, you can only achieve half the available marks. Try to give as wide an answer as you can, without stepping outside the subject matter of the question altogether. Make sure that you cover each issue in appropriate detail in order to demonstrate that you have the relevant knowledge. Giving relevant examples is a good way of doing this.

We mentioned earlier the value of using the syllabus to plan your revision. Another useful way of combining syllabus study with examination practice is to create your own exam questions by adding one of the words you might find at the beginning of an exam question (such as 'explain' or 'identify' or 'outline') in front of the syllabus topic areas. In this way, you can produce a whole range of questions similar to those used in the exam.

Before the Exam

You should:

- Know where the exam is to take place.

- Arrive in good time.

- Bring your examination entry voucher (which includes your candidate number), photographic proof of identity, pens, pencils, ruler, etc. (Remember, these must be in a clear plastic bag or wallet.)

- Bring water to drink and sweets to suck, if you want to.

During the Exam

- Read through the whole exam paper before starting work, if that will help settle your nerves. Start with the question of your choice.

- Manage your time. The exam is two hours long. You should attempt to answer all 11 questions in the two hours. To do this, you might spend:

    - 25-30 minutes answering Question 1 (worth 20 marks), and then

    - 8-9 minutes on each of the ten remaining 8-mark questions.

- Check the clock regularly as you write your answers. You should always know exactly where you are, with regard to time.

- As you start each question, read the question carefully. Pay particular attention to the wording of the question to make sure you understand what the examiner is looking for. Note the verbs (command words), such as 'describe', 'explain', 'identify' or 'outline', that are used in the question. These indicate the amount of depth and detail required in your answer. As a general guide:

    - 'Explain' and 'describe' mean give an understanding of/a detailed account of something.

    - 'Outline' means give the key features of something.

    - 'Identify' means give a reference to something (could be name or title).

- Pay close attention to the number of marks available for each question, or part of a question - this usually indicates how many key pieces of information the examiner expects to see in your answer.

- Give examples wherever possible, based either on your own personal experience, or things you have read about. An example can be used to illustrate an idea and demonstrate that you understand what you are saying.

- If you start to run out of time, write your answers in bullet-point or checklist style, rather than failing to answer a question at all.

- Keep your handwriting under control; if the examiner cannot read what you have written, then he or she cannot mark it.

- You will not be penalised for poor grammar or spelling, as long as your answers are clear and can be understood. However, you may lose marks if the examiner cannot make sense of the sentence that you have written.

Health and Safety Practical Application

Introduction

The aim of this unit is to help you prepare for your NEBOSH Construction Certificate Unit NCC2: National Construction Health and Safety Practical Application.

Some people think that this unit is simple, don't bother to prepare themselves properly, and fail as a result. Make sure you don't fall into this trap! While the process you have to work through is straightforward, in order to succeed you need to understand what NEBOSH expect. If you work carefully through these notes, we are confident that you'll be a successful candidate!

NOTE: Tutors are unable to comment on your practical application before submission or marking. Please read the guidance carefully before submitting.

Contents

Aim of the Practical Assessment

The aim of the practical assessment is to test your ability to carry out two activities:

A safety inspection of your workplace:

A written report to management:

- What are the common hazards?

- Are they adequately controlled?

- Give any appropriate, cost effective control measures that are required.

- Outlining what you found in your inspection.

- Explaining why action is needed (and persuading management to do it!) including reference to possible breaches of legislation.

- Identifying what management need to do to resolve the issues you have highlighted.

NEBOSH advise that the whole assessment should be completed within two hours, although there is no time limit. The inspection should take approximately one hour and the report should be written immediately afterwards and completed in the second hour. Let's look at these two stages in detail, starting with the workplace inspection.

The assessment may be word processed or submitted in the candidates own handwriting.

Workplace Inspection

For this assessment, you have to show NEBOSH that you can competently complete an inspection of a construction workplace, identifying any uncontrolled hazards or unsafe practices, their consequences, what needs to be done about them, and how quickly action should be taken.

You will have already covered the types of hazards you are likely to come across in the workplace in Unit NCC1 of your course, so we will not go into the detail of those here. Instead, we are going to concentrate on how you should approach the inspection to give you the best chance of success.

So what do you need to do?

The stages you need to work through are shown in the diagram below; let's take a look at each stage in a little more detail.

Select a suitable area of a construction workplace for inspection that is large enough to provide a sufficient range of hazards but contained enough that you can comfortably walk around the entire area in a reasonable period of time (say 1 hour) making notes as you go.

Identify poorly controlled hazards, unsafe practices and good practice. Walk around the area and look carefully at the working environment and activities to identify poorly controlled hazards, unsafe practices and two examples of good practice. These might include physical, chemical, ergonomic and biological hazards.

Complete the NEBOSH Observation Forms. You need to note down all of your observations on the correct NEBOSH form. You must record the right things in the right places and your notes must be detailed enough to allow the examiner to understand your meaning. You'll use these notes to help you write your management report in the next stage of the assessment and the examiner will use them to check that your report is accurate, so make sure they are clear and legible!

Inspection Area

In order to complete this assessment, you have to select an area of a construction workplace that will be suitable. To be suitable, your workplace should be large enough to provide a sufficient range of hazards, but contained enough that you can cover all of the issues you find there in your assessment.

If your workplace is very large, think about limiting your inspection area to a single office, or workshop.

If you read through the rest of this guidance, you will see the types of hazards that you will be expected to cover in the assessment.

Bear in mind that you should consult the management of the premises to ensure that they are happy for you to complete your assessment there, and so they can ensure that you can carry out the inspection without endangering your own health and safety. You might like to inform your employer that the inspection you are undertaking is for "educational purposes only" to fulfil the requirements of the NEBOSH National Construction Certificate. In other words, you have to complete the inspection and write the report to gain the full NCC qualification.

Identifying Hazards and Consequences

So, you have selected your construction workplace area and you are ready to begin your inspection - where do you start?

HINTS AND TIPS

Start by taking a good look at your surroundings. Some hazards may leap out at you immediately, but try to take a minute or two just to survey the whole area first. It's important that you show a wide range of hazards (at least five 'types') so, before you start noting things down, think about the environment as a whole to get a feel for the sorts of hazards and unsafe practices you should be looking for.

Begin by making a few notes about the area you are about to inspect, as you will need these when you write the introduction to your management report. This should include where and when the inspection took place, a description of the area, a description of the activities taking place in the area and any equipment that is being used. An indication of the number of staff working in the area will be helpful, too.

Next, you need to turn your attention to any hazards in the area. To score well, you should aim to identify **at least 25 examples** of uncontrolled hazards and unsafe practices. NEBOSH recommend that you identify **more than 20, but no more than 30**, to avoid duplication, or inappropriate hazards being identified, so try to give at least 25 hazards. As well as identifying hazards, it is very important that you also state the **consequences** of exposure to each hazard. In other words, you should indicate the risk that the hazard will create. For example, you may have identified 'Boxes stored in pedestrian walkways' as a hazard. This will not be enough for full marks - **you must also state the consequences**. So, your entry in this column might be 'Hazard - boxes stored in pedestrian walkways. Consequence - obstruction of access and egress and/or risk of musculoskeletal injury if lifted'.

You need to make sure that these hazards cover a range of different topics (at least five different types of hazard). Try to picture in your mind all the various topics you have studied in your course (some of which are covered below) and attempt to cover as many of them as possible in your examples. If you repeat a hazard (for example, if you reference three items of work equipment that all require portable appliance testing), you will only be marked once.

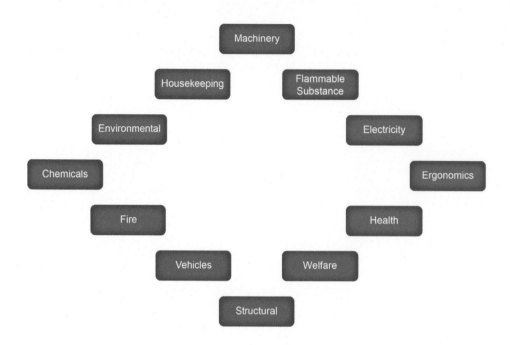

- **Hazards**

  In almost any workplace you should be able to find a range of hazards, such as:

  - A pothole in the floor (or trailing wires/cables), creating the risk of slips, trips and falls.

  - An unguarded pedestal drill, creating the risk of entanglement and severe hand injury.

  - Poorly stored combustible waste, creating a fire risk.

  If you've studied your course notes thoroughly, you should be aware of lots of other such examples.

  For the purposes of completing your inspection, it is important that you describe properly whatever hazard you have identified. So, it is not enough to just say "defective floor" or "fire risk"; you must include enough information so that the examiner can understand what the hazard was, where it was and what the consequences of exposure to the hazard might be. So, on your observation form, rather than "defective floor", you will need to say: "Potholes in the floor outside the workshop door create a risk of slips and trips"; and instead of "fire risk", put: "Fire exit route at rear of site partially obstructed by build-up of heavy boxes; risk of being trapped in the event of fire".

- **Unsafe Practices**

  As well as hazards, you need to look for examples of unsafe practices.

  Again, in almost every workplace these should be fairly easy to spot and could include:

  - Careless forklift-truck driving, creating a risk of collision with workers, buildings and other vehicles.

  - Workers smoking in designated 'No Smoking' areas, creating a fire risk.

  - A ladder in use against a wall at the wrong angle, creating a risk of falling from height.

  Remember to describe any examples you give in detail so the examiner can understand the issue.

  You should focus on physical conditions and not on poor policies and procedures.

- **Good Practices**

  As well as unsafe practices, note down a couple of examples of good practice, such as the provision of good welfare facilities. However, it is best not to include more than one or two examples of good practice, as the main point of the exercise is to assess your ability to identify hazards and unsafe practices - **there is only one mark available for good practices anyway!**

So, now you know what you should be looking for in terms of hazards and unsafe and good practices, take a look around your own workplace and think about the following questions.

Safe Premises	Safe Plant and Machinery
<ul><li>Are the premises clean?</li><li>Are the workplace, equipment, systems and devices maintained in an efficient state, efficient working order and in good repair?</li><li>Are floors in good condition and free of obstructions?</li><li>Are floor openings adequately protected against falls?</li><li>Is there a risk of someone falling out of a window?</li><li>Are staircases safe and fitted with a handrail?</li><li>Is an adequate level of lighting provided?</li><li>Is the workplace too hot or too cold?</li></ul>	<ul><li>Are machines adequately guarded and fitted with appropriate safety devices?</li><li>Are power sources to machinery properly connected?</li><li>Can machinery and plant be cleaned safely?</li><li>Are machines maintained in an efficient state, efficient working order and in good repair?</li><li>Is there a formally documented, planned preventive maintenance schedule for machinery?</li><li>Are hand tools in good condition, well-maintained and used correctly?</li></ul>
Safe Processes	**Safe Materials**
<ul><li>Are the various operations carried out safely? Look particularly at:<ul><li>– Manual handling.</li><li>– Driving of forklift trucks.</li><li>– Storage of raw materials and finished products.</li><li>– Ergonomic aspects of machine operation.</li><li>– Use of hazardous substances.</li></ul></li></ul>	<ul><li>Are materials being handled safely?</li><li>Are some of the materials dangerous, such as radioactive substances, chemical substances or biological agents?</li><li>Are these substances correctly packaged and labelled?</li><li>Is there adequate information on the safe handling of materials and substances?</li></ul>
Safe Systems of Work	**Safe Access to Work**
<ul><li>Are safe systems of work established for potentially hazardous operations?</li><li>Are these safe systems of work followed implicitly?</li><li>Is a permit-to-work system used where there is a high degree of foreseeable risk?</li></ul>	<ul><li>Are access roads and internal gangways kept clear, maintained and well-lit?</li><li>Are specific provisions made for ensuring safe work at height and below ground level, e.g. scaffolds, mobile access equipment, protection of excavations?</li><li>Are ladders well-maintained and used correctly?</li></ul>

Adequate Supervision	Competent and Trained Personnel
• Is the level of safety supervision adequate? • Are line managers adequately trained in their health and safety duties?	• Are competent persons, e.g. for electrical maintenance work, clearly identified? • Are operators adequately informed, instructed and trained in safe systems of work? • Are first aiders adequately trained?
Care of the Vulnerable	**Personal Hygiene**
• Are vulnerable groups exposed to specific risks? • Do such persons need to receive some form of medical or health surveillance? • Are specific provisions made for the supervision of vulnerable groups?	• Is there a risk of occupational skin conditions through poor levels of personal hygiene? • Are adequate welfare facilities provided? • Is the consumption of food and drink in working and storage areas prohibited?
Personal Protective Equipment	**Careful Conduct**
• Does Personal Protective Equipment (PPE) provided meet the requirements necessary for the particular hazards and risks of the workplace? • Is there a formal procedure for selection and assessment of PPE? • Do those employees exposed to risks wear their PPE correctly and all the time that they are exposed to those risks?	• Do operators behave safely during their work? • Were any unsafe practices noted?

These are the sorts of questions you need to ask about conditions in the inspection area and, as you can see, a lot of these hazards are quite simple to identify - but don't forget: you need to think about the consequences, too! You can probably think of a lot of similar questions to add to the list.

If you remember to look out for these types of issues when it comes to completing your workplace inspection, you'll have no problem in achieving the required standard.

HINTS AND TIPS

Identifying Safe Systems of Work and Legal Standards

While you won't need to record it on your observation form, keep in mind any possible breaches of laws or standards as you will need to make a note of these in your management report.

Completing the NEBOSH Observation Forms

You should now have a good idea of the sort of things to look for as you walk around your workplace inspection area.

As you carry out your inspection, you need to complete the NEBOSH Candidate Observation Form (available to download from the NEBOSH website), which will provide you with notes to work from when it comes to completing your management report. **Remember that these notes will be submitted to your examiner, who will use them to decide how effective your management report is, so they must be clear and legible**!

The Observation Form has three columns:

Observations	Control measures	Timescale
Hazards and consequences	Immediate and longer-term actions	

As you can see, NEBOSH have already given you a big clue as to what to include in each of the columns, but here's a brief summary:

Observations

As it says, here you should include the hazards and consequences that you identified - the sorts of things we have just covered. You must clearly outline the hazard to enable the marks to be awarded for the control measures.

Control Measures

Here, you need to state the action required to eliminate or control each hazard or unsafe working practice. You should think about what is needed to immediately control the risk from each of your hazards AND identify the need for longer-term actions.

One- or two-word statements, such as 'fit a guard' or 'segregate area', are not enough; although you need to be concise, you still need to give the examiner more detail than that, so it becomes clear what your recommendations are. For example, you might say:

- [For boxes stacked in gangways] - Immediate: Remove boxes from gangways. Longer term: Storage areas should be clearly marked out and gangways kept clear at all times.

- [For a spillage] - Immediate: Clean up and inform supervisor. Longer term: Supervisor training, regular inspections and investigate the source of the leak.

- [For a missing guard] - Immediate: Take machine out of use and inform supervisor. Longer term: The adjustable guard to the circular saw should be replaced and supervisors should ensure it is maintained in position during use.

Most hazards will have more than one recommended action - an immediate action to make the hazard safe and another longer-term action that fixes the underlying problem (the root cause). So, for example:

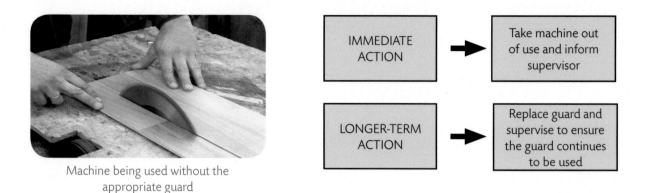

Machine being used without the
appropriate guard

If adequate controls are already in place, remember to think about whether any measures are required to maintain this level of control.

Remember to avoid using generic phrases such as 'monitor' or 'train staff'. Let the examiner know what needs to be monitored, or the type of training that will be required.

Timescale

Here, you need to indicate how quickly action needs to be taken - the higher the risk, the more urgent it is likely to be, while longer-term actions may take much longer to put in place.

This is where you need to pause and think carefully. It is tempting to treat everything as requiring immediate action, but NEBOSH want to see that you can realistically identify what is required to immediately control the risk and what longer term measure is also needed. You are required to distinguish between the immediate and root causes. The following table should give you some helpful hints.

Immediate	Where there is a risk of serious or imminent danger, or where there is a flagrant breach of legal requirements. This can also be used for actions that can be done quickly at no cost. The timescale for an immediate should be short.
Longer term	Where hazards can be eliminated or controlled without the need for capital expenditure and where there is no serious or imminent danger present; or Where there may be a need, for example, to provide information, instruction and training, to write a safe system of work, or to introduce health surveillance.

Criteria for Assessment of Observation/Inspection Stage

The following marking matrix should give you a good idea of what you need to do to achieve maximum marks in each of these areas:

Marks to be awarded				
		11-15	**6-10**	**1-5**
Completion of observation sheets	**Range and outline of hazards and consequences**	• 4-5 different types of hazards outlined • 14-20 uncontrolled hazards/consequences outlined	• 2-3 different types of hazards outlined • 7-13 uncontrolled hazards outlined (hazards/consequences)	• 1 type of hazard outlined • 1-6 uncontrolled hazards outlined (hazards/consequences)
		11-15	**6-10**	**1-5**
	Identification of suitable control measures and timescales	• Immediate and longer-term actions identified for majority of hazards • Majority of recommended actions effective in reducing risk and realistic in terms of timescales	• Identification of immediate and longer-term actions for some of the identified hazards • Some recommended actions generally effective in reducing risk and realistic in terms of timescales	• Reference to mainly immediate actions only • Recommended actions limited in reducing risk and unrealistic in terms of timescales

Example of a Completed Observation Form

Now we know the theory, let's see what your completed form should look like in practice.

NEBOSH NATIONAL CERTIFICATE IN CONSTRUCTION HEALTH AND SAFETY

UNIT NCC2 - CONSTRUCTION HEALTH AND SAFETY PRACTICAL APPLICATION

Candidate's observation sheet

Sheet Number   of

Student Name   Student Number

Place inspected   Hotel Renovation   Date of inspection   /   /

Observations	Control Measures	Timescale
Hazards and consequences	**Immediate and longer-term action**	
Housekeeping	**Immediate**	24hrs
1. Old timber with protruding nails left on the floor in the main entrance to the building.	Remove or flatten nails.	
	Medium Term	1 week
	Identify suitable storage area and remove timber from entrance.	
Consequences: puncture wounds.	**Long Term**	Every 2 weeks
	Schedule regular housekeeping inspections.	
2. Extension leads causing tripping hazard at top of stairway.	**Immediate**	1 day
	Re-route cable away from stairway.	
	Medium Term	1 week
Consequences could include significant injury to employees such as broken bones, cuts and lacerations.	Remind workers of the dangers with a toolbox talk.	
	Long Term	1-6 months
	Consider enforcing use of cordless tools.	
3. Piles of offcut timber left in walkways.	**Immediate**	Within 1hr
	Tidy away to more suitable area.	
Consequences could include risk of tripping resulting in broken bones, cuts and lacerations.	**Medium Term**	1 week
	Provide suitable waste bins/skips.	
	Long Term	Every 2 weeks
	Introduce regular cleaning regime.	

Observations	Control Measures	Timescale
Hazards and consequences	**Immediate and longer-term action**	
Fire Safety	**Immediate**	Ongoing
4. Open jar of paint thinners left on ledge above electric heater. Consequences, if spilt, are increased potential for fire and loss of life.	Remove jar and properly stopper.	
	Long Term Ensure good storage and supervision of flammable substances.	At induction and annually
	Long Term Training for employees on fire safety.	1 day
5. General waste and packaging left in piles where hot work may be carried out. Consequences: increased potential for fire and loss of life.	**Immediate** Remove waste.	1 day
	Medium Term Introduce cleaning regime to ensure correct disposal of waste.	1 week and ongoing
	Long Term Schedule housekeeping inspections.	Every 2 weeks
6. Good selection of suitable fire extinguishers.	Good practice.	Ongoing
Working at Height	**Immediate** Secure ladder at top of stiles.	Within 10 mins
7. Roof access ladder not properly secured. Consequences of a fall from height resulting in severe disabling injury or death.	**Medium Term** Consider using more suitable means of access such as MEWP.	1 month
	Long Term Provide ladder safety training to all ladder users.	At induction and ongoing
8. Materials being carried up a ladder to roof level - potential for fall from height due to insecure hand hold with consequences of severe injury.	**Immediate** Stop the work.	Straight away
	Medium Term Introduce hoist system for movement of materials.	1 week
	Long Term Brief supervisors to look out for unsafe climbing practices.	Ongoing
	Long Term Train staff not to carry anything in their hands when climbing ladders.	At induction
9. All roof edge protection properly secured and in good order.	Good practice. Maintain edge protection.	Ongoing

Observations	Control Measures	Timescale
Hazards and consequences	**Immediate and longer-term action**	
Hazardous Substances	**Immediate**	Straight away
10. High levels of solvent vapours from use of adhesive in unventilated bedrooms during carpet fitting.	Open doors and windows during and after use.	
	Immediate and Long Term	Within 1hr and ongoing
	Supervisors to ensure use of suitable vapour mask by carpet fitter.	
Consequences: solvent narcosis and/or respiratory sensitisation. Possible risk of fire.	**Medium Term**	1 week
	Tool box talk on dangers of solvent fumes.	
11. Large amount of silica dust produced during block cutting in new toilet extension.	**Immediate and Long Term**	Within 1hr and ongoing
	Supervisors to ensure operator is wearing suitable PPE, e.g. dust mask.	
Consequences may include silicosis through inhalation of dust.	**Immediate**	1 day
	Consider moving operation outside.	
	Medium Term	2 weeks
	Install ventilation if job cannot be moved outside.	
	Long Term	1 month
	Investigate use of water spray suppression for future jobs.	
12. Cleaning chemicals left on sink tops.	**Immediate**	Within 1hr
	Remove chemicals from sink top and place in temporary secure storage.	
Consequences may include chemical burns and skin irritation following exposure.	**Medium Term**	1 week
	Provide suitable chemical storage container area for chemicals.	
	Long Term	1 month
	Investigate using non hazardous cleaning chemicals.	

Observations	Control Measures	Timescale
Hazards and consequences	**Immediate and longer-term action**	
13. Workers observed standing in ready mixed concrete above the level of their boots, allowing wet concrete to come into contact with skin. Consequences: severe alkaline burns to skin which may require skin grafts or even foot amputation.	**Immediate** Evacuate workers from the area immediately. Remove contaminated clothing and footwear, wash with fresh water and examine for skin damage.	Straight away
	Immediate Refer to medical help if skin is burned.	Within 10 mins
	Medium Term Supervisors to deliver toolbox talks on the dangers of working with wet concrete.	3 weeks
	Long Term Introduce skin monitoring by occupational health nurses for employees working with wet concrete.	1 month and ongoing
Noise 14. High noise levels produced when using block cutting machine. Consequence: noise-induced hearing loss from exposure to noise.	**Immediate and Long Term** Supervisors to ensure operators wear ear muffs at all times when using block cutting.	Within 1hr and ongoing
	Medium Term Deliver toolbox talk on the dangers of noise induced hearing loss.	1 week
Vibration 15. High levels of vibration experienced by workers using block cutting machine. Consequence: risk of Vibration White Finger (VWF) and Hand Arm Vibration Syndrome (HAVS).	**Immediate and Long Term** Supervisors to ensure workers wear appropriate PPE (gloves) and only operate the block cutter for restricted periods of time.	Within 1hr and ongoing
	Medium Term Deliver toolbox talk on the dangers of VWF and HAVS.	1 week

Observations	Control Measures	Timescale
Hazards and consequences	Immediate and longer-term action	
Tools and Equipment	**Immediate**	2 days
16. No evidence of portable electrical tool having been PAT tested - potential for tool to cause electric shock with the consequence of severe burns or fatality to employee.	Supervisors to visually inspect all electrical tools.	
	Medium Term	Within 1 week
	Ensure all electrical equipment brought on to site has been PAT tested.	
	Long Term	1 month
	Toolbox talks delivered to train staff in visual inspection and pre-use checks.	
Site Security and Access	**Immediate**	Within 3 days
17. Access to site is not restricted. Unauthorised access by the public, children, etc. is possible.	Secure site using plywood or Heras fencing with a fixed entry and exit point.	
	Medium Term	2 weeks
Consequences may include injury to the public and increased risk of arson.	Employ a security guard to control access to the site.	
	Long Term	1 month and ongoing
	Put viewing windows in hoarding and deliver safety talks in local schools and neighbourhood.	
Vehicle Movement	**Immediate**	1 day
18. Site and emergency vehicles obstructed by workers' cars parked on driveway.	Move cars and brief staff not to obstruct emergency and site vehicles.	
	Medium Term	1 week
Consequences: lack of access for fire/ambulances in the event of an emergency.	Introduce a No Parking Zone on driveway.	
19. Site vehicles being driven on unsuitable surfaces.	**Long Term**	3 weeks
Consequences: vehicles at risk of turning over, resulting in injuries to occupants.	Lay hardcore to large open area at rear of building to allow car parking.	

Observations	Control Measures	Timescale
Hazards and consequences	**Immediate and longer-term action**	
Falling Objects	**Immediate**	Within 1 hr
20. Materials stored on a tower scaffold without fitted toe boards.	Remove stored materials from tower scaffold and arrange for competent person to fit toe boards.	
Consequences may include falling objects causing head injury to people beneath the tower scaffold.	**Medium Term** Provide tower scaffold training to employees.	2 weeks
	Immediate and Long Term Scaffold inspected by a competent person.	Within 1hr and then every 7 days
Manual Handling	**Immediate**	Within 2 days
21. Workers unpacking bags of cement and carrying them long distances to cement mixer area.	Carry out a Manual Handling Risk Assessment on this job.	
	Immediate Provide workers with sack trucks or trolleys to move the cement sacks.	Within 2 days
Consequences: risk of musculoskeletal disorders, back pain and strains.	**Medium Term** Have cement sacks delivered on a pallet that can be transported to the cement mixer by rough-terrain lift truck.	1 week
	Long Term Have cement delivered directly to where it is required by mobile cement mixer and extendable dispensing nozzle.	3 weeks and ongoing
Welfare/Hygiene	**Long Term**	Within 1 week and ongoing
22. Workers required to eat meals on site. No facilities provided for workers to sit in comfort in a dry, covered area.	Provide a workers' hut or room where employees can sit in comfort and where they are provided with fresh drinking water and facilities to make tea/coffee.	
Signage	**Immediate**	Within 2 days
23. Vehicles driving too quickly on site. No signs to indicate any speed restriction.	Erect speed restriction signs (10km/h).	
	Medium Term Introduce a section in the induction training informing drivers on site of the speed limit.	1 week
Consequences: vehicles may collide with workers causing broken bones or fatality.	**Immediate and Long Term** Ensure supervisors enforce the speed limit on site.	Ongoing

Report to Management

Hopefully you've now got a good understanding of what you need to do in the workplace inspection, but your work is not yet finished! Once you've completed the inspection, you need to write a report to management that successfully persuades them to take appropriate action. To do this, you'll need to explain why such information is needed and identify the remedial measures that should be implemented.

HINTS AND TIPS

The report can be typed or written on lined paper in your own handwriting. The recommended word count is between 700-1,000 words in length, which is equivalent to two or three handwritten sides of A4 paper. You will not be penalised for reports that are shorter or longer than this.

You can consult reference books when preparing the report but be sure not to plagiarise. Your report should not contain photographs or any other extra material.

This is supposed to be a report to management so **it should not just duplicate your observation sheets**. You need to think carefully about the issues you need to bring to the management's attention and only concentrate on those. It must give management sufficient information to allow them to take reasonable action based on the facts you have presented to them and, crucially, persuade them of the need to take that action.

Structuring your Report

You will need to structure your report using the following headings:

- **Title**

  Give your report a title and format it as a title on the page. Use the format for the report that is provided on the NEBOSH website as a standard template.

- **Introduction, including overview of area inspected and activities taking place**

  In this section, you should explain **where, when and why** the inspection was carried out. This needs to include a clear **description of the chosen area, the people that work there and the activities** that take place there.

- **Executive Summary**

  This should be written after you have completed the rest of the report but should be inserted after the Introduction. The aim of this section is to provide a **concise** overview of the important points and **summarise** your main conclusions and recommendations.

  Here, you will need to convince a busy manager of the need to read your full report and, crucially, act on your recommendations.

- **Main Findings of the Inspection**

  The report should clearly **identify the 5 or 6 key issues you have found during the inspection and what corrective action must be taken,** with an indication of cost implications and some explanation of why this corrective action is necessary.

  The report should **not duplicate the observation sheets** but should include balanced argument on why action is needed and the possible effects it will have on the business. You need to identify the Acts and Regulations that may have been breached and show a clear understanding of the reasons for the breach. Giving clear moral, legal and financial arguments that will convince management to take the actions you suggest. Financial benefits, such as increased productivity could be mentioned or the possible costs of not taking the action.

- **Conclusions and Recommendations**

  The conclusions should **summarise the findings identified in the main body** and should persuade management to take action. You should not introduce any new issues at this stage.

  Recommendations **must follow on logically from your conclusions**. Use the following table to set out your recommendations. All recommendations must be sensible and realistic, appropriately prioritised and have appropriate resource implications in terms of cost or time. It is the assessment of the magnitude of the cost rather than precise figures that are needed.

Recommendations	Likely Resource Implications	Priority	Target Date

Remember, these conclusions and recommendations need to convince your manager of the need to take action.

The report should be **signed and dated**.

As a general note, the report should be written in **concise**, **formal language**. It should be factual and avoid technical jargon as far as possible. Your report should not contain photographs, printed text (e.g. policies or extracts from textbooks), or other extraneous material.

Criteria for Assessment of the Report to Management

The following marking matrix should give you a good idea of what you need to do to achieve maximum marks in each of these areas:

Marks to be awarded				
Management Report - Introduction and Executive Summary		**4-5**	**2-3**	**1**
	Introduction providing an overview of the chosen area	• Clear and appropriate description of the chosen area and of the activities occurring in the area	• Some description of the chosen area and of the activities in that area	• Limited description of the chosen area • Lack of details of the activities taking place in the area
		4-5	**2-3**	**1**
	Executive Summary	• Concise overview of important points and main conclusions/ recommendations	• Overview of some important points and some conclusions/ recommendations	• Limited overview
		11-15	**6-10**	**1-5**
Management Report - Main findings of the inspection	**Quality of interpretation of findings**	• Logical progression from the observation sheets • Does not duplicate observation sheets • Majority of key issues identified in the observation sheets have been appropriately selected and discussed	• Logical progression from the observation sheets but some duplication of observation sheets • Some key issues identified in observation sheets have been appropriately selected and discussed	• Limited progression from the observation sheets and duplication of observation sheets • Minority of key issues identified in the observation sheets have been appropriately selected and discussed

Marks to be awarded					
Identification of possible breaches of legislation	**5**	**4**	**3**	**2**	**1**
	Appropriate references to 5 possible breaches of international standards with a clear understanding of the reasons for the breaches	Appropriate references to 4 possible breaches of international standards with a clear understanding of the reasons for the breaches	Appropriate references to 3 possible breaches of international standards with a clear understanding of the reasons for the breaches	Appropriate references to 2 possible breaches of international standards with a clear understanding of the reasons for the breaches	A list of legislation with no explanation of how the international standard was breached, or how it relates to the hazards, unsafe conditions or work practices selected

Marks to be awarded				
		8-10	**4-7**	**1-3**
Management Report - **Main findings of the inspection**	**Persuasiveness/ conciseness/ technical content**	• Clear legal, moral and financial arguments • Convinces management to take action • Report is well structured and appropriate length	• Some legal, moral and financial arguments • Some persuasion in management action • Report is reasonably well structured	• Limited legal, moral and financial arguments • Limited persuasiveness in management action • Report is poorly structured

Marks to be awarded				
		11-15	**6-10**	**1-5**
Management Report - Conclusions and Recommendations	**Clear and concise conclusions which are clearly related to report findings and are effective in convincing management to take actions**	• Findings identified in report summarised clearly and concisely • Relevant and appropriate information provided to convince management to take actions	• Logical progression from the report • Some key issues identified in report have been appropriately discussed	• Limited progression from the report • Limited discussion of the key issues identified in the report
	Recommendations which present realistic actions to improve health and safety in the chosen area	• Recommendations based upon conclusions • Realistic recommendations and target dates • Appropriately prioritised recommendations • Appropriate resource implications for all recommendations	• Most recommendations follow on from the conclusions • Most recommendations and target dates are realistic • Some attempt at prioritisation • Appropriate resource implications for all recommendations	• Limited progression from conclusions • Recommendations and target dates not all realistic • No prioritising • Limited resource implications

TABLE 1			
Range of issues identified and number of hazards			
Issues description	**Issue range (✓ if covered)**	**Number of hazards identified**	**Comments**
Electricity			
Ergonomics			
Falling objects			
Fire			
First aid			
Good practice			
Hazardous substances			
Housekeeping			
Information			
Machinery			
Manual handling			
Noise			
Obstructions/ trailing cables			
Personal protective equipment			
Signage			
Vehicles/routes			
Vibration			
Welfare/hygiene			
Work at height			
Work environment			
Any other appropriate			
TOTAL			

Example of a Completed Report To Management

Report on an Inspection of a Hotel Renovation Project

Introduction including Overview of Area Inspected and Activities Taking Place

This report represents the main findings of an inspection of the health and safety precautions at the above worksite. Internally, the renovation includes: replacement of old panels, flooring and fittings and renewing wiring and plumbing. Externally, the flat roof is to be re-covered, all brickwork re-pointed and a new drainage system installed to accommodate a leisure facility at the back of the hotel. Although most equipment is brought on and off by the contractors as required; a cement mixer, a dumper truck and a rough-terrain forklift are permanently on site. There are approximately 30 workers on site on a daily basis, although this may vary according to the precise nature of work being done on any particular day. The vast majority of those present on site are contractors, all of whom have been selected on the basis of their competence and experience of similar projects. The project is managed by a team of five who are always present on site during working hours.

Executive Summary

This report focuses on five principal areas where improvements are required to ensure the safety of workers on site and guard against both the threat of prosecution by enforcing authorities and substantial financial losses incurred by a serious accident:

- **Housekeeping**

    Timber with protruding nails and trailing extension leads creating tripping risks show the site housekeeping is not up to standard. Housekeeping should be addressed by flattening nails in timber before taking it off site and promoting the use of battery operated tools to eliminate trailing cables.

- **Fire Safety**

    Open jars of paint thinners and general waste packaging left near to hot works taking place are potential sources of fire. They can be controlled through improved management and provision of a suitable storage area.

- **Hazardous Substances**

    Hazardous substances such as cement, silica dust and solvent-based glue were present without adequate precautions in place. This issue can be addressed very quickly and at relatively little cost, by introducing Personal Protective Equipment (PPE), training and effective supervision.

- **Tools and Equipment**

    The portable electrical tools on site did not have stickers indicating that they had been PAT tested, and so the safety and integrity of that equipment could not be guaranteed. Management should address this by implementing inspection and testing regimes.

- **Site Security**

    Site security is inadequate. Children and members of the public could enter the site at any time and be injured by unfamiliar hazards or even set fires. This is easily remedied by installing fencing and controlling access to the site.

The improvements suggested in this report will help to reduce the added cost of accidents and ill health, reduce the likelihood of prosecution by the enforcing authorities and will help to develop a happier and better motivated workforce.

Main Findings of the Inspection

Housekeeping

The standard of housekeeping on site was poor, with little care being taken to keep the different work areas clean and tidy. Managers have a duty under the **Construction (Design and Management) Regulations 2015** to ensure that work areas are kept free from obstruction. Failure to maintain a clean workplace is bad for workers' morale and could cause tripping accidents. This, in turn, could result in lost-time accidents, compensation claims and possibly action by the enforcement authorities leading to fines. The organisation has a clear duty of care to prevent these injuries happening.

Two main issues identified were timber with protruding nails and extension leads causing trip hazards. Housekeeping should be addressed in these instances by flattening nails in timber before taking it off site and promoting the use of battery operated tools to eliminate trailing cables. General housekeeping can be improved relatively easily and at little cost by introducing a 'clean as you go' policy and by conducting regular inspections.

Fire Safety

With the amount of work using 'hot' tools (blow lamps, bitumen heaters, etc.) on site, the use and storage of flammable materials must be closely controlled. Leaving uncovered solvents in the area of a source of ignition is a breach of the duty to take general fire precautions under the **Regulatory Reform (Fire Safety) Order 2005**. The cost of any resulting fire could be catastrophic for the company. The remedy is almost cost-free, with good training and supervision being the key.

While not a fire risk, blocking a fire exit could prevent timely escape in the event of a fire. The employer has a duty under the **Health and Safety at Work, etc. Act 1974** to provide safe access and egress and under the **RRFSO** to maintain a safe fire escape route. If injury should occur as a result of failing to do so, the employer could be prosecuted and fined in the criminal courts.

Hazardous Substances

The control and safe use of hazardous substances on site needs to be improved. There were a number of instances of substances being used (e.g. adhesives for carpet laying) or produced (e.g. airborne silica dusts from block cutting) without any basic precautions being taken to protect either the workers or others. This is a breach of the **Control of Substances Hazardous to Health Regulations 2002**.

This issue can be addressed very quickly and at relatively little cost. The alternative might well be a complaint by an employee to the enforcing agency resulting in a visit by inspectors and a possible improvement or prohibition notice as there may be a risk of serious harm.

Tools and Equipment

It was noticed during the inspection that none of the portable electrical tools had any stickers indicating that they had been PAT tested. There is a duty on management to ensure that all such equipment is regularly tested. This is a requirement of the **Electricity at Work Regulations 1989**.

Without regular testing and checking of work equipment it is impossible to guarantee its safety and integrity and may lead to employees receiving electric shocks. Electric shocks from portable electrical tools operating at 220-240 volts are capable of causing severe internal burning or even death from heart fibrillation.

Management should ensure that:

- All portable electrical equipment has a visual inspection as a matter of urgency.
- A regime of testing is introduced as a high priority.

- Assessments in manual handling are carried out.
- Staff are trained in how to identify potential defects with electrical equipment before use.

The estimated cost of these measures is £100 plus in-house risk assessor's time and employee time. The benefit of preventing possible electric shocks makes the cost of testing seem insignificant.

Site Security

Building sites are dangerous places for trespassers and the **Health and Safety at Work, etc. Act 1974** Section 3 imposes obligations on you to protect non-employees, including children. In addition, the **Construction (Design and Management) Regulations 2015** require you to prevent unauthorised access. Incidents of children using sites as playgrounds not only carry risk of prosecution and/or civil actions for compensation, but also attract damaging publicity. One basic security measure needed to remedy this costs little as existing fencing panels from our yard can be brought to site. The more significant cost of a gateman for the duration of the contract will also help, and will almost certainly be partially offset by reduced pilfering of tools and materials.

Conclusions

While there are other issues that need to be dealt with, such as noise and waste disposal, those that have been raised in this report are the most pressing and require the most urgent action. Housekeeping is poor but can be remedied relatively easily and at little cost by introducing a 'clean as you go' policy and by conducting regular inspections.

Fire risks are a perennial problem on construction sites and this site is no exception. Care should be taken to control fire hazards as the consequences of a serious fire on site could be catastrophic.

Ill health is another major cause for concern - especially that which can be caused by exposure to hazardous substances such as dusts and fumes. To prevent the threat of long-term ill health from the hazardous substances used on site, which may well give rise to claims for compensation from those affected and deprive the company of experienced workers, suitable personal protection equipment such as masks and gloves should be provided.

Portable electrical tools are generally poorly maintained, which can give rise to the risk of electrocution. This issue can be easily remedied by the introduction of an appliance testing regime and by training staff in how to identify potential defects with electrical equipment before use.

Finally, site security will need to be tightened up so as to reduce the risk of children and members of the public entering the site and either sustaining injury or causing malicious damage. This will also deter those who wish to steal from site or set fires deliberately.

If management can be seen to be taking a lead in improving the safety conditions on site, then it will go a long way towards improving morale and the workforce playing their part in maintaining a safe and healthy workplace.

Recommendation	Likely Resource Implications	Priority	Timescales
Housekeeping			
Clean the area immediately.	The estimated immediate cost is £110 and 1 hour of employee's time.	High	1 day and ongoing
Hold a toolbox talk to remind workers of the need for good housekeeping.	1 hour of management time.	Medium	1 week
Fire Safety			
Provide training to ensure all workers understand the need for control of flammable materials.	The estimated cost of these measures is £560.	High	2 weeks
Hazardous Substances			
Provide all workers with effective personal protective equipment and proper instruction and information about the use of the equipment.	The estimated cost of these measures is approximately £1,000.	High	Within 2 or 3 days
Tools and Equipment			
All portable electrical equipment has a visual inspection as a matter of urgency.	The estimated cost of these measures is £110 plus in-house risk assessor's time and employee time.	High	2 days
A regime of PAT testing is introduced as a high priority.		High	Within 1 week
Assessments in manual handling are carried out.		Medium	1 week
Site Security			
Security fencing.	Estimated cost of hiring Heras fencing or placing boarding around the site is £400.	High	3 days
Remove/secure ladder at night. Secure building at night.	Negligible time expenditure only.	High	1 day
Employ daytime gateman.	£2.2k in wages for contract duration.	Medium	2 weeks

Signed   A. Smith   Dated   1/8/2016

Submitting your Completed Assessment

Once completed, your assessment should include the following:

- **Your completed observation sheets** showing between 25 and 30 examples of hazards and their consequences, together with at least one example of good practice. Remember that these should cover a wide variety of different types of hazard (multiple examples of the same type of hazard will only be marked once).

- **Your completed management report**, following the structure laid down by NEBOSH earlier in this guidance. Look at the marking schemes provided to check that you have given yourself the best chance of getting as high a grade as possible.

- **Your signed declaration**, confirming to NEBOSH that this assessment is all your own work. Don't forget to include this - NEBOSH will not accept your assessment without it!

- **Your completed Practical Assessment must be received by RRC within the following timescales**:

    - no more than two weeks before your nominated exam date; and

    - no more than one week after your nominated exam date.

    Any Practical Assessments received outside this timeframe will not be submitted to NEBOSH for marking. RRC will confirm these deadlines nearer the time.

    If you do not meet these deadlines, NEBOSH will not accept your Practical Assessment and additional costs will be incurred for re-submission.

Once you have completed your assessment and are happy for it to be marked, send it into our Exams department at the following address:

Exams

RRC International

27-37 St George's Road

London

SW19 4DS

We suggest that you take a copy of your assessment before you send it off to us (just in case it gets lost in the post) and send it to us by trackable means.

Final Reminders

Workplace Inspection		Report to Management	
✓	Start by taking a good look at your surroundings. Try to get a feel for the sorts of hazards and unsafe practices you should be looking for.	✓	Keep in mind that the report to management has to successfully persuade management to take appropriate action.
✓	Identify between 25 and 30 examples of hazards and their consequences, as well as some good practices, and explain them in enough detail.	✓	The report should be approximately 700-1,000 words in length, which is equivalent to two or three sides of A4 paper.
✓	Ensure you include hazards under a range of different topics (at least 5, e.g. fire, electricity, etc.). Two separate examples of a training need will only get you 1 mark!	✓	The report needs to be structured appropriately, as follows: • Title • Conclusions • Introduction • Recommendations • Executive Summary • Date and Signature • Main Findings The report should be written in concise, formal language and be broken down into distinct sections.
✓	Remember to include timescales. You need to show you can differentiate between them.	✓	The report should clearly identify what the main findings of the inspection were, with sufficient detail to allow the examiner to understand what was observed, what the risks were and what legal breaches have occurred.
✓	When explaining what action is required to eliminate or control each hazard or unsafe working practice, be concise but give the examiner enough detail.	✓	The report should clearly identify what corrective actions must be taken, with an indication of cost implications and some explanation of why this corrective action is necessary.

Workplace Inspection		Report to Management	
✓	Give more than one recommended action for each hazard - an immediate action to make the hazard safe and another longer-term action that fixes the underlying problem.	✓	Keep in mind the areas that the examiner is going to be looking at when marking your report:
✓	Keep in mind the areas that the examiner is going to be looking at when marking your inspection: • Range and number of issues identified - 0-15 marks • Identification of suitable control measures - 0-15 marks **You need to score well in each of these areas to pass.**		• Introduction - 0-5 marks • Executive summary - 0-5 marks • Interpretation of findings/quality of interpretation of findings - 0-15 marks • Identification of breaches of legislation - 0-5 marks • Persuasiveness/conciseness/technical content - 0-10 marks • Conclusions - 0-15 marks • Recommendations - 0-15 marks **You need to score well in each of these areas to pass.**
✓	Remember to include everything when you submit the practical assessment for marking, including: • **Your completed observation sheets** • **Your completed report (laid out in the required structure)** • **A signed declaration that the submission is your own work (if this is missing, your result may be declared void!)**		

No Peeking!

Once you have worked your way through the study questions in this book, use the suggested answers on the following pages to find out where you went wrong (and what you got right), and as a resource to improve your knowledge and question-answering technique.

Element 7: Fire Safety

Question 1

The processes of heat transmission/fire spread are:

(a) Convection.

(b) Radiation.

(c) Conduction.

Question 2

Direct burning is not shown.

Question 3

(a) Friction is the process whereby heat is given off by two materials moving against one another. In the absence of a lubricant or cooling substance, it can result in the surfaces of the materials becoming hot or actually producing sparks, either of which may be sufficient to cause ignition. Friction can be caused by impact (one material striking another), rubbing (when moving parts of a machine contact stationary surfaces) or smearing (e.g. when a steel surface coated with a softer light metal is subjected to a high specific bearing pressure with sliding or grazing).

(b) A space heater is designed to give off considerable heat and, close to the heater, temperatures may be very high. Fire may be started by combustible materials being placed too close to the source of the heat (through radiation) or by them actually touching the hot surfaces of the heater itself.

Question 4

The three ways of extinguishing a fire are starvation (removing the fuel), smothering (removing the oxygen) and cooling (removing the heat).

Question 5

The classifications of fire are:

(a) Class C - fires involving gases or liquefied gases.

(b) Class B - fires involving flammable liquids or liquefied solids.

(c) Class A - fires involving solid, mainly carbonaceous, materials (here, most likely paper and furniture, etc.).

Question 6

The fire risk assessment should address three topics: a site plan; the fire hazards and their level of risk; and fire control and evacuation measures.

Question 7

This means looking around the construction site, including existing buildings that are being worked on and temporary accommodation, for sources of heat, fuel and oxygen which, together, might lead to fire.

Question 8

The site-specific emergency plan should cover the location of all main fire hazards and protective measures on site. It should be kept in the Construction Phase Plan. The precautions identified will become part of the site induction training.

Question 9

Fire risk can be minimised by ensuring that wood shavings and dust are cleared regularly and ignition sources such as sparks from electrical equipment do not come into contact with combustible materials.

Question 10

The volume of flammable liquids in use at any one time should be minimised (up to 250 litres is usual) and it should be held in appropriate (usually metal), correctly labelled containers with secure lids. The need to decant highly flammable liquids from one container to another should be minimised, thereby reducing the risk of spillages. Storage areas should be well ventilated and drip trays and proper handling aids should be provided. A method for dealing with spillages and the disposal of empty containers and contaminated waste is required.

Question 11

LPG is a colourless liquid which readily evaporates into a gas to form a flammable or explosive mixture. It is heavier than air and can collect in drains, gullies, cellars and excavations, where it can accumulate and lead to possible asphyxiation. It is not easily detected by smell.

LPG can also cause frost/cold burns to the skin, and the risk of either a fire or explosion happening, especially in confined or unventilated places.

Cylinders are vulnerable to impact from equipment near them. Leaks can also occur from faulty valves and pipe connections.

Cylinders can also give rise to possible manual handling problems and a proper risk assessment is required.

Question 12

To store LPG safely:

- LPG contained in cylinders should be stored upright (unless designed otherwise, e.g. LPG-fuelled forklift trucks).

- It should be stored in suitable containers with the valves uppermost and kept in open air positions protected from sunlight or from falling materials.

- It should be in a safe storage area constructed of non-combustible material which is adequately ventilated and in a safe position (at least three metres away from buildings/structures/drains/excavations), e.g. a meshed cage in the open air.

- All storage areas should be suitably signed and marked and with a warning sign for where an explosive atmosphere may occur.

- LPG storage is classified as a hazardous place, i.e. in zonal classification (**DSEAR**).

- It should not be stored beneath overhead power cables or in the path of falling materials.

- Planning is required to ensure that the number of cylinders is kept as small as is reasonable.

- Each cylinder should be clearly marked 'Highly Flammable LPG', with the design pressure and temperature.

- The correct regulators should be used, as well as the hoses being colour-coded orange.

- LPG should not be stored next to either oxygen cylinders or other flammable gases, e.g. acetylene or oxidising agents, or near any cellars, drains or excavations.

- Full cylinders should be stored separate from empty cylinders and separate from bulk containers.

- Suitable fire extinguishers should be available in the event of an accident, e.g. foam or powder.

Question 13

(a) The fire resistance of timber depends on the 'Four Ts' – the thickness or cross-sectional area of the piece, the tightness of any joints involved, the type of wood and any treatment received.

(b) The fire resistance of reinforced concrete depends on the type of aggregate used and the thickness of concrete over the reinforcing rods.

(c) The fire resistance of a brick wall depends on its thickness, the applied rendering or plastering, whether the wall is load-bearing or not, and the presence of perforations or cavities within the bricks.

Question 14

The beam will distort, possibly causing the collapse of any structure it is supporting. It will also conduct heat and increase the possibility of fire spread.

Question 15

Flame-retardant paint, when exposed to heat, bubbles rather than burns, thereby giving additional protection to the covered timber.

Question 16

- Zone 0 - explosive atmosphere present continuously or for long periods.

- Zone 1 - explosive atmosphere likely to occur in normal operation.

- Zone 2 - explosive atmosphere not likely to occur in normal operation; if it does, it is only for short time.

Question 17

Manual systems alone can only raise an alarm over a limited area and for a limited time. There needs to be some means for the person raising the alarm to make it more widespread - by using a phone or public address system, or a manual/electric system.

Question 18

Three fire detection methods include:

- Detection of smoke or other fumes by ionisation or optical smoke detectors.

- Detection of flames by ultraviolet and infrared radiation detectors.

- Detection of heat by fusion or expansion heat detectors.

Question 19

Classes of fire and suitable extinguishers are:

(a) Water - class A.

(b) Carbon dioxide gas - classes B and electrical fires.

(c) Dry powder - suitable for all classes of fire except F.

(d) Foam - class A and B. (Only specialist foams are suitable for some electrical fires.)

(e) Fire blankets - classes B and F.

Question 20

Under BS EN 3-10:2009 all extinguishers are now red, with colour identification on each, as follows:

- Water - white lettering.

- Carbon dioxide - black.

- Foam - cream.

- Dry powder - blue.

- Halon - green (rarely found - generally replaced with other gas or vaporising liquids).

Question 21

Fire extinguisher training should cover:

- General understanding of how extinguishers operate.

- The importance of using the correct extinguisher for different classes of fire.

- Practice in the use of different extinguishers.

- When and when not to tackle a fire.

- When to leave a fire that has not been extinguished.

Question 22

The purpose of signs used along an escape route is to direct occupants to the means by which they can safely leave the premises.

Question 23

The escape route should be clearly signed, as short and straight as possible, lead directly to a place of safety (usually outdoors), be clear of obstructions and free of materials which could pose a fire hazard. It should well lit and wide enough throughout (including at doorways and openings) to provide for the unrestricted flow of people.

Question 24

An assembly point should be a place of ultimate safety (outside the building, in the open air, away from any further danger from the fire); a refuge is a temporary place of comparative or relative safety, in a fire-protected area (usually within a building).

Question 25

There should be a roll-call at the assembly point to ensure that all people in the affected area are present.

Question 26

Fire marshals/wardens are responsible for:

- Ensuring all occupants leave by the designated safe escape routes.

- Searching all areas to ensure that the area is clear (people have left).

- Ensuring that fire escape routes are kept open and clear at all times.

- Ensuring all doors and windows are closed on leaving the area.

- Conducting the roll call at the assembly area (in the absence of senior management).

- Meeting the fire service on arrival and informing them of any relevant details.

- Ensuring special assistance is available to the disabled or infirm (perhaps using 'evac-chairs' in multi-storey areas).

- Investigating the location of the fire (as indicated by the fire alarm system controls).

Element 8: Chemical and Biological Health - Hazards and Risk Control

Question 1

The physical forms of chemical agents which may exist in the workplace are dusts, fibres, fumes, gases, mists, vapours and liquids.

Question 2

The five main health hazard classifications of chemicals are toxic, harmful, corrosive, irritant and carcinogenic.

Question 3

Mists are usually small liquid droplets (aerosol) suspended in the air, while fumes are fine solid particles which are created by condensation from a vapour, given off in a cloud.

A potential source of mists is where paint is being sprayed; fumes are emitted from welding processes.

Question 4

Acute ill-health effects arise where the quantity of a toxic or harmful substance absorbed into the body produces harmful effects very quickly, i.e. within seconds, minutes or hours. Chronic ill-health effects arise where the harmful effects of a substance absorbed into the body take a very long time to appear - months or perhaps years.

Question 5

The main routes of entry are inhalation, ingestion, absorption and injection. A further route is aspiration.

Question 6

Inhalable substances are capable of entering the mouth, nose and upper reaches of the respiratory tract during breathing. Respirable substances are capable of deeper penetration to the lung itself. They are generally 7 or 8 microns or less. It is the size of the individual particle that determines whether a substance such as a dust is inhalable or respirable.

Question 7

A product label must give the following information:

- Name, address and telephone number of the supplier.
- Nominal quantity of the substance/mixture (though this may be elsewhere on the package) - but only where made available to the general public.
- Product identifiers:
  - for substances: name and identification number (EC number, CAS number or inventory number);
  - for mixtures: trade name, and the identity of all the substances (maximum of 4) in the mixture which contribute to its classification.
- Hazard pictograms.
- Signal word (as applicable).
- Hazard statements (as applicable).

- Precautionary statements (as applicable).
- Supplementary information.

Question 8

Safety data sheets are intended to provide users with sufficient information about the hazards of a substance or preparation for them to take appropriate steps to ensure health and safety in the workplace in relation to all aspects of its use, including its handling, transport and disposal.

Question 9

In passive sampling devices, the air sample passes through/into the device by means of natural air currents and diffuses into a chamber containing an absorbent material which can be removed for later analysis. In active sampling devices, the air sample is forced through the instrument by means of a pump.

Question 10

The limitations of stain tube detectors are as follows:

- They provide a spot-sample for one moment in time rather than an average reading.
- They can have an accuracy of +/-25%, which is not particularly accurate.
- The correct number of strokes must be used; losing count and giving too few/too many will give inaccurate results.
- The volume of air sampled may not be accurate due to incorrect assembly interfering with the air flow (through leaks, etc.) or incorrect operation.
- There may be the possibility of cross-sensitivity of tube reagents to substances other than the one being analysed.
- There may be problems caused by variations in temperature and pressure.
- The indicating reagent in the tubes may deteriorate over time.
- There may be variations in the precise reagent make-up between tubes.

(Note: only three were required.)

Question 11

Smoke tubes are used to test the effectiveness of ventilation or air-conditioning systems and chimneys, to detect leaks in industrial equipment, to assess relative air pressures used in certain types of local ventilation system, and to provide general information about air movements in a work area.

Question 12

Guidance Note EH40 sets out the workplace exposure limits for substances hazardous to health.

Question 13

A Workplace Exposure Limit (WEL) is the maximum concentration of an airborne substance, averaged over a particular period, to which employees may be exposed by inhalation under any circumstances, as contained in the HSE Guidance Note EH40.

Question 14

WELs are expressed as time-weighted averages, meaning that measurements are taken over a particular time period (15 minutes for short-term limits or 8 hours for long-term limits) and then averaged out. The concept of time-weighted averages allows concentration levels to exceed the limit, provided that there are equivalent exposures below it to compensate.

Question 15

The limitations of WELs are as follows:

- They are designed only to control absorption into the body following inhalation.

- They take no account of human sensitivity or susceptibility (especially in relation to allergic response).

- They do not take account of the synergistic effects of mixtures of substances.

- They do not provide a clear distinction between 'safe' and 'dangerous' conditions.

- They cannot be applied directly to working periods which exceed 8 hours.

- They may be invalidated by changes in temperature, humidity or pressure.

(Note: only three were required.)

Question 16

The two reference periods are 15 minutes (for STELs) and 8 hours (for LTELs).

Question 17

The principles of control are:

(a) Substitution.

(b) Work process change.

(c) Reduced time exposure.

(d) Substitution.

Question 18

Local Exhaust Ventilation (LEV) is a control measure for dealing with contaminants generated from a point source. Dilution ventilation deals with contamination in the general atmosphere of a workplace area.

Question 19

Dead areas are areas in the workplace which, owing to the air-flow pattern produced by the positioning of extraction fans and the inlets for make-up air used in the ventilation system, remain dormant and so the air is not changed. This is a problem for dilution ventilation as the harmful contaminant remains in this area.

Question 20

The four main types of respirator are: filtering facepiece respirators; ori-nasal or half-mask respirators; full-face respirators; and powered visor respirators.

For breathing apparatus, the three main types are: fresh-air hoses, compressed airlines and self-contained systems.

Question 21

Key factors in the selection of the appropriate respirator:

- Contaminant concentration and its hazardous nature (e.g. harmful, toxic).
- Physical form of the substance (e.g. dust, gas, vapour).
- Level of protection offered by the RPE.
- Presence or absence of normal oxygen concentrations.
- Duration of time that it must be worn.
- Compatibility with other PPE that must be worn.
- Shape of the user's face and influences on fit.
- Facial hair might interfere with an effective seal.
- Physical requirements of the job, e.g. the need to move freely.
- Physical fitness of the wearer.

Question 22

The main purpose of routine health surveillance is to identify, at as early a stage as possible, any variations in the health of employees which may be related to working conditions.

Question 23

Six chemical agents from: petrochemicals; organic solvents; isocyanates; lead; silica; cement dust; asbestos; fibres; carbon dioxide; carbon monoxide; nitrogen.

Four biological agents from: blood-borne viruses; tetanus; leptospirosis (Weil's disease); Legionellosis (Legionnaires' Disease or Pontiac Fever); hepatitis.

Question 24

Gases described as 'asphyxiant' (e.g. carbon dioxide (CO_2) and carbon monoxide (CO)) do not cause direct injury to the respiratory tract when inhaled, but reduce the oxygen available to the body.

Question 25

Sources of organic solvents used in construction: paints, varnishes, adhesives, pesticides, paint removers and cleaning materials.

(Note: only three were required.)

Ill-health effects include irritation and inflammation of the skin, eyes and lungs, causing dermatitis, burns and breathing difficulties including occupational asthma and sensitisation. Vapours given off are usually flammable, and may be narcotic (e.g. toluene) progressively causing drowsiness, nausea and unconsciousness. Some organic solvents are carcinogenic.

Question 26

Controls used to avoid or reduce exposure to cement dust and wet cement:

- Eliminating or reducing exposure.
- Use of work clothing, and PPE such as gloves, dust masks and eye protection.
- Removal of contaminated clothing.
- Good hygiene and washing on skin contact.
- Health surveillance of skin condition to control chrome burns and dermatitis.

Question 27

The three main types of asbestos are:

- White (chrysotile).
- Blue (crocidolite).
- Brown (amosite).

Question 28

A procedure must be in place covering the actions to take on discovering asbestos in unknown locations:

- Stop work immediately.
- Prevent anyone entering the area.
- Arrangements should be made to contain the asbestos – seal the area.
- Put up warning signs – 'possible asbestos contamination'.
- Inform the site supervisor immediately.
- If contaminated, all clothing, equipment, etc. should be decontaminated and disposed of as hazardous waste.
- Undress, shower, wash hair; put on clean clothes.
- Contact a specialist surveyor or asbestos removal contractor.

Question 29

Sampling for asbestos in the air should be carried out by trained staff, in three situations:

- **Compliance sampling** - within control or action limits.
- **Background sampling** - before starting work (i.e. removal).
- **Clearance sampling** - after removal and cleaning the area.

Question 30

Such persons have a responsibility to:

- Manage the waste legally.
- Ensure it does not escape from control.
- Transfer waste only to an authorised person.
- Adequately describe the waste.
- Provide adequate documentation, i.e. transfer notes.

Question 31

Factors to consider when handling and storing waste for disposal:

- The hazardous nature of the waste.
- The waste may present a manual handling risk.
- Storage equipment such as skips, bins and compactors may be difficult to access and may require steps or platforms to allow safe use.
- Compactors will have moving parts that must be effectively guarded to prevent access.
- Collection vehicles such as skip lorries present a significant hazard when manoeuvring, especially when reversing.
- The waste may present a temptation to scavengers (e.g. waste metals) and to vandals (unlocked storage tank valves).
- Any escape may have the potential to cause pollution.
- Waste types (streams) must be segregated to prevent the mixing and contamination of one type of waste with another.
- Appropriate documentation should accompany the waste and the duty of care, to dispose of waste in line with legal requirements, must be fulfilled.

(Notes: only six were required.)

Element 9: Physical and Psychological Health - Hazards and Risk Control

Question 1

This refers to a daily personal exposure to noise ($L_{EP,d}$) at a level of 85 dB(A) over the course of a working day (8 hours), or an equivalent exposure over a shorter period. The significance of the level it relates to is that it is the upper exposure action level.

Question 2

Ear defenders can be uncomfortable when worn for long periods and users may be tempted to either remove or constantly adjust them. They may also be incompatible with other items worn such as spectacles or other items of PPE, and they must be routinely inspected, cleaned and maintained to ensure their effectiveness.

Ear plugs are difficult to see when properly fitted, leading to problems of supervision and enforcement, and workers not replacing them on a regular basis can lead to ear infections. In addition they are easy to lose or misplace.

There is a general limitation on the level of noise reduction that can be achieved, depending on the quality and type of ear protection. Taking off the protection reduces its effectiveness. In addition, the seal between the ear and the protective device may be less than perfect due to long hair, thick spectacle frames and jewellery, incorrect fitting of plugs or the wearing of helmets or face shields.

Question 3

Audiometry allows:

- Recognition of existing hearing loss (before starting employment).

- Further damage or hearing loss during employment to be identified.

- The removal or exclusion of workers from high noise areas (to protect from further loss).

- An evaluation of the effectiveness of noise controls.

Question 4

Symptoms of hand-arm vibration syndrome include:

- Fingers turning white, before becoming red and painful when the blood supply returns (vibration white finger).

- Loss of pressure, heat and pain sensitivity (nerve damage).

- Reduction in grip strength and manual dexterity (muscle weakening).

- Abnormal bone growth at the finger joints (joint damage).

Question 5

There are a number of preventive and precautionary measures which can be taken in regards to tools and equipment:

- **Choice of equipment**:
    - Mechanise the activity - use a concrete breaker mounted on an excavator arm rather than hand-operated.
    - Change the tool or equipment for one with less vibration generation characteristics.
    - Use tools that create less vibration, e.g. a diamond-tipped masonry cutter instead of a tungsten hammer drill.

- Support the tools (e.g. tensioners or balancers), allowing the operator to reduce grip and feed force.

- Add anti-vibration mounts to isolate the operator from the vibration source.

- **Maintenance**:

  - Keep moving parts properly adjusted and lubricated.

  - Keep cutting tools sharp.

  - Replace vibration mounts before they wear too badly.

  - Ensure rotating parts are checked for balance.

  - Keep all equipment clean - especially look for corrosion.

Question 6

Regulation 7 of **CVAWR** requires that health surveillance should be conducted where appropriate, e.g. in cases where the risk assessment shows a risk of developing vibration-related conditions, or employee exposure reaching action levels. Records of this health surveillance should be kept.

Where an identifiable disease related to vibration exposure is discovered, monitoring is required to minimise the health effects and maintain adequate control.

Question 7

The non-ionising radiation types are:

(a) Radio frequency.

(b) Infrared radiation.

(c) Ultraviolet radiation.

(d) Visible radiation.

Question 8

Acute effects of exposure to high doses of ionising radiation include:

- Sickness and diarrhoea.

- Hair loss.

- Anaemia, due to red blood cell damage.

- Reduced immune system due to white blood cell damage.

All of the cells of the body are affected by the radiation, but some more than others. A large enough dose can kill in hours or days.

Question 9

Artificial optical radiation has effects such as:

- Burns or reddening of the skin.

- Burns or reddening of the surface of the eye (photokeratitis).

- Burns to the retina of the eye.

- Blue-light damage to the eye (photoretinitis).

- Damage to the lens of the eye that causes early cataracts.

Question 10

Radon is a naturally occurring radioactive gas originating from uranium, occurring naturally in rocks and soils - radon levels are much higher in certain parts of the UK. The highest levels are found in underground spaces such as basements, caves, mines, utility industry service ducts and in some areas in ground floor buildings, as they are usually at a higher pressure than the surrounding atmosphere. It usually gets into buildings through gaps and cracks in the floor.

All workplaces can be affected in radon-affected areas.

Question 11

Where controlled areas have been designated, the employer must appoint a qualified Radiation Protection Adviser (RPA). Usually from external organisations, RPAs must have particular experience of the type of work the employer undertakes and be able to provide advice and guidance on the following matters:

- Compliance with current legislation.

- Local rules and systems of work.

- Personnel monitoring, dosimetry and record-keeping.

- Room design, layout and shielding.

- Siting of equipment emitting ionising radiation.

- Siting and transport of radioactive materials.

- Leakage testing of sealed sources.

- Investigation of incidents, including spillages or losses.

(Note: only four were required.)

Question 12

The main causes of work-related stress include:

- **Demands**, in terms of workload, speed of work and deadlines - these should be reasonable and where possible, set in consultation with workers. Working hours and shift patterns should be carefully selected and flexible hours allowed where possible. Workers should be selected on their competence, skills and ability to cope with difficult or demanding work.

- **Control** - employees should be encouraged to have more say in how their work is carried out, e.g. in planning their work, making decisions about how it is completed and how problems will be tackled.

- **Support** - feedback to employees will improve performance and maintain motivation. All feedback should be positive, with the aim of bringing about improvement, even if this is challenging. Feedback should focus on behaviour, not on personality. Workers should have adequate training, information and instruction.

- **Relationships** - clear standards of conduct should be communicated to employees, with managers leading by example. The organisation should have policies in place to tackle misconduct, harassment and bullying.

- **Role** - an employee's role in the organisation should be defined by means of an up-to-date job description and clear work objectives and reporting responsibilities. If employees are uncertain about their job or the nature of the task to be undertaken, they should be encouraged to ask at an early stage.

- **Change** - if change has to take place, employees should be consulted about what the organisation wants to achieve and given the opportunity to comment, ask questions and get involved. They should be supported before, during and after the change.

(Note: only one example of a preventive measure was required for each.)

Question 13

Work-related stress has adverse effects on the individual employee and the organisation.

For the **employee**: physical or psychological, including headaches, dizziness, panic attacks, skin rashes, stomach problems, poor concentration, difficulty sleeping and increased alcohol consumption. If stress is intense or prolonged, it can lead to the onset of serious physical and mental health conditions, such as high blood pressure, heart disease, gastro-intestinal disturbances, anxiety and depression.

(Note: only six effects required.)

For the **employer**: sickness absence can have effects on output and costs of a replacement. Work-related stress also affects morale and motivation, resulting in lower productivity, reduced performance, tensions between colleagues and increased incidence of industrial relations problems. In the long term, it may cause workers to leave, with the consequential costs of recruiting and training replacements.

(Note: only three effects required.)

Element 10: Working at Height - Hazards and Risk Control

Question 1

The **Work at Height Regulations 2005** call for a hierarchy of measures where there is a risk of a fall liable to cause personal injury, namely:

- Avoid work at height.
- Use work equipment or other measures to prevent falls where work at height cannot be avoided.
- Use work equipment or other measures to minimise the distance and consequences of a fall where the risk of a fall cannot be eliminated.

Question 2

The safe method of working on fragile roofs is by the use of roof ladders or crawling boards. These are laid across the surface, supported by underlying and load-bearing roof members, and distribute the load of the worker over a wider area, enabling the roof structure to sustain the load safely. Roof ladders also provide a good foot-and-hand hold for the worker.

Fall arrest equipment should be worn when shown to be required by a risk assessment.

Question 3

Commonly, falls occur:

- From the edge of a completed roof.
- From a roof where work is being completed.
- Through openings or gaps.
- Through fragile materials making up part of the roof.

Question 4

To prevent materials from falling in the first place, the following control measures should be used:

- Not stacking materials near edges, and particularly unprotected edges.
- Close boarding of working platforms to minimise the gaps between scaffold boards, or placing sheeting over the boards so that material cannot fall through.
- Avoiding carrying materials up or down ladders, etc. by using hoists and chutes to move materials.
- Using physical safeguards such as toeboards and brick guards.

Question 5

Any platform used for construction work where a person could fall more than two metres must be inspected in its place of use before being used. This inspection is only valid for seven days. For mobile platforms, inspection at the site is sufficient without inspection again every time it is relocated on that site.

Question 6

Safety features include sole boards, base plates, toeboards, guardrails, boarding, brick guards and debris netting and waste chutes.

Question 7

The main hazards of using ladders are:

- Not being tied or not resting on firm ground, which may cause the ladder to tip.
- Poor storage and maintenance allowing the ladder to rot or warp, which may cause the rungs to break.
- Objects falling from height.
- Contact with live overheads.

Question 8

Detailed requirements for edge protection are:

- Top guardrail to be at least 950mm above the working platform.
- Intermediate rails so no unprotected gap of more than 470mm between toeboard and guardrail.
- Toeboard must extend to at least 150mm above the working platform.

Question 9

In respect of scaffolding:

(a) Standards are the vertical tubes (the uprights), ledgers are the horizontal tubes running parallel to the face of the building and transoms are the tubes spanning across ledgers to secure a scaffold transversely.

(b) Tying secures the scaffolding to the building, whereas bracing is used to stiffen the framework.

Question 10

Safety precautions for use of MEWPs:

- Select the type of MEWP to suit the terrain it will cross/work on.
- Site the MEWP on firm, stable ground.
- Ensure clearance from obstructions around and overhead when operating.
- Place barriers to prevent the MEWP being struck by vehicles or mobile plant.
- Same barriers keep people from beneath the working platform (cradle).
- Cradle to have guardrails; safety harnesses to be worn as additional precaution.
- Controls of the MEWP should be inside the cradle so the operator has some control while at height.
- MEWP should not moved with cradle raised unless designed to do so.
- Must not be overloaded.
- Must be inspected (six-monthly) as item of lifting equipment designed to carry people.
- Restrict use to trained, authorised operators.

Question 11

Ladders should be positioned at an angle of 75° (4:1).

Question 12

Roof access methods include: independent scaffolding, fixed scaffold towers, mobile scaffold towers, ladders, or by a valley or parapet gutter.

Question 13

Fall arrest equipment is intended to minimise the effect of a fall once it has happened and is used as part of a safe system of work. The provision of fall arrest equipment is subject to the **Personal Protective Equipment at Work Regulations 1992** and the **Work at Height Regulations 2005**.

Question 14

(a) The two main types of safety netting are personnel nets (100mm mesh) to catch persons falling from above - maximum fall distance six metres; and material or debris netting (12-19mm mesh) to catch falling objects.

(b) Safety nets should be:

- – Properly secured and slung efficiently.

- – Higher at the outer edge than at the inner to allow access of any rescue craft.

- – Erected as close as possible to the working level.

Question 15

Drowning can occur if workers fall from a construction site into water. Hazardous areas include harbours, docks, wharves and piers; lakes, rivers, streams and the sea; swimming pools, ponds (natural and man- made), reservoirs and lagoons; chemical works or factories containing open tanks, vats or water holding tanks; culverts, sewers, outfalls and other discharge points. In coastal areas, the tide may cause problems of drag or undertow.

Question 16

Legislative requirements when working over or in the vicinity of water:

- A suitable and sufficient risk assessment of the work involved, as well as risk prevention and protective measures, are required.

- Any boat or small craft used to convey a person to and from a place of work must provide for his or her safe transport, and be suitably constructed, maintained and operated by a competent person.

- Suitable rescue equipment must be provided nearby and persons trained/instructed in its use.

- Guardrails are required if there is a possibility of falling from the edge of adjacent land, a structure, scaffolding, or a floating stage - these may be removed temporarily to allow materials to be moved but must be replaced as soon as possible.

- Safety nets can be used where it is not possible to provide a full and proper scaffold or gangway with handrails and toeboards, etc., provided that everything practicable has been done in respect of providing scaffolding.

- Safety harnesses can be used instead of nets provided that secure anchorage points exist and the harness is constantly worn and attached. Everything practicable must have been done in respect of providing safety nets.

- Employers must do everything that is reasonably practicable to provide information, instruction, training and supervision.

- Employers must provide a safe place and system of work with safe access/egress and must ensure that provision is made for safe use and handling of materials, etc.

Question 17

Additional precautions include: warning notices, buoyancy aids, safety boats, platforms and gangways, ladders, good housekeeping, illumination of the water surface, consulting the weather forecast, first-aid facilities, protective clothing and equipment, life jackets, lifebuoys, rescue lines, safe operating procedures, safety nets and emergency procedures.

Question 18

Types of protective clothing and equipment that can be worn are:

- Safety helmets - these must be worn at all times, as anyone struck on the head and then falling into water is at a particular risk of drowning.

- Footwear - this should have non-slip soles. Rubber and/or thigh boots should be avoided due to them filling with water, which could result in the wearer being dragged under water.

- Safety harnesses and belts - these are permitted under the **Work at Height Regulations 2005** where it is not possible to provide a standard working platform or safety net, provided that they are always worn and always secured to a safe anchorage. There are a number of types, e.g. chest harnesses, full-body harnesses, safety rescue harnesses, etc. which are required to be properly selected for a particular use and the operatives trained and instructed in their use.

Element 11: Excavation Work and Confined Spaces - Hazards and Risk Control

Question 1

The hazards of work in and around excavations include:

- Buried services.
- Falls of persons/equipment/material into the excavation.
- Collapse of sides.
- Collapse of adjacent structures.
- Water ingress.
- Use of cofferdams and caissons.
- Contaminated ground.
- Toxic and asphyxiating atmospheres.
- Mechanical hazards.

Question 2

Risk assessment factors to consider for excavations include:

- Depth.
- Soil type.
- Type of work.
- Use of mechanical equipment.
- Proximity of roadways/structures.
- Presence of the public.
- Weather.

Question 3

Controls that may be necessary during excavation work are:

- Identification and marking of buried services, and using safe digging methods to avoid contact with them.
- Methods of supporting excavations (e.g. steel sheets, support boxes).
- Safe means of access.
- Safe crossing points.
- Barriers.
- Lighting and warning signs.
- Safe storage of spoil.
- De-watering.
- Positioning and routing of vehicles, plant and equipment.

- PPE.

- Additional controls will be required when working with contaminated ground, e.g. separate welfare facilities.

Question 4

Hazards that may arise during the excavation of contaminated ground:

- Digging will uncover buried materials or contaminants within the ground which are hazardous to health.

- The contaminants themselves can change over time due to bacterial or chemical action, which may also alter their properties. This may be the result of the decomposition of organic matter or from the dumping or spillage of hazardous substances.

- Certain contaminants are subject to specific legislation, namely asbestos, lead, anthrax, radioactive materials and buried explosives, and well established procedures need to be followed to deal with each of these situations.

- There may be radioactive hazards from the ground itself (probably as a result of previous occupancy).

- Toxic and asphyxiating atmospheres may be present, for example:

  - Flammable gases such as methane (marsh gas) and carbon monoxide from plant and machinery used in connection with excavation, including pumps involved in de-watering operations.

  - Toxic gases such as hydrogen sulphide.

  - Chemicals and metal compounds, either in containers or within the soil.

Question 5

No person is allowed to work in an excavation before it has been examined by a competent person.

The **CDM Regulations** require that a competent person shall inspect the working areas of an excavation at the start of each shift. Additional inspections will be required after any event likely to have affected the strength or stability of the excavation, or any part of it, e.g. flooding or other incidents such as an accidental fall of rock or earth or other material.

A report must be made and records kept of such inspections.

Question 6

(a) A confined space is any enclosed space where there is a reasonably foreseeable specified risk of any serious injury associated with it.

(b) Typical confined spaces found in construction work include trenches, sewers, manholes, tunnels, excavations, chambers, tanks, pits, cellars and unventilated rooms. Cofferdams and caissons by their enclosed nature may also be included.

Question 7

Hazards associated with confined spaces include:

- Exposure to toxic, explosive and oxygen-deficient atmospheres.

- Heat.

- Water.

- Free-flowing solids.

- Restricted space.

Question 8

Precautions that are necessary for safe entry into a confined space include:

- Avoidance where possible.
- Risk assessment.
- Planning.
- Permit-to-work procedures and implementation of their requirements.
- Training.
- Use of competent persons.
- Atmospheric testing.
- Means of access.
- PPE.

Question 9

Factors that might be involved in a safe system of work for confined space entry include:

- Adequate, competent supervision.
- Experienced and competent workers.
- Proper isolation of plant and equipment.
- Pre-cleaning and correct disposal of debris and sludge.
- Adequate lighting and ventilation.
- Atmospheric testing.
- Provision of specialist, non-sparking tools; breathing apparatus; and rescue harnesses.
- Emergency arrangements/plans.

Element 12: Demolition and Deconstruction - Hazards and Risk Control

Question 1

Three other methods of demolition are:

- Pre-weakening.
- Progressive demolition.
- Overturning by wire rope pulling.

Question 2

Transport-related accidents in construction work are due to:

- Poor, unstable and uneven ground.
- Poor control of vehicle movements.
- Use of unsuitable plant or vehicles.
- Unauthorised use of vehicles and plant by untrained operators.
- The potential proximity of private or road-going trade vehicles to heavy demolition plant.
- Vehicles left in unplanned areas, causing obstructions and obscuring sight lines.

(Note: only three were required.)

Question 3

The method statement and demolition plan should outline:

- How the presence of hazardous substances is to be identified.
- The means of disposing of such substances.
- The requirements for any protective equipment.

Question 4

To avoid the premature collapse of a building/structure during demolition, designers should consider:

- How structural stability can be maintained throughout the process and include relevant information with their designs in order to avoid such events taking place.
- That structures can become unsafe during the demolition process and temporary scaffolding/support may be required, e.g. for heavy overhanging cornices.
- The need to ensure that these temporary structures are able to support the loads required, so that overloading does not occur.
- That the removal of certain parts of the building or structure during demolition can result in other parts of the building becoming unsafe.
- That there are a number of types of temporary structural support for shoring, propping and facade retention including tube and fittings scaffolding; system scaffolding; screw jack propping; shoring systems; facade retention systems; and buttresses.

- That temporary structural supports should be used in accordance with the appropriate standards and should be sufficient and suitable for the work required.

- That temporary structural supports should be:

  - In position prior to the disturbance or removal of the existing supports.

  - Fit for purpose and founded on secure and effective footings.

  - Adequately laced and braced.

  - Capable of resisting dynamic loadings.

  - Checked both prior to and during demolition for effectiveness, including for the effects of vibration.

In addition:

- Scaffolding should normally be an independent tied scaffold. When completed, it should conform to the requirements of the statutory regulations and with any local authority requirements, e.g. inspected, adjusted as necessary and removed in a progressive and planned manner as the work proceeds, to ensure its integrity.

- Any shoring and propping should be adequate for its purpose, placed in position at the appropriate time and designed not to interfere with subsequent construction. The shoring should be checked for effectiveness as the demolition proceeds and should never be loaded in excess of the design limits.

- The temporary support system should not be weakened by removal of components until the facade in that location is fully supported either by the new structure or by an alternative, temporary structure.

Question 5

A number of steps need to be taken to avoid noise and provide protection for people working in, or living near, demolition sites.

- A noise assessment is required in accordance with the **Control of Noise at Work Regulations 2005,** which will identify all potentially noise-sensitive areas on the site.

- Monitor background noise prior to work beginning at any noise-sensitive areas.

- State actions taken to reduce noise levels (in the demolition method statement).

- Use plant and equipment with low operating noise levels, and mains-generated electricity in preference to diesel generators.

- Use solid-panelled fencing around the site instead of wire fences.

- Restrict deliveries to daytime working hours, i.e. not early morning or late at night.

- Display project contact details prominently in residential areas, to allow any nuisance issue to be addressed quickly.

- Post warning notices to warn people to keep away from the danger area.

- Fit appropriate silencing/soundproofing to all machinery and plant on site.

- Provide personnel working within the noise zone with, and ensure they use, adequate hearing protection.

Question 6

Protection against dust from demolition activities may include the following:

- A **COSHH** assessment.

- Maintaining a high standard of housekeeping, regularly cleaning and sweeping the site roads.

- Using techniques that produce low levels of dust; damping down.

- Designating vehicle routes to and from the site to limit the problem.

- Maintaining plant and equipment to a high standard, so that it is less likely to break down and will emit fewer pollutants, and to prevent spillage of oil and fuel to the environment.

- Using wheel-washing facilities at exits onto public traffic routes.

- Using water sprays as a dust suppressant, taking care as to the potential consequences of environmental contaminants or the proximity to electrical services.

- Using air movers or LEV where possible.

- Using covered wagons and skips and restricting the speed of vehicles.

- Using PPE as a last line of defence.

- Where asbestos might be present, take samples to verify its presence and carry out the necessary precautions, actions and required notification.

- Put precautions in place if lead is found to be present.

Question 7

To ensure the safe siting of plant and machinery:

- The plant and machinery should be properly sited within a compound and isolated or immobilised at the end of each shift.

- Sufficient and suitable parking areas should be provided for all vehicles using the site - including employees' and visitors' private vehicles.

- Vehicles should not be left in unplanned areas, otherwise the safe operation of the site may be jeopardised - for example, by obscuring sight lines.

- Safe areas for loading and unloading skips and collection vehicles should be provided.

- Prevent parking of vehicles near any scaffolding, stacks of materials, compressed gas or storage compounds containing toxic or flammable materials, especially transport carrying LPG.

Question 8

Environmental information relating to any underground tanks or potential chemical/biological hazards or the presence of contaminated land, along with the building's former use, should be supplied to the contractor prior to demolition.

Types of contaminated sites (including both ground and buildings) are numerous and can include waste disposal sites; gasworks, power stations; sewage treatment works; railway land including sidings and depots; coal-yards (contaminated by phenols); oil refineries, petrol stations and associated sites; metal mines, smelters, electroplating works, refineries and foundries; chemical works; Industrial Revolution era workshops and warehouses; slaughter yards and abattoirs; fish and meat markets; tanneries; paper and printing works; wood preservative treatment sites; hospitals, including isolation and quarantine premises; and buildings with animal hair used as insulation in roofs, etc. (anthrax).

Protection is required from noise, dust, waste and asbestos. Any particular problems that might arise from these should be taken account of in the risk assessment and detailed safety precautions should be put in place.

All the information should be included in the health and safety plan for the demolition project.

Question 9

To ensure the competence of the workforce for demolition purposes:

- All personnel should be competent for the tasks that they undertake.

- The **CDM Regulations 2015** place responsibilities on the client and other persons involved with demolition works to ensure that competent persons are employed on the project.

- Management should ensure that the necessary levels of competencies exist and are developed by appropriate training as required, e.g. health and safety.

- In the case of a subcontractor, the presence of a health and safety policy, the suitability of method statements, previous work and accident history, quality of risk assessments and the level of training of staff would be a guide to such competence.

- The CITB issue, at various grades, certificates of competence, e.g. labourer, etc. following successful completion of training.

- The training and competence of workers can be further enhanced by site induction training, or other training covering the hazards and legislation involved in the demolition process, e.g. NVQs.

Question 10

Information is to be considered in a pre-demolition survey:

- The presence (or absence) of asbestos; of what types and in what locations.

- The identification of key structural elements including pre- and post-tensioned components.

- The identification of the location and types of services.

- The identification, significance and extent of any dilapidation of the structure.

- A review of the drawings and structural calculations, and the existing health and safety file relating to the structure.

- A review of all structural alterations carried out on the structure in the past.

Question 11

The method statement should identify the work procedure, associated problems and their solutions. It should include:

- Name and address of demolition contractor and site.

- Sequence and method of demolition.

- Details of personnel access, working platforms and machinery requirements.

- Details of any pre-weakening of structures which are to be pulled down or demolished using explosives, and temporary propping required.

- Arrangements for protecting workers and the public, and the exclusion of unauthorised people from the work area.

- Site security including the provision of suitable fencing and/or barriers; controlling of spectators and/or site visitors; use of exclusion zones; and containment of demolition materials.

- Details of the removal or isolation of electrical, gas and other services.

- Details of temporary services required and welfare services provided.

- Arrangements for the disposal of waste.

- Details of environmental considerations (dust, noise, pollution of water, contaminated ground).

- Details of controls covering substances hazardous to health and flammable substances, e.g. asbestos, LPG and compressed gases, and any permit-to-work system.

- Arrangements for the control and co-ordination of the site, e.g. transport, contractors, storage.

- Training requirements and competencies of personnel involved in the demolition process.

- Identification of people with special responsibilities for the co-ordination and control of safety and emergency procedures/arrangements.

Question 12

Typical emergency arrangements that a demolition contractor might need to consider include:

- Containing a localised chemical spillage or gas/vapour release.

- Dealing with emergencies caused by damage to utility supplies that have not been isolated, particularly gas explosion.

- Fire evacuation.

- Plans to deal with premature or unplanned collapse of structures.

- Rescue of persons trapped under collapsed structures.

- Recovery of persons fallen from height (perhaps from collapsing structure).

- Rescue of persons fallen into cellars, pits, voids, etc.

- First-aid treatment.